The Saint Giles Library

NO. 30

A SERIES OF UNCOMMON EVENTS

A list of the books included
in The Saint Giles Library
will be found at the end of
this volume

CAPTAIN GEORGE ROBERTS

A Series of Uncommon
Events

THE
SAINT GILES
LIBRARY

JONATHAN CAPE
THIRTY BEDFORD SQUARE LONDON

FIRST PUBLISHED 1726

FIRST ISSUED IN
THE SAINT GILES LIBRARY
1940

JONATHAN CAPE LTD. 30 BEDFORD SQUARE LONDON
AND 91 WELLINGTON STREET WEST, TORONTO

J. AND J. GRAY, PRINTERS, EDINBURGH
BOUND BY A. W. BAIN & CO., LTD.

The Four Years
VOYAGES
OF
Capt. George Roberts;
BEING A
SERIES *of Uncommon* EVENTS,
Which befell him

In a Voyage to the Iflands of the Canaries, Cape de Verde, and Barbadoes, from whence he was bound to the Coaft of Guiney.

The Manner of his being taken by Three Pyrate Ships, commanded by *Low, Ruffell,* and *Spriggs,* who, after having plundered him, and detained him 10 Days, put him aboard his own Sloop, without Provifions, Water, *&c.* and with only two Boys, one of Eighteen, and the other of Eight Years of Age.

The Hardfhips he endur'd for above 20 Days, 'till he arriv'd at the Ifland of St. *Nicholas,* from whence he was blown off to Sea (before he could get any Suftenance) without his Boat and biggeft Boy, whom he had fent afhore; and after Four Days of Difficulty and Diftrefs, was Shipwreck'd on the Unfrequented Ifland of St. *John,* where, after he had remained near two Years, he built a Veffel to bring himfelf off.

With a particular and curious Defcription and Draught of the *Cape de Verd* Iflands; their Roads, Anchoring Places, Nature and Production of the Soils; The Kindnefs and Hofpitality of the Natives to Strangers, their Religion, Manners, Cuftoms, and Superftitions, *&c.*

Together with Obfervations on the Minerals, Mineral Waters, Metals, and Salts, and of the Nitre with which fome of thefe Iflands abound.

WRITTEN BY HIMSELF,
And interfpers'd with many Pleafant and Profitable Remarks, very inftructive for all thofe who ufe this Trade, or who may have the Misfortune to meet with any of the like Diftreffes either by Pyracy or Shipwreck.

Adorn'd with feveral COPPER PLATES.

LONDON:
Printed for A. Bettesworth, at the *Red Lyon,* in *Pater-Nofter-Row,* and J. Osborn, at the *Ship,* at St. *Saviour's Dock-Head,* near *Horfely-Down.* 1726.

"To My Dear Brother

Percy,

from George,
Xmas 1944.

INTRODUCTION

*

THE old title-page, which is reproduced overleaf, told the prospective reader plainly enough that here lay a remarkable story of adventure, in addition to a manual of deportment for any who should fall into the hands of pirates, and a handbook for those who had business with the Cape Verde Islands. But neither in the title nor elsewhere in Roberts' work will you find a hint that the book combines amusement with these varied utilities.

The first few pages have a very ordinary, sober look, and the comic element bursts in suddenly, when a pirate with a taste in dress bawls at Captain Roberts from across the harbour, 'You dog, you son of a bitch, you speckled-shirt dog!' And then Roberts goes on board to interview the pirate captain and finds him sitting on a gun, to look martial, though his cabin was full of chairs; the whole company felt the craving to look martial, and therefore used to snap their food like dogs. But after this picture comes the revelation that law-breakers on the unmastered ocean were as sternly set around with laws (though of their own making) as any of their victims. Moreover, being only amateurs in legislature, pirates sometimes found that to keep one of their statutes involved breaking another, with the result that shiploads of desperadoes wasted day after day in quibbling argument. Roberts had been thrown into such a band of sea-lawyers, the matter of whose argument was nothing of less moment to him that his liberty, or perhaps his very life; for ten days the wretched man waited while they split endless forensic hairs, with the blackness of his fate becoming ever more discernible. Never has comedy such flavour as when it holds grim possibilities within it, and these fatuous debates, so tragic to him, are set down in the artless language of the old-fashioned music-hall, which adds immeasurably to their absurdity.

Since Roberts declared himself to be a married man, with five children and one more 'on the stocks,' he should legally have been exempt from piratical service, but the Dago with the interest in clothes had taken a dislike to him from the first

7

glance at his shirt. This fellow, who aspired to be English, once attempted to murder Roberts just to illustrate the strength of his Jacobite feeling; the shot went wide, but he nearly achieved the same result by means of his eloquence. For he talked his associates into setting their prisoner adrift in his leaky sloop with a crew of one boy and a child, without food or water or sails.

By great ingenuity, Roberts succeeds in regaining the Cape Verdes, 150 miles away. The boy goes ashore in their boat to get water, and before he can return a sudden wind drives the sloop to sea. Some of the local negroes come out to Roberts' aid, but refuse to stay with him as the wind is driving him away from their island; meanwhile, however, they make such use of his cask of rum that three of their number remain insensible in the hold, forgotten by their companions. Even when sober, this unexpected reinforcement fails to save the ship; the captain tries to harrow us with the funny stories of how the three flung overboard in disgust the shark that he had caught with such pains, how they repeatedly struck work at the critical moment, how they mispiloted him and deserted him, so that he finally had to anchor in an exposed bay and lost the sloop on the rocks for lack of assistance.

His subsequent adventures on the islands have not the same grotesqueness, yet this latter half of the book has a notable success in imparting the quaint sweetness of primitive life in a small community, remote and isolated to a degree unparalleled to-day. The islands lie 300 miles west of the mainland of Africa (at Cape Verde), and so had not been peopled until their discovery in 1460 by some Genoese explorers in the Portuguese service; at the most they found only a few negroes who had arrived by the accidents of wind and current. Slaves, who were gradually brought over by the Portuguese, intermarried with the whites and produced a race with a standard of living lower than either of the parent stocks had possessed. For on these arid volcanic rocks an occasional rainless year brought a famine, disastrous owing to the lack of communications, while a normal rainfall meant sickness to the entire population. The heavy agricultural work had necessarily to be performed at the rainy season, when the north-easter no longer cools the air and the atmosphere turns moist and oppressive. Sir Richard Hawkins twice called at the islands, and on each occasion lost half his crew through 'fevers and fluxes: to these two diseases, proceeding from the air,' as he justly remarked, 'some add the Gripes or Belly-ach.' Roberts, however, had the good fortune to be wrecked on Brava (St. John), the greenest and most wholesome member of the archipelago, among a people less corrupted by stress of climate. He found them living almost in the style of their African ancestors, whose pagan ritual had been incorporated into their Christianity; they still retain the religious dances and the ceremonies at marriage and burial, of which Roberts enumerated those suited to polite ears (p. 224).

Interspersed with the account of Brava are two instalments of the story of a lonely Welshman, the account of his wanderings in Guinea, but unhappily the narrative breaks off with his arrival in the Koinadugu district, back of Sierra Leone, saying no word on his route from there to the Cape Verdes. This is the greater pity, considering that no previous European traveller had penetrated so deeply into the interior of West Africa, so far as we know. The story agrees with other sources as to conditions at Sierra Leone and up-country, but of course all rests merely on the word of the traveller himself, on the soundness of Roberts' memory, and on the general truthfulness of his work (which has been doubted).

This, Roberts says, was his first book; he contemplated writing another if the venture proved acceptable to the public, but presumably it did not, for his name occurs on no other publication. The amazing popularity of *Robinson Crusoe*, which appeared seven years before under the disguise of an autobiography, called forth plenty of adventure stories, both fact and fiction, but only the more startling romances showed any signs of rivalling Defoe's success: Roberts failed through not stirring the blood. Still, a lengthy summary of the book came out in 1745, in the first volume of the *New General*

Collection of Voyages printed at London, and a contemporary German collection also included it. It next met with attention in 1830, when Walter Wilson declared that the hero was another of Defoe's imaginary travellers: it had become the fashion to attribute quite a large proportion of the better work of his time to Defoe, encouraged by his habit of anonymity and by the freedom of his style from mannerisms which could at once determine its authorship. The ingenuous narrative of Roberts has, of course, little in common with the concise brilliance of the most competent writer of the age, so that the reasoned criticism of the Victorian period could not hesitate to condemn the theory—as in several other cases, one of them being that of the *Military Memoirs*, by George Carleton, already published in this series. Inevitably, however, faith in the authenticity of the alleged author remained shaken, though the connection with Defoe had been abandoned; and so it happens that the British Museum still catalogues the name of Capt. George Roberts as a pseudonym. The *Dictionary of National Biography* (Sir John Laughton writing) remarks upon the fact with evident disapproval, though unable to admit any outside evidence of the captain's reality; it had been suggested that he was identical with a Mr. Roberts who suffered shipwreck in 1692, but from his statement to the pirates (p. 54), his age at a date thirty years later may be guessed at thirty-five or forty; besides, he would surely have mentioned the published account of the shipwreck to introduce this book.

The dedication (to Mr. William Killet of Gorleston) is dated from Shad-Thames, *i.e.* the London docks, July 1726, but supplies no further information. One possible source remained untried—the wills at Somerset House. Fortunately, George was an uncommon name at that period, doubtless because the Hanoverians had not reigned long enough for a generation to grow up, and the register only refers to three persons called George Roberts between 1726 and 1741. One of the three was a cooper, one died intestate in Surrey in 1728, while the third died abroad; the will described him as 'belonging to the *Crollee*, Capt. Clark, a merchant-ship.' He bequeathed all his property to his wife, Jane, who as sole executrix swore to his death and proved the will on 23rd April 1741; it had been signed in 1736. Our Roberts appears to have been unmarried in 1725, and his book does not mention the name of either Elzebath Anderson or Robert Wallis, who witnessed the will; but these points have no significance. The great obstacle to identifying the two Roberts as the same man lies in the absence of proof that the testator ranked higher than an ordinary seaman, though his lawyer would probably not have taken the trouble to insert a long list of the possible forms of his property—lands, tenements, chattels, etc.—had he been a man of very small substance. The author had a temporary engagement as chief mate in 1721, and may well have joined the *Crollee* in a similar capacity, which would explain the absence of his title. At the time of death, 1740 or 1741, he might have reached the age of sixty, and it appears that his constitution fifteen years earlier had been far from robust; the date therefore would suit admirably.

This tempting identification must remain uncertain, nor even can its probability be accepted until the veracity of the book is established. The author himself put a note at the end to confound any doubters: in these days, however, no other record of the story exists, and inference alone can give any assurance of its truth. Now, in the original edition, one-sixth of the total length is filled with an elaborate account of the Cape Verde Islands, which lays particular insistence on all marketable products and minutely describes every harbour and roadstead; a block of seventy pages (omitted in this reprint) deals in turn with each island of the group, while similar information lies scattered through the narrative. In addition the author published a map of his own drawing as a frontispiece.

If the story itself were an invention by some imitator of Defoe, who gathered his local colour by questioning sailors, he could not have avoided errors in such a flood of detailed information upon an archipelago which was badly charted, only cursorily described in any existing work, and of no interest to shipping apart from three or four out of its dozen islands. On the contrary, his directions for finding anchorages are correct, his soundings seldom differ by more than a fathom or two from those marked in the Admiralty charts, while he gives the names of more capes and bays than could be obtained from any other publication till 1910, when the Portuguese Government issued a set of maps which agree with his data in all respects. He must have picked up these names from an illiterate population (a process harder than anyone can imagine without experience of it), and wrote them phonetically, according to the rules of English and not Portuguese spelling, with such success that they can be recognised with ease. His map, too, was the first to reproduce the outline of each island with any approach to accuracy, only failing with two un-inhabited rocks which he does not claim to have visited, but merely to have seen in passing: while fantastic misrepresentations prevail in a couple of Dutch maps ascribed to 1695 and 1700. The relative positions of the group had already been laid down fairly satisfactorily, and here Roberts made few improvements; his anonymous editor of 1745 complains that he seems to have taken no observations of longitudes, and indeed he had lost most of his instruments, according to his own account.

It is significant that the point in which Roberts' map especially excels its predecessors is its treatment of the island on which he claims to have spent most of his time. The two Dutch maps I have mentioned show Brava (St. John, he prefers to call it) as a narrow island, straggling away to east and west, whereas he drew it as in nature, thick and lying north and south: contemporary maps sometimes put it on the north instead of the west of its neighbour. Roberts slightly underestimated its girth at the centre, but drew all details of the coast correctly, here again giving evidence of unusual local knowledge; for ever since Drake had failed to find a harbour it had been commonly believed that none existed, while the French naval chart of the nineteenth century marked it at the wrong end of the coast. It was from this harbour that Roberts rode up to the town by what is still the only track on the island; he had lain beneath cliffs that rise unbroken to a ridge 3000 feet high, until his rescue by the one little boat which the community possessed. This lack of shipping sounds incredible, seeing that the Brava people have become intrepid sailors, even taking their own schooners as far as Europe and America; yet a Portuguese visitor of 1797 corroborates the author's statement in this respect, as in many others.[1]

Now that the authenticity of his book can be established, no doubt it will soon appear in a library edition. The present volume aims at being enjoyable, and therefore cuts it into chapters, presents it without the topographical sections, and shortens the last part of the narrative. The printer was instructed not to retain the uses of the initial capital for all nouns, of italics for proper names, and of the apostrophe in words like 'wish'd,' since these merely follow the custom of the age; but no changes, other than the correction of obvious misprints, have been made in the author's own peculiarities of punctuation or spelling. Who would alter 'quoils' to 'coils,' or 'Antonio Gumms' to 'Antão Gomes'?

[1] In *Memorias Economicas da Academia Real das Sciencias de Lisboa*, V, 1815. Notes by older travellers are collected by Roberts' editor of 1745.

CONTENTS

CONTENTS

CHAPTER ONE

*

IN the year of our Lord 1721, on the 14th day of September, I made a contract with Mr. Dennis Langton, merchant and goldsmith, living at the Wheatsheaf in Lombard Street, Mr. William Ady, packer, living in the house that was Sheriff Cornish's near Blackwell-Hall-Gate, and Captain Andrew Scott, living then on Little Tower-Hill, to go to Virginia, and take possession of a sloop there called the *Dolphin*; and there to buy a cargo to slave with on the coast of Guinea; and from thence to proceed to Virginia or Barbadoes, as I found would be most to the gentlemen's advantage who were concerned with me; from thence to load or take freight to London: To which the before-mentioned gentlemen signed an obligation for the payment of their dividends, both for sloop and cargo; and by their order I shipped a chirurgeon to go from London to Virginia for half pay, and from thence to be in whole pay till arrived in the Thames. Captain Andrew Scott at the same time being commander of the *King Sagamore*, a ship of twenty-two guns, and bound from the Thames, to touch at the Island of Madera, at the Cape de Verd Islands, at the Island of Barbadoes, from thence to Virginia, and from Virginia, upon the coast of Guinea, etc. And I agreed with Captain Scott, by consent of the other owners, who were to be concerned with me in the above-mentioned sloop and cargo, to go his chief mate in the *King Sagamore*, till we arrived at Virginia, and then and there to be discharged, to take possession of the before-mentioned sloop. We met with nothing very remarkable all the passage until we made the Island of Sal, which is one of the windwardmost of the Cape de Verd Islands, for which reason I always endeavoured to make that island first, when bound to touch at any of the Cape de Verd Islands: We made this Island of Sal in the morning, and I, by the captain's order, went ashore with the pinnace and six men armed, in a bay called Palmera, to see what we could observe: At our landing, we found some huts, which were in good repair, and seemed by the grass which was in them, that some people had lately been there, which made me suspect that there might be some turtle-catchers here since the last turtle season, or they might be men shipwrecked, or by other accidents left there, as by pirates, etc. After I had gone a little farther towards the palm-trees, I saw two fire-places, which, by the freshness of the ashes, seemed to have been but lately made; and some heaps of fish-bones lying by the fire-places, which were not thoroughly dry; the under part of them, as also the middle of the heap being moist, which I turned up on purpose; these reasons, I say, farther confirmed my opinion that there were some people upon the island, the certainty of which I was willing to be satisfied in; for which cause I divided my men into two companies, resolving, if possible, to discover whether there was any people on the island, or not: We walked and searched as high up as the middle of the island, without discovering any creature of humane kind; we saw abundance of small land birds, asses, etc. And Captain Scott fearing that some accident might have befallen us, made a signal for us to come on board, which I did as soon as I could get the men together. We got on board about eight o'clock at night, and brought off with us some land-crabs, dates, and three or four of the wild bitter gourds, whereof there is great plenty there (with which the natives in those islands commonly purge themselves, as we do here, under the name of Coloquintidum or Alhandal); these were all we found there that was remarkable, at this time. As soon as we came on board, and got the boat in, we made sail for the Island of Bona Vist, it being the island resolved upon to make a cargo of salt, and the next day we arrived at Bona Vist, and anchored in the English Road, as they call it, under the little island, about ten o'clock at night, in about five fathom water, clear sandy ground within the sunken rock.

Next day I went ashore with Captain Scott, to agree with the inhabitants for their assistance to bring the salt from the salt-ponds down to the water-side; as also to settle the prizes of our goods, and also of their horses, asses, etc., for we were to take in horses and asses, after we had got our salt on board.

Captain Scott being an utter stranger to all these islands, as well as the Canary Islands, both as to their language and trade, I was forced to be with him, as well on the trading account, as of speaking the lingua; so having settled all matters relating to our trading and business there, we went to work to make our salt as fast as we could; it being customary in those voyages for the ship's crew to make the salt for the cargo themselves, and after it is made, to carry or wheel it out a little way from the ponds, to a dry place, and there to heap it up in large heaps to drain and dry; from thence the natives bring it down upon asses at so much *per diem*, per ass, and likewise to the black that drives the asses; one black being commonly allowed to every fifteen asses, who is employed to drive them; every master of a ship bespeaking his asses and drivers in proportion to his company and craft that he has to ship it off with; for it must not be brought down to the landing-place any faster than it can be shipped off, for if it be, the sand is so light, and there being commonly in the day a fresh breeze of wind, that the salt would be blown so full of sand, that it would spoil your salt, and make it good for nothing, as I have often seen experienced, and at several times by masters (both at this island and also at the Isle of May) who were over-hasty to have their salt brought down, and not having hands enough, or their craft being out of order, have caused a sail to be spread on the sand to lay the salt upon, and notwithstanding they took all the care they could to keep it covered with another sail, except when they were a starting the salt brought down, or carrying down to ship off; yet, I say, notwithstanding all their care, the salt was so full of sand, that they had better a hove it overboard than took it in, for I am perswaded it did more harm to the sale of their cargo, than it was worth; but there are some men think if they can but get their ship loaden, that's enough. Sometimes when a ship's company is but few, the masters are forced to hire some of the natives to work in the salt-ponds while the salt is making, and also to work in the shipping the salt off. I advised Captain Scott, as he had brought but little hay with him out of England for his live cargo, to get the blacks to bring some down every day while we were making the salt; but he depended on the blacks' words, who told him, they would supply him with hay enough in one day, for his voyage, which made him think it needless to provide hay before-hand, though I knew to the contrary, as having experienced them before; but yet, Captain Scott depended on their words, which in the end had like to have been the loss of all our live cargo; and as it was, it spoiled the sale of them at Barbadoes, as you will find in the sequel of the story. No ship being here but ourselves, we had all the salt-ponds, to pick and chuse the best, and had but little trouble to make our salt, to what it is sometimes, as I have seen when ships have been forced to wait three weeks or a month for a birth, to make salt in the ponds, and then be forced to take up with, perhaps, such ordinary ponds, that ten or a dozen ponds in that poor ground might not yield much more than one or two ponds would yield where it is a rich salt soil, and yet have as much labour, in a manner, with those ponds, as you would have in tending the best ponds; but we in the making our cargo, had little more to do but to rake the salt out of the ponds, and wheel it out to the heap. While we lay here, came in a sloop belonging to Philadelphia, but last from Santa Cruz, on the Island of Teneriff, and bound to Jamaica; he hindered us almost a day's work; for we not knowing but it might be a pirate got all our hands on board, and so kept ourselves in readiness to receive him, until he sent his boat on board, which we commanded, and satisfied us what he was. Now Captain Scott having bought more asses by far than he could stow on board, and it being all in the sloop's way, they agreed, that the sloop should take in as many asses as she could stow, at so much per head, to be delivered at Barbadoes. After we got our salt all on board, we took in horses and asses, as many as we could stow, and also put as many asses on board the sloop as she could stow; after which, we were forced to stay twenty-four hours for grass and hay, and then neither, we could not get half enough for the voyage; but our water also being almost expended, we could tarry no longer; for you must know, that the Island of Bona Vist, has no drinking water but what lies a long way up in the country, and those ships that come there only to make salt, must bring fresh water enough with them to serve while they are making and shipping off their salt, or they must pay dear for that water that must be brought down out of the country by the natives, on asses' backs; but those that come here to buy cattle, if they do not bring water with them, it is next kin to an impossibility, at least, it would be so chargeable, as well as tedious, to have their water brought out of the country, that it would cost more than the beasts; neither could you ever get a stock of water this way, for your cattle would drink it, in a manner, as fast as it could be brought down. So having got in all that we could get, we and the sloop sailed in company together, and touched at the Isle of May, where we met with five sail of ships loading there with salt for the East country, up the Baltick Sea, among whom we got some water, and also tobacco, the want of which had almost brought a West country famine on us, as the sailors used to term it. We took in six cows to carry down to St. Jago, and one was given to Captain Scott for freight. We stayed one night at the Isle of May, and the next morning weighed for St. Jago, which was the place we designed to take in water, hay, and wood for the voyage, the sloop also being in our company. Captain Scott being ambitious to keep ahead of the sloop, who went very well, as did we in the ship also, crouded all his small sails, and would not shorten sail before we came the length of the Port of Villa de Praya, and it blowing a fresh gale of wind, and generally off the high land, and in the bay there comes off very hard flaws of wind; so that standing with all our sail out until we brought the bay open, before we could hand our small sails, and take a reef in each top-sail, to luff into the bay, we were drove to leeward of the road, and it holding such taut gales, and our decks being cluttered with the cattle, that we could not work the ship so well as we otherwise might, it was three days before we could get into the road; in which time several of our asses died, and the rest were so dispirited, that they never recovered during the voyage. The sloop got into Villa de Praya the evening after we came from the Isle of May, and by the time that we got into the bay, he had got all his water on board for the voyage: As soon as we got in, and were moored, Captain Scott went on shore to buy hay and wood, and to work we went with all our boats to water. After we had watered, wooded, and got as much hay, green cocoa-nuts, etc., for the cattle, as could be gotten, we unmoored and weighed from thence with the sloop in company, and steered away for the Island of Barbadoes, meeting with little remarkable in our passage down, saving that we met with a dead whale about the middle of the passage, having an innumerable quantity of fowls about it, notwith-standing it could not be less than three hundred leagues from any land. We had mostly light winds all the passage down till we arrived at the Island of Barbadoes, which was on the latter part of March, in the year 1722. The first we did was to get our live cargo out, which we did as soon as we had liberty from the Governor and custom-house, but both horses and asses were so weak and poor, that none of the horses, and very few of the asses, were sold while we lay here; so that if a country gentleman had not given Captain Scott the feeding of his horses and asses in the country gratis, after he saw he could not sell them, the cheapest way would have been to have knocked them all on the head, for they would have cost more to have put them in a market case than they would sell for: And likewise the wine did not go off very well; for the inhabitants of this island, as likewise all our islands in the West Indies, being for the most part used to Madera wine, they did not seem to like so well our Canary wine; nay, most of them were afraid to buy it, thinking it was not good, because different in flavour from that of the Island of Madera, their accustomed wine, though the wine which we brought, as it cost almost double the price which wine commonly costs in Madera, so it was of twice the goodness of any wine commonly brought from that island, though it rather sold here under the price of common Madera wine. These disappointments in the cattle, wine, etc., and some other reasons which I shall forbear mentioning here, made Captain Scott entirely decline, and fully resolve of not proceeding to Virginia, notwithstanding the scheme of the voyage was to have proceeded there directly from Barbadoes, as also were his orders and instructions from his owners; however, resolved he was not to go to Virginia, but to contrive or lay a scheme to proceed some other way, which new resolutions of his, did not only surprize me at the present, but likewise dissatisfied me very much, and I could not resolve with myself what course to take in this unexpected disappointment; but it being in vain to sit unresolved what to do, I at last fixed my resolution, which was thus; To make up my account with Captain Scott, and cause him to pay me the ballance, and so to return home to give the gentlemen an account how finely they and I were deluded, they by having such a partner concerned with them, and I by having such an owner as Captain Scott was. Now you must know that I had lent Captain Scott some money at several times before our departure from London, to be repayed me at our arrival at Virginia, which, with the wages that were due to me on board the *King Sagamore*, came to near ninety pounds, which I demanded of him; on which his answer to me was, That he could not raise that money at present, by reason he could not dispose of his effects, but if I thought well of it, he could buy a sloop in his own name, for which he could have credit on his effects till they were sold, and would make a bill of sale to me, to hold a part in the sloop proportionable to the debt; and I considering how difficult it would be for me to recover my money of him there, if not impossible, resolved to accept of his offer; for though he was reputed at London to have considerable effects in Maryland, yet when I came to Barbadoes, I understood by some masters of vessels that came from, and belonged to the place where he pretended his effects lay, that he was so far from having any effects there, that it was the reverse; for they believed that he was so much in debt there, that they thought for that reason he did not much care to come there; wherefore I was after a sort, as it were, necessitated to accept of his proposals, for fear of entirely losing my money;

though I believed I had obliged my friends more, and especially those gentlemen who were to be concerned with me, had we proceeded to Virginia, and I am sure done my self more service to have run the hazard of losing my money, and come home; as the sequel hath fully made manifest.

Accordingly we pitched upon a sloop that was to be sold there; I forget the gentleman's name at present that owned her, neither is it much material. She was then called the *Margaret*, and the then master's name was Alexander Fisher; she was about sixty tun of cask, indifferently well found for those parts, and by the register she was between four and five years old, and was an extraordinary penny-worth. I was discharged by Captain Scott from the *King Sagamore* the 24th April 1722, and the same day took possession of the sloop; and being obliged to register her anew, the old Register Certificate being pretty much torn, and the property now altered, accordingly a new Register Certificate was taken out in Captain Scott's name, and also that of Mr. George Johnson, a merchant who then lived at Barbadoes; after which, I shipped hands and began to get things ready as fast as I could; but found Captain Scott very backward to furnish me with money towards the fitting of her out, or for a cargo; however I made shift to rub along, and what I could not have of Captain Scott, I pieced out with the little money I raised there. I often asked him to come to an account, that we might settle our affairs; but he still put me off from time to time with one excuse or another: However, we concluded and agreed upon the voyage, which was for me to go to Guinea, and thence to the Cape de Verd Islands to trade, or only to the Cape de Verd Islands, as I thought proper; but the cargo was all that remained in dispute: However, Captain Scott did put in a small quota, namely thirty bushels of maiz, four hogsheads of rum, and then he fell sick, and got up in the country: However, I made shift as well as I could, and had some corn, rice, flower, etc., put on board of me by some gentlemen who, rather than I should be baulked, were resolved to venture with me; and I was to make them such returns, if I succeeded, as I thought might be reasonable. I

24

likewise purchased what rum I was able, as also sugar, tobacco, etc., and in short, one way or another, I got together a pretty cargo, sufficient to have answered my design, if it had pleased God that I had escaped the pirates; as in the sequel of the story you shall hear.

By this time Captain Scott's ship was ready for sailing, and he understanding what goods I had on board, offered to barter some of his goods that would answer at the Canaries, in lieu of some of my goods which would answer where he was intended to go; provided I would alter my voyage and go to the Canaries, which I did not approve of, and so there was no more said on that head. We were both ready to sail, and I urged him to come to an account, which he said was then impossible; but as we had agreed to keep company together till we came in the latitude of the Cape de Verd Islands, so we should have time enough to settle before we parted; and abundance of suchlike discourses: Besides, he said, he could not yet hold a pen in his hand by means of his late sickness. Having no other remedy, I was forced to acquiesce, he promising me, to make me a bill of sale not only in proportion to the debt he owed me, but, if I had a mind, he would make me an assignment of the whole bill of sale, and pay him when I thought fit.

So we concluded to sail together the next day, which accordingly we did, being about the middle of July 1722, and were to keep company together till we arrived in the latitude of the Cape de Verd Islands, which I was desirous of, on two accounts; first, that I might have an opportunity of settling accounts between us, and also to have a consignment made over to me of a part of the sloop in proportion to the debt, which would have been for half the sloop at least. The other reason was, I was apprehensive of some pirates which we had an account of at Barbadoes, that lay lurking about the Caribees.

We had a fresh trade-wind, considering the time of year, about the north-east and by north, with some squalls of wind and rain; I was indisposed before I sailed from Barbadoes with a dejection of the spirits, faintness, and want of appetite, which might be occasioned by my fretting and vexing at my disappointments. I had the advice of some gentlemen of the faculty of physick there, who ordered me what they thought proper, and withal told me, as I also believed and hoped, that the fresh air of the sea would carry off my indisposition.

The *King Sagamore* and I kept company three days; and about half an hour past six in the evening the third day, came on a taut squall of wind and rain which split my main-sail at the head, insomuch that I was forced to lower it down; and the ship keeping on her way, I lost sight of her in that squall which continued until duskish. We were then got clear of the islands, and Captain Scott, as I suppose, concluded that he was clear of the pirates, which we had had an account of at Barbadoes; which, with some other reasons, I believe, might be the cause why he did not shorten sail for me when my main-sail split, but made the best of his way; neither was I much concerned then, not doubting but I should meet with him at some of the Cape de Verd Islands, where he designed to trade, and, as I supposed, might be another reason of his making the best of his way to get to the islands before me; for he knew that I had goods in for these islands, though my design was, if winds and weather permitted, to touch on the windward part of the coast of Guinea, about the Rio Grande, before I came to the islands, and did not much doubt but to have been at the islands time enough to have done my business with Captain Scott before he left the islands; my sloop sailing much better than his ship, especially on a wind, which, in crossing the trade, is a great advantage: But my illness encreased after I came out to sea, which was contrary to what I expected, as well as to the opinion of the doctors; insomuch, that after struggling with it as much and as long as I could, I was at last forced to keep my bed ten days with a fever accompanied with excessive cold, clammy sweats, with faintings; after which, growing better, as soon as I was able to keep an account of the vessel's way, I demanded of my mate the latitude and longitude we were got into by his account, which he gave me; which, upon perusal, made me conjecture that we were not got so far to the eastward as his account made out; wherefore I required his logg-book, to see how far that might agree with his general account; for sometimes the best of men may make a mistake, either in transcribing the day's work, by misplacing of a figure, or even by an error or mistake in the working.

There were about fourteen leagues' difference between what I made out, as I took it out of his logg-book, and the general account he first gave me, he being so much to the eastward of what he made out by his logg-book; which farther confirmed me in my opinion, that we were not so far to the eastward, as he reckoned we were.

We had light gales, and sometimes calms, after we were got to the northward of the trade, with heavy showers of rain, which is usual at that time of the year in these latitudes; we stood as far to the northward as thirty-one degrees of latitude, and then I bent my course southerly, and to the eastward withal, till we got into the trade again: My suspicion, as I observed to you before, that we were not so far to the eastward as our reckoning made us, caused me to run about eighty leagues to the eastward of the meridian of the islands, before I came into the latitude of them, and the winds after we got into the trade, holding from the east to the east-south-east, I could not possibly, without losing a great deal of time, get hold of the coast of Guiney, so far to windward as I had at first resolved; therefore, I concluded to run directly for the Cape de Verd Islands, and designing to make the Isle of Sal first, it being the windwardmost of the Cape de Verd Islands, I stretched to the southward till I got into the latitude of it, and then, by our account, we were between sixty and seventy leagues to the eastward of it; but my mate was very positive, that the vessel was considerably farther to the eastward than our reckoning made her. After we were in the latitude, I run down west by day, and lay too by night; for though I had a good observation two or three times every twenty-four hours by the stars, and sometimes a meridian observation by the sun, yet I would not venture to run in the night, for fear of missing the island, by reason the weather was sometimes hazy, sometimes overcast, and a taut gale of wind from the east-south-east, to the south-east, and south-south-east. I run down about one hundred leagues west, without making any of the islands; and then concluding, as good reason I had, that we were to the westward of the islands, I had no other remedy left, but to stand to the northward again, till out of the trade, to get into a variable wind's way, and so to get to the eastward, and that way to gain the islands; for the time of the rains being almost come, I did not much care then for touching on the coast of Guiney, as I had before proposed; so made the best of my way for the islands, which by the ignorance or carelessness, or both, of my mate, we had missed. I stood to the northward with a very hard gale of wind at south-south-east, with rain and a very deep hollow sea, which held for about four days; after which the weather being more moderate, I stood to thirty-one degrees thirty minutes of north latitude, and then run my easting out, and so bent my course to the southward, till we got into the latitude of the Isle of Sal again, without meeting with any thing worth noting here: I then bore away west till we made the island, and it being green turtle season, I stretched in, and anchored in a road under the west side of the island called Palmera, I suppose so called, from the date-trees growing there, in the valley in the southermost bay.

After we came to an anchor I sent my boat ashore, to see if there were any signs of the turtle landing, or if any people were there a turtling, and if so, and they had any fresh caught, to bring one on board; for the French oftentimes come there to make a turtle-voyage, salting their turtle on the shore, and drying it, much after the same manner as they do cod at Newfoundland, of which and the oil, they make good markets at their islands in the West Indies; they saving the shell for the French market, where it generally yields a better price than with us in England, especially the shell of that turtle caught about these islands, which is of the thinnest sort, and extraordinary clear, as well as finely clouded; besides, there are oftentimes found greater quantities of ambergreese at this island, than at any of the Cape de Verd Islands, and were it not for the wild cats that eat it (as also does the green turtle) there would be much more found than there is.

In about two hours after the boat went ashore, she came off, and brought a green turtle which might weigh, I believe, between two and three hundredweight, and also a black, being a native of St. Nicholas's Island, who told me, that his companions ashore sent me that turtle which the boat brought off, as a present; and that there were about sixty persons natives of the Island of St. Nicholas, who were brought hither in a sloop belonging to a place, the name of which he could not remember. I asked him if he was an Englishman? and he told me yes; so I named several places in England, but he still said no; till at last, among other places, I named Bermudas, and then he said he was a Bermudian. I asked him if he was sure of it? and he said yes; he was certain that the master told him he belonged to Bermudas, and that he brought them from St. Nicholas's hither, to catch and cure turtle, and that about ten weeks ago he sailed from hence, and told the blacks he would go to Bona Vist, and take in some salt, and then stretch over to St. Nicholas, to take in some provisions for them, and promised them, without fail, to be with them in ten days at farthest; but they had heard nothing of him since, and therefore they had given him over, and believed that he was either lost, or had altered his mind, and was gone some other voyage, and offered me half their turtle, oil, shell, ambergreese, etc., to transport them with the other half to the Island of St. Nicholas. I told him I was bound down to St. Nicholas, and if any of them had a mind to go, I would give them their passage for nothing; but I likewise told him, I would carry none of the effects off the island until I knew the right of the matter, which I supposed I might when I arrived at St. Nicholas, and according as I found how it was, I did not know but I might come back again to the Isle of Sal. He desired me to let the boat put him ashore, that he might go and tell his companions, which accordingly I did, and gave him two bottles of rum, and his hat full of Indian corn, to drink and eat with his companions, when he came on shore: He was very thankful; and I ordered the boat to put ashore, which accordingly was done: And in about an hour's time it came off again, and brought an old man and a woman, who begged that I would give them their passage to St. Nicholas, adding, that they had nothing to pay for it, but the turtle oil, and shell which they had made here, and if I pleased to accept of that, they would freely give all that they had, rather than to stay here; for they said they were almost starved, having nothing to eat but the fish that they catched. I told them I would consider of it, and it being almost night, I sent them ashore, and told them I would come ashore in the morning and talk with them.

Next morning I went ashore, and they all came about me that were in the bay, which were eight men and two women, one of them having a young child; for when they began to be out of hopes of the sloop's coming again, they separated into companies, and each company went to a several bay, for the greater conveniency of living; for were they all to stay in one place, they could not so well supply their wants, all their food being then what fish they daily catched. There being, as I observed before, eleven souls at this Bay of Palmera, they begged that I would give them a passage to St. Nicholas, and they would give me all their shell, oil, and part of their dried turtle, to carry them and the other part of their dried turtle to St. Nicholas. I answered, as the day before, that I would meddle with none of the goods till I had been at St. Nicholas, to understand the right of the story; and if in case that the sloop which brought them hither was gone, or had come to any disaster, as it was very likely, we should hear something of it there, and they need not much fear, but that I should come up again to the Isle of Sal, and carry them down to St. Nicholas; but then I should expect as they had offered me now; to wit, all the turtle, oil, turtle-shell, and half the dried turtle. They said they were sure every-body would be very glad to agree to that now, without giving myself any farther trouble. But I not knowing upon what terms they were sent there, and what might be the reason of the sloop's tarrying so long, and not being willing to disappoint any man, not knowing what charges the man might have been at in relation to them, and the little credit that is to be given to any thing that those blacks say, made me resolve not to meddle with any thing till I heard farther of the business; and so I told them, if any of them wanted to go down to St. Nicholas, I would carry them for nothing, but would not carry off any of the effects; and that I was resolved to sail that evening: upon which they told me, that they should not have time to send to their comrades who were in the other bays; but if I pleased to give them their passage, and liberty to carry a little dried turtle with them for food, they should be very thankful: Which I granted, and so six men and the two women, and a little child, agreed to go, and two old men stayed on the island, and promised to send the rest word as soon as they could, of what had happened, and the great likelihood of their good fortune to get home in a short time, etc. I ordered those who designed to go with me to St. Nicholas, to get themselves ready, and also to bring the turtle they designed to carry with them for the voyage, down to the water-side, that it might be put on board: This they readily complied with, and brought down as much as the boat could carry at twice, which I ordered on board, and they would have brought more, but I would not permit them; So on board I came, and brought off with me a live green turtle, which the blacks had catched the night before; and after dinner I sent my boat ashore to bring them off, which they immediately did to the number of six men, two women, and a sucking infant. About seven o'clock in the afternoon we weighed from Palmera, and steered away for the Island of St. Nicholas; and after we got clear from under the lee of the land, which might be about ten o'clock at night, we had a pleasant fresh gale, and by day-dawning we were off of the east-point of the Island of St. Nicholas; but after we got under the lee of the island, it being high steep land, with a great many deep gullies, we met with such hard squalls of wind coming down those gullies, that it was nine at night before I could get to an anchor; which I did in a road at the west-end of the island, called Trefall Road, in about six fathom water.

Next morning the Priest, who was a native of Portugal, came down from their town, and I sent the boat ashore for him: Who told me, when he came on board, that he had sent the sloop to the Isle of Sal with the blacks; and that the sloop was all his own, he having bought her from the master, whose name was James Peer, living at Bristol; and that he had sent her to the Isle of Sal with the blacks to make turtle, some of which were his own slaves, the rest being hired, some at two dollars, some three, and other some at four dollars per month; and that all the turtle, oil, shell, etc., that they had made, was intirely his: and that his sloop had been here at St. Nicholas, since she came last from the Isle of Sal, and he had sent her to trade at St. Jago, and the other islands to the leeward, and that she was to be back again in three weeks or a month at farthest: that it was now almost three months since he sent her away, and, therefore, was afraid she was come to some accident, or else blown off from the islands, they having had two or three travadoes since she went. He also offered to freight me to the Isle of Sal, to bring off the effects and men, the turtle season being in a manner over, and their remaining upon that island, being now only a expence to him, without any farther view of making much more profit this season. He added, that he did not much fear his sloop's being safe; but as it might possibly be some time before she could arrive to transport his people from the Isle of Sal, he would gladly agree on reasonable terms to freight me thither; and if not, he must even wait the coming of his own sloop. I told him, if I undertook the matter, I would not be unreasonable; but as yet I was not resolved whether to go to the Isle of Sal, or not; but was designed in the evening, or the next morning, if the weather proved moderate, to weigh my anchor, and turn up into Paragheesi Road, and then I would resolve him.

Now the blacks which I had brought from the Isle of Sal told me, that the Island of St. Nicholas, as also all the windward islands of the Cape de Verd, were in great want of provisions;

and that the famine had raged so at this island, in particular, that within the last twelve months, there died no less than five hundred souls purely for want of food, the famine having been for several years past at the other windward islands; but although St. Nicholas had groaned under it but one year, yet it was visited the severest of all the islands during the time that it held. Now this was the reason why I resolved for Paragheesi, because it was nigher their town, and for the most part a level way (which is very rare in those islands, they being generally very steep and rocky), my intent being to truck or barter away some of my corn, rice, etc., with the inhabitants, in exchange for cotton-cloths (such as we trade with on the coast of Guiney, called by the Portuguese, and from them by the blacks, barrafools), likewise for ambergreese, dragons'-blood,[1] money, etc., the road of Trefall, where I lay, not being so convenient for trading, by reason of its distance from the town, which was about sixteen or eighteen miles, and that being a rocky way, with very high and steep ascents and descents.

The Priest went ashore in the afternoon, as also did some of the blacks which I brought from the Isle of Sal, and went up to town; and understanding that I designed for Paragheesi, they desired that I would let their turtle remain on board till the vessel came there, which I did.

Next morning I weighed from Trefall, and got up to Paragheesi about nine o'clock that forenoon, and anchored in the old road in six fathom water; the reason why I did not go to Paragheesi, was, because the blacks I had on board informed me that if I went in there I should be so pestered with the inhabitants, when they came to hear I had provisions to sell, that I should never be able to keep my vessel clear of them; and, perhaps the greatest number of them that would flock on board, would be poor, and unable to do any thing but beg or steal; whereas, as I lay off at an anchor, there could none come on board but such as I thought fit to bring off in my boat, and then I need not be troubled with any, but those who brought something with them to trade.

[1] The red gum of a tree, used by apothecaries.

I approved and made use of their advice; however, few or none came down besides the Priest, and those who waited upon him, or were his followers; whether it was because I did not moor in the harbour, or that the Priest prevented them, for fear that it should hinder my agreeing with him to go to the Isle of Sal, I am not able to determine; however, I was willing to lay hold of the freight offered, for fear his sloop should come, being satisfied I should have time enough to make my market at St. Nicholas, after my return from the Isle of Sal, which would not take up above a week's time if no accident happened: besides I did not fear any vessel coming with provisions to spoil my market, by reason it was the wrong time of the year, being the season for shifting winds, and Captain Scott, as I heard, had been there about ten days before my arrival, but could supply them but with very little provisions, which was the only thing they then wanted; and that Captain Scott was gone to Bona Vist, and so from thence to trade among the Leeward Islands.[1] So the Priest and I agreed for me to sail to the Isle of Sal, and bring off all the people and effects that belonged to him, or on his account, and he was to pay me one hundred dollars, and a lusty, stout, sound man slave, about thirty years of age; to be paid and delivered at our return to the Island of St. Nicholas, before any of the effects brought from the Isle of Sal were landed; the Priest also engaging himself to go along with me, to make the better dispatch in embarquing the goods from that island.

So I concluded to weigh anchor from Paragheesi next morning, and turn up to Currisal, a road lying on the south-east side of the island, being very commodious for watering; the fresh water running down to the sea; where I resolved to recruit my store of water and wood, which was almost spent; the Priest promising to meet me there the next morning, with some blacks to assist my men in that work. Accordingly next morning I weighed before day, and got up and anchored in Currisal Road before noon; where, according to promise, the Priest met me with four blacks. We were not long a watering,

[1] The northern members of the Cape Verde archipelago.

the water being, as I observed, so nigh the seaside; but the
wood was a long way to fetch, and over steep rocks, so that if
it had not been for the blacks' assistance, I believe my own
men would not have been able to have found it, or to get it
down when found. The last turn of wood we got on board
about eleven o'clock at night, and it proving calm in the road,
I could not weigh anchor that night as I designed. The Priest
with his four blacks, being sea-sick, lay ashore on the sand all
night according to their desire; and if I saw an opportunity of
weighing, I was to send the boat for them. He had sent some
other blacks, while we were wooding and watering, to hunt for
wild goats, who brought in two, whereof he sent me one on
board.

CHAPTER TWO

*

NEXT morning about dawning, as it was my usual custom, I turned out, it continuing still calm; and as the day broke out, looking about, I espied three sail of ships off the bay, one ship to the eastward, another ship to the westward, and the third right off the middle of the bay; the first of them that I made plain with my glass was the eastwardmost ship, which seemed to be a full-built and loaden ship, and I took the rest to be the same, and of her company, and imagined that, perhaps, they might want water, etc. They had but very little wind in the offing, and it continued still calm in the bay. I saw them bring to, then edge away, but could not perceive any signals made by them; and seeing them act thus, I still continued in my first opinion, that they wanted to touch at the island for wood, water, etc., but that, perhaps, they might be unacquainted with the roads or harbours of the island; insomuch that I was almost of the mind to send my mate off with the boat to conduct them in.

As soon as the day broke up clear, that they made me, the middlemost of the three stood right in for me, and as the sun rose, the wind freshened and backed more to the eastward, as is usual there after calm night. As she drew nigher, I made her with my glass to be a scooner, and full of hands, all in their white shirts, and likewise I saw a whole tier of great guns; and, then, indeed, I began to suspect what they were: But I had no remedy but patiently to wait the event, for I could do nothing, except I put the vessel ashore, which would have been meer madness to have done, although I had been sure they were pirates; and I was so surrounded by them, that there was no possibility of escaping from them, and especially, it holding calm within the bay; and they coming in with the day-breeze, came in as fast as the wind. He came in under an English ensign, jack, and pendant, and as soon as I perceived his colours, I hoisted my ensign; he had eight guns, and six pattereroes, and seventy men. He stretched ahead of us, and haled us; I answered him: He asked, *Where the sloop belonged to?* I answered, *To London.* He asked, *From whence we came?* I told him, *From Barbadoes.* He said, *It was very well; he knew that*; and so brought to a-head of us, and bid me send my boat on board of him; which accordingly I did, with two hands in her, and I myself kept walking on the deck. The captain of the scooner, whose name was John Lopez, a Portuguese (as I was told afterwards; but then went by the name of John Russel, pretending, though falsely, that he was born in the northern parts of England), asked the people who came on board of him with the boat, *Where the master of the sloop was?* who answered, *That he was on board, and sent them with the boat to know what they wanted.* He asked them, *Which was the master of the sloop!* So they shewed me to him as I was walking the sloop's deck, and then he immediately called to me, saying, *You dog! you son of a b – ! you speckled-shirt dog!* (for I had a speckled Holland shirt on, and was slip-shoed, and without stockings, being just as I turned out of my cabin). So he still continued calling in that manner, and I considering what hands I was fallen into, and that it would be easie for them to send a ball through me for my silence, which, perhaps, they might deem contempt of them, as indeed it was, I thought it was the safest and wisest course, to answer, according to the proverb, *When your hand is in the lion's mouth, get it out as easie as you can*, and not, in the least, to seem to resent anything that they said, or did to me, but endeavour to submit, if not with a willing mind, yet with a seeming patience, as in truth I could do no otherwise, except I would, with a foolish rashness, provoke them to be my executioners; and, God knows, a small provocation, nay, if they do but conceit it so, will occasion the taking any honest man's life away. So I answered him, *Ho lo:* He said, *You dog, you, why did not you come on board with the boat, you son of a b – ? I will drub you, you dog, within an inch of your life, and that inch too.* I made him answer, *That he only commanding the boat on board, I did not think he required me; but if he pleased to send the boat, I would come and wait upon him on board.* He answered, *Ay, you dog, and I will teach you better manners.* Upon this, he ordered some of the pirates into my boat, to fetch me, as also eight or ten more of them, to take possession of the sloop mean while; which accordingly was done, and I came along side of the scooner. The captain of her still continued to threaten me with drubbing, *to teach me better manners than so to affront him.* I answered, *I did not design to affront him, or any of the company.* *D – n you, you dog,* said he, *do not stand there to chatter; come on board.* So up the side I came, this glib-tongued captain standing at the entring-place with his cutlash ready drawn in his hand, to receive me. The least I expected was a sound drubbing bout, and I had abundance of reason to apprehend even worse than that, he still continuing to threaten what he would do to me when I came in: But a man in a gold laced hat, whom afterwards I understood to be the gunner, looked over the side, as I was coming up, and said, *Come up, Master, you shall not be abused.* After I got in, the captain up with his cutlash, as though he was going to cleave me down, and said, *You dog, you, what was the reason you did not come on board when the boat first came? What do you think you deserve?* I answered, *If I had done amiss, it was through ignorance, and for want of knowing better; and hoped that he would excuse this my fault, I not knowing who or what they were.* Then he rapped out an oath, with a *Damn you, you dog, what, or who do you think we are?* I paused a while, not well knowing what answer to make, for fear of offending them again; for one displeasing word is as much as the best man in the world's life is worth, while in their clutches. However, after a little pause, I told him, *I believed they were gentlemen of fortune belonging to the sea.* At which he answered and said, *You lie, by G – , we are pirates, by G – .* Then I answered again, and said, *Well, gentlemen, now I know who you are, but not before, and am sorry I have not carried myself as I should; but,* as I had told them before, I said, *It was my ignorance, never having been taken by such gentlemen as they before, and, therefore, did not know the way of behaving myself to them, as they might have expected, had I been acquainted with their ways or customs* (though I had been once taken by pirates before, coming from Newfoundland, when I was a youth, but I did not then think it proper to take notice of it to them, but the reverse; and thought it the safest course at present, to pretend ignorance, as the only way to appease his unmerited, though dangerous and threatning wrath). So after he had hectored and bounced thus a while, he asked me, in a gaming way, *Why I had not put on my best cloaths, when I came a visiting such gentlemen as they were?* I told him, *That that was the common dress which I wore on board my own vessel in a morning, and did not know that I should have paid a visit to such gentlemen as they were, when I dressed myself. Besides, when he called me to come on board of him, he threatned me so, that I came from on board my own vessel as it were in a fright, that made me have but very little thought, or stomach either, to change my present dress; but if he pleased to let me go on board the sloop, and grant me the liberty, it would not be too late yet, to dress myself in better cloaths. No, damn you,* said he, *now it is too late: What cloaths we took you in, you shall keep: But your sloop, and what is in her, is ours.* I told him, *I perceived it was, but still hoped, as I wholly lay at his mercy, he would be so generous as to take only what they had occasion for, and leave me the rest.* He answered, *As to that, he could say nothing as yet, that being a company-business to decide*; and withal demanded of me, an account of every thing that was on board the sloop, particularly the cargo, and what money I had, or knew to be on board; and if I did not give a true and exact account, and discover to him every thing; and if upon their rummaging, they found the least thing on board which I did not discover, they would set the sloop on fire, and me in her. He added, that he had a full account of what cargo I brought out from Barbadoes, and, therefore, if I had touched anywhere, and disposed of any of it, I must not conceal the money; for if I did, I should fare the worse. All the rest of the Johns that were standing by, in a seeming friendly manner, told me, that it would be much better for me, to make a full and true discovery of every thing, especially of money, arms, and ammunition, which, as they said, were the principal things they sought after; for it was their manner to punish

39

liars and concealers, especially of those things they had now mentioned, in a very severe manner. I told them, I would give them an account of everything on board, as exact as my memory would suffer me, which accordingly I then did; and withal told them, that if I failed in giving them an exact account of every thing, that it was not with a design to conceal any thing from them, but meerly the fault of my memory, for which, if any happened, I hoped they would excuse me, and not punish me, as culpable for that, which was not a wilful or designed ommission. *But*, said I, *if you please, gentlemen, to give me liberty to go on board of the sloop for my papers, and to peruse them, I shall then be able to give you a very exact inventory, I think, I may say of everything on board, except what properly belonged to my men.* But Captain Russel told me *No, and as for my papers, he would take care of them, and if anything was found on board, more than I had given an account of, I must stand clear.*

All this while the pirates were rommaging on board the sloop, which, when they had done, I suppose, as much as they thought fit, some of them came on board, with an account of what they had found or seen there, which was nothing more than what I had told them of before, saving a ring, and my silver buckles, which really I had forgotten, otherwise I should have mentioned them: However, they were so generous as to keep them.

By this time the Priest and the blacks, mistrusting how the game went, were got a pretty way up the rocks, in order to escape into the mountains, which the pirates observing, Captain Russel asked me, *If I knew who those people were?* I not knowing but the same question might have been asked of some of my people, and that, perhaps, they might have told them, and not being willing, and, indeed, I may say, not daring, to be caught in a lye, ingenuously told them the truth, and said, *They were the Priest and some blacks with him, who were to have gone with me to the Isle of Sal, if I had not thus met with them.* He then asked, *What we were to have done at the Isle of Sal?* So I told him the occasion, and also of the bargain which I had made with him on that head. He said, *The Priest would never see his sloop more.* I asked him, *If he heard anything of her?* He said *Yes, they had taken her, and their own gang, that they had put on board of her, ran away with her, with a booty of eight hundred pounds in money, besides other goods;* and also he said, *He had an account of me, and what cargo I brought out of Barbadoes, and that in all probability, I was then arrived at St. Nicholas; which information, and also that the Priest and Governor of St. Nicholas had a pretty large bag of dollars, which each of them had hoarded up, was the only occasion of their coming here: otherwise, if they had not received this information, they were designed to have gone directly from the Island of Bona Vist, after they had cleaned and fitted their vessels, on their intended enterprize.*

I told him, *I could not imagine who could give him that information of me, for that I had hardly communicated my design of touching at these islands to any, that I thought was or could be liable to fall into their hands, except one person.* He told me, *It was one that came out in company with me from Barbadoes;* and to be short, said, *it was Captain Scott told them, and how that all the sloop was his, and he had filled my hold full of sugar, rum, etc., and that he was sure I was, by this time, arrived at the Island of St. Nicholas, St. Antonia, or some of the windward islands, unless I was run away with his sloop and cargo; and likewise that he had seen, when he was last a trading at St. Nicholas, both the Priest's and Governor's money, which, as he reported to them, he was certain, neither of them could have less than sixteen hundred or two thousand dollars apiece.* So I asked them, *How it was with Captain Scott?* They told me, *He was but indifferent yet, they thought he was better than he deserved; and told me how they had burnt his ship, and that he had been put ashore by them at Bona Vist, where they believed he at present was.*

Russel, still eyeing the Priest and blacks, asked me, *If I thought it was possible to go ashore and catch them?* I told him, *I thought not.* He asked me, *Why? For, he had men on board could out-walk or out-run them, he was sure.* I told him, *I believed not; for before his boat could put ashore, they would be got two or three miles up into the country, and that the way there was so steep and rocky, that I was sure his men could not climb up, much less pretend to catch them.* He answered, *It did not signify much; for he would have him,* meaning the Priest, *and some more of them, before this time to-morrow;* and asked me, *Which was the nighest anchoring-place to the town?* And also *from which anchoring-place was the smoothest path or road up to it?* I told him, *I did not know for certain; neither was I any-ways acquainted on the island, having never been half a quarter of a mile up from the sea-side, on any part of it.* He said, *I might have heard from the inhabitants.* I told him, *I did hear some of the inhabitants say, that the road of Paragheesi was the nighest anchoring-place to the town, of all the roads about the island; but what sort of pathway it was up to town, I had not so exactly inquired, as to be able to satisfy him in that.* *Well,* says Russel, *we will go to Paragheesi; and,* says he to me, *you shall pilot us thither.* I told him, *I never had been there, and did not know, but there might be sunken rocks in the way; and, therefore, thought myself very unqualified to take charge of the vessel thither; but,* I told him, *there were two blacks on board the sloop, both natives and fishermen of that island; and that one of them was my pilot, and might be, as far as I knew, very capable to pilot their vessel into the road; or, perhaps, might discover to them some more convenient place to anchor or land at.* Upon this, he swore and damned, saying, *What! do you think I will let a negro pilot me?* *No, no;* but swore *I should pilot the vessel into an anchoring-place, and stand clear if the least accident happened to her.* I told him, *I would do as well as I could, and that I had acquainted him already of my little knowledge of the island.* *Well,* says he, *do as well as you can: Do as you would do, was it your own vessel.* I told him *I would: Well,* said he, *we desire you to do no more;* and immediately he gave orders to make the best of our way down to Paragheesi, which accordingly was done; and the pirates on board my sloop slipped the cable, because they would not take the pains to weigh the anchor, and so, through sloth and laziness, left a good cable and anchor behind.

All this time, the other two ships lay too in the offing, but as soon as they saw us make sail down to leeward, the *Rose Pink*, having thirty-six guns mounted, commanded by Edward Loe, who was then Commodore of them, edged in towards us, upon which we edged off towards him, and spoke with him, and Russel gave him an account of what had passed, and of his design of landing that evening upon the Island of St. Nicholas, in order to take the Priest and Governor, if he approved of their resolution. Which the Commodore said he did, and immediately ordered his great launch to be manned, and sent some more of his ship's company to join and reinforce the scooner's crew, and to go ashore with them in the expedition; which was accordingly done.

Then we haled in for the shore again, and when we were got the length of Porto Lappa, which is a road, or bay, lying about midway, or a little more, between Currisal and Paragheesi, one of the scooner's company raps out a great oath, *That that was the best place to land at, and the nighest to the town;* upon which Captain Russel, whom I understood then to be, not only captain of the scooner, but also quarter-master-general of all the companies, asked me, *If it was as the fellow said?* I told him, *I could not tell; it might be so as far as I knew; for all the knowledge I had as to that, was only by the relation of the inhabitants, and therefore could not be certain myself, not knowing but they might deceive me in the relations they made me.* The fellow swore, *That he knew the place perfectly well; and that he had landed there before, and was acquainted with the way up to the town:* Upon which, Captain Russel ordered to stand in for the bay of Porto Lappa, and likewise directed the gang, that was to go ashore, to have their arms ready, and every man to prepare so many rounds of cartridges, both for pistols and pieces, and to be in a readiness to embarque in the boats, as soon as we should be got nigh enough to the land. When we came within about half a league of the shore, the boats were manned by Russel's order, who also went ashore, and headed them, to the number of thirty-five, besides those which went in the boats to bring them off again. We were ordered by

Russel, as soon as the boats were put off, to make the best of our way down to Paragheesi, and come to an anchor, and stay there till farther orders, and the boats were to follow us down to the bay, after they had landed the men at Porto Lappa.

All this was accordingly performed, and we cast anchor in the old road, where I had anchored before in the sloop; and the boats, after they had landed the men, also came down, and got on board of us about six o'clock that evening; the two ships keeping plying off, and on, open with where we lay.

Here we rid all night, during which, the Commodore kept out a light, as we also did to answer him; and next day Captain Russel, with all his company, came down to Paragheesi, and brought with them as prisoners, the Priest and the old Governor's son, with five or six men-blacks; and upon their haling the scooner, the boats were manned and sent ashore for them, and they were all brought off together. It was about one o'clock in the afternoon when they came on board, and immediately we weighed, and stood off to the ships, which were then lying too in the offing; and when we were come within call of the Commodore, he haled us, and asked, *How all fared? And what luck?* And was answered by Russel, *That he would wait on him on board, and give him a full and particular account.* Accordingly the launch was forthwith manned, and the men sent from the Commodore, to join the scooner's men, for the shore expedition, were ordered to embarque in her, to go on board their own ship; which being done, I was ordered also to get into her, to present myself, and pay my respects to the great Captain Loe, their Commodore: Accordingly I went into the launch, and Russel followed us in his own boat, with the Priest and the other prisoners, which they had brought off the Island of St. Nicholas.

CHAPTER THREE

*

WHEN I came on board the *Rose Pink*, the company welcomed me on board, and said, *They were sorry for my loss; but told me I must go to pay my respects to the captain, who was in the cabbin, and waited for me.* I was ushered in by an officer, who, I think, was their gunner, and who, by his deportment, acted as though he had been master of the ceremonies; though I do not remember to have heard of such an officer or officers mentioned among them, neither do I know whether they are always so formal on board their Commodore, at the first reception of their captivated masters of vessels. When I came into the cabbin, the officer who conducted me thither, after paying his respects to the Commodore, told him, *That I was the master of the sloop which they had taken the day before*, and then withdrew out of the cabbin, leaving us two alone.

Captain Loe, with the usual compliment, welcomed me on board, and told me, *He was very sorry for my loss, and that it was not his desire to meet with any of his countrymen, but rather with foreigners, excepting some few that he wanted to chastise for their rogueishness*, as he called it: *But however*, says he, *since fortune has ordered it so, that you have fallen into our hands, I would have you to be of good cheer, and not to be cast down.* I told him, *That I also was very sorry, that it was my chance to fall into their way; but still encouraged myself in the hopes, that I was in the hands of gentlemen of honour and generosity; it being still in their power whether to make this their capture of me, a misfortune or not.* He said, *It did not lie in his particular power; for he was but one man, and all business of this nature, must be done in publick, and by a majority of votes by the whole company; and though neither he, nor, he believed, any of the company, desired to meet with any of their own nation (except some few persons for the reasons before-mentioned), yet when they did, it could not well be avoided, but that they must take as their own what Providence sent them: And as they were gentlemen, who entirely depended upon fortune, they durst not be so ungrateful to her, as to refuse anything which she put into their*

45

way; for if they should despise any of her favours, though never so mean, they might offend her, and thereby cause her to withdraw her hand from them; and so, perhaps, they might perish for want of those things, which in their rash folly they slighted. He then, in a very obliging tone, desired me to sit down, he himself all this time not once moving from his seat, which was one of the great guns, though there were chairs enough in the cabbin; but, I suppose, he thought he should not appear so martial, or hero-like, if he sat on a chair, as he did on a great gun.

After I had sat down, he asked me, *What I would drink?* I thanked him, and told him, *I did not much care for drinking; but out of a sense of the honour he did me in asking, I would drink anything with him which he pleased to drink.* He told me, *It would not avail me anything to be cast down: It was fortune of war, and grieving or vexing myself, might be of no good consequence in respect to my health; besides, it would be more taking,* he said, *with the company, to appear brisk, lively, and with as little concern as I could. And come,* says he, *you may, and I hope you will, have better fortune hereafter.* So ringing the cabbin-bell, and one of his *valet de chambres*, or rather *valet de cabins*, appearing, he commanded him to make a bowl of punch, in the great bowl which was a rich silver one, and held, I believe, about two gallons; which being done, he ordered likewise some wine to be set on the table, and accordingly two bottles of claret were brought; and then he took the bowl and drank to me in punch; but bid me pledge him in which I liked best; which I did in wine. He told me, *That what he could favour me in, he would, and wished that it had been my fortune to have been taken by them ten days or a fortnight sooner, for then,* he said, *they had abundance of good commodities, which they took in two Portugueze outward-bound Brasile men, viz. cloth, as well linens as woollens, both fine and coarse, hats of all sorts, silk, iron, and other rich goods in abundance, and believed, he could have prevailed with the company even to have loaded my sloop. But now they had no goods at all, he believed, having disposed of them all, either by giving them to other prizes, etc., or heaving the rest into David Jones's locker (i.e. the sea); but*

46

did not know, but it might be his lot, perhaps, to meet with me again, when it might lie in his way to make me a retaliation for my present loss; and he did assure me, that when such an occasion as he was but now a speaking of, offered, I might depend he would not be wanting to serve me in anything that might turn to my advantage, as far as his power or interest could reach. I could do no less, in common civility, and the truth is, I dared do no less, than thank him.

By this time, word was brought into the cabbin, that the Quarter-Master-General Russel was come on board, with the Priest and the other prisoners, which they had brought off from the Island of St. Nicholas. Captain Loe ordered Captain Russel, the Priest and the Governor's son of St. Nicholas, to be called into the great cabbin, and accordingly they came, and the cabbin was immediately filled with officers, and some others of the principal pirates, who, I suppose, by their long standing, or their activity in villainy, had signalized themselves for principals of the crew; out of whom, as occasion served, they also chose their officers, etc. The cabbin having been thus filled, Loe, after compliments passed, bid Russel and the prisoners sit down, and then asked Russel, *What news? And how the game went?* Upon which, Russel began his relation, in these words, as near as I can remember.

'According to our last agreement in consultation, says he, we landed with thirty-five men, on the Island of St. Nicholas, yesterday in the afternoon, as soon as possibly we could after the taking of the sloop, and putting things in such order as was proper; and immediately after our landing, we apprehended two blacks of the natives, who were come down to know who we were, and what account we were upon, that they might go and acquaint the Governor of us, as they said. But we retarded their journey, by making them our guides, to direct and shew us the way to the town; and it was well we happened to meet them, for night coming on, we should never have found the way. But by our taking those men, we prevented any rumour or notice of our coming, and so were assured there was no booty there, but what we found. We got to town about nine o'clock at night, and, by estimation, from the place of our landing to the town, was about twelve miles. We went directly to the Governor's house, and having set a guard there, to prevent anybody's going out, or in, that there might be no opportunity of conveying any thing out of the house, I took some hands with me, and went to the Priest's house, whom we found not to have been long come home, from Currisal, and had not the least thought of our so sudden arrival here, believing it was impossible that we could reach the town till the day following, if we were designed to come up; neither had he any notice of our arrival before, till his own eyes confirmed it. But, however, he did not seem to be much surprised. I set a guard, to prevent anything being conveyed out; and the Priest ordered such victuals as he had, to be set on the table, and wine enough, and told me, *That he could not entertain us at such an unseasonable time of night as he would, and hoped we would excuse him for not being better provided, and take the will for the deed;* adding, *That to such as we found, we were very welcome, wishing it had been better; but if we tarried till next day,* he said, *we should be supplied plentifully, with whatever the island afforded.* Upon which I thanked him, and told him, *I came of an errand, and must perform it, which was, That we had a positive informations, from very good hands, who had been eye-witnesses, that he, as also the Governor, had good store of dollars, as well as gold hoarded up, and that we were come to share it with them, it being one great branch of our trade not to let money lie rusting and cankering in old bags or chests, but to make it move and circulate, whenever we could come at it.* At which, the Priest, without any apparent concern, replied, *That whoever gave us that information gave a false one, as anyone might easily conceive, if they but gave themselves leave to consider how unlikely, nay, he might very well say, impossible it was, to get money in those barren, uncultivated and commerceless islands.* I told him, *I was master of but two senses that could give me satisfaction whether the information was false, or what he now said was true, which were seeing and feeling.* He said, *I was welcome to make use of those senses to my satisfaction, which I am sure,* says he, *will then fully confirm the truth of what I have said;* and immediately ordered wax-candles (they having no other there, and them only for the use of the Church, being all consecrated, and sent thither by the Bishop of St. Jago, whose business it is to send consecrated candles, oil, etc., for the use of the Church, to all the adjacent islands) to be lighted; and we searched all the house, chests, trunks, and everywhere throughout and about the house, and found nothing worth taking, and only about twenty dollars in money, which I did not think it worth our while to take from him. From thence I went to the Governor's house, and seached there as narrowly as we could, and found less there; after which I disposed of my men as I thought most convenient for the reposing and refreshing them after their fatiguing journey, but yet with a due regard withal to our own security, by setting a guard, and ordering the rest to repose as well as they could, and not one of them to offer to stir out of the Governor's house; and withal giving them a strict charge to be ready with their arms at all calls, and at a moment's warning, and not one of them to unarm, or unfling his pistols: Which was accordingly very regularly and orderly performed; and next morning we concluded, that not having lighted on the booty according to information given, or rather the information being false, no such booty being there, we had therefore agreed to seize and bring on board the Governor, Priest, and four or five besides of the principal inhabitants for your more ample satisfaction.'

Captain Loe sitting as demure and attentive all the while, as a judge upon the bench, of a sudden started, as it were, out of a deep study, and interrupting Russel in his story, said, *Z – ds, what satisfaction is this to me or the company? We did not want these fellows, d – n them; No, we wanted their money, if they had any; and if not, they might have stayed ashore, or gone to the Devil where they belong to, so we had had the money:* To this Russel replied in a something more stern tone, and said, *Captain Loe, we had as much reason for, and interest in getting the money, if there had been any, as you had, or any of the company could have, and we did as much as could be done to find it; neither do I believe they have any more than what we saw, and which had I taken it, would not have amounted to sixpence apiece when shared among the company, as it was not worth having our name called in question for such an insignificant trifle. For my part, I am for something that is worth taking, and if I cannot light with such, I never will give the world occasion to say I am a poor, pitiful, or mean-spirited fellow: No, I will rob for something of value, or else will not rob at all, especially from these people among whom we may reckon one of our places of refuge in case any of us should be separated from the company, or the company break, etc., and therefore I boldly affirm, that by drawing on us an odium from these people for a trifle, might be of pernicious consequence to us, and more especially, if any of us should be put to such extremities as might happen.*

Hereupon Captain Loe interrupting him, replied, *That what he said was very true*, and asked the Priest several questions, after which, he directed them to be put on board the scooner, and from her to be put ashore; but I was ordered to remain on board the Commodore till by a general vote of the company it should be determined how I and the sloop were to be disposed of; and Captain Loe ordered a hammock and bedding to be fixed for me, and told me, *That he would not oblige me to sit up later than I thought fit, nor drink more than suited my own inclination; and that he liked my company no longer than his was agreeable to me;* adding, *That there should be no confinement or obligation as to drinking, or sitting up, but I might drink, and go to sleep, when I pleased, without any exceptions being taken, ordering me to want for nothing that was on board; for I was very welcome to anything that was there, as to eatables and drinkables.* I thanked him, and told him, *I would, with all due gratefulness, make use of that freedom which he was so generous to offer me, etc.* About eight o'clock at night, I took my leave of him, and went to my hammock, where I continued all night, with thoughts roving and perplexed enough, not being able, as yet, to guess what they designed to do with me, whether they intended to give me the sloop again, or to burn her, as I heard it tossed about by some, or to keep me as a prisoner on board, or put me ashoar.

My two boys and mate remained still on board the sloop, but all the rest they took on board of them, not once so much as asking them whether they would enter with them, only demanding their names, which the steward writ down in their roll-book.

About eight o'clock in the morning I turned out, and went upon deck, and as I was walking backwards and forwards, as is usual amongst us sailors, there came up one of the company to me, and bid me good-morrow, and told me, *He was very sorry for my misfortune.* I answered, *So was I:* He looked at me, and said, *He believed I did not know him.* I replied, *It was true, I did not know him; neither, at present, could I call to mind that ever I had seen him before in the whole course of my life.* He smiled, and said, *He once belonged to me, and sailed with me when I was commander of the 'Susannah' in the year* 1718 (At that time I was master of a ship called the *Susannah,* about the burthen of three hundred tons, whereof was sole owner Mr. Richard Stephens, merchant, living at this present writing in Shad-Thames, Southwark-side, near London –). In the interim came up two more, who told me they all belonged to me in the *Susannah,* at one time. By this time I had recollected my memory so far as just to call them to mind, and that was all; and then I told them I did remember them. They said, they were truly very sorry for my misfortune, and would do all that lay in their power to serve me, and told me, they had among them the quantity of about forty or fifty pieces of white linnen cloth, and six or eight pieces of silk, besides some other things; and they would also, they said, make what interest they could for me with their consorts and intimates, and with them would make a gathering for me of what things they could, and would put it on board for me as soon as the company had determined that I should have my sloop again. They then looked about them as though they had something to say that they were not willing anybody should hear; but as it happened, there was nobody nigh us, which was an opportunity very rare in these sort of ships, of speaking without interruption: But we lying too all night, nobody had anything to do, but

51

the lookers-out at the topmast-head; the mate of the watch, quarter-master of the watch, helmsman, etc., being gone down to drink a dram, I suppose, or to smoak a pipe of tobacco, or the like. However it was, we had the quarterdeck intire to ourselves, and they seeing the coast clear, told me, with much seeming concern, That if I did not take abundance of care, they would force me to stay with them, for my mate had informed them, that I was very well acquainted on the coast of Brasile, and they were bound down along the coast of Guinea, and afterwards designed to stretch over to the coast of Brasile: That there was not one man of all the company that had ever been upon any part of that coast; and that there was but one way for me to escape being forced; but I must be very close, and not discover what they were going to tell me; for if it was known that they had divulged it, notwithstanding they were entered men, and as much of the company as any of them, yet they were sure it would cost them no smaller a price for it than their lives. I told them, I was very much obliged to them for their good-will, and did not wish them to have any occasion for my service; but if ever it should be so, they might depend it should be to the utmost of my power; and as for my betraying anything that they should tell me of, they could not fear that, because my own interest would be a sufficient tye upon me to the contrary; and were it not so, and that I was sure to get mountains of gold by divulging it to their prejudice, I would sooner suffer my tongue to be plucked out.

They said, they did not much fear my revealing it, because the disclosing it would rather be a prejudice to me than an advantage, and therefore out of pure respect to me they would tell me; which was thus: *You must know*, said they, *that we have an article which we are sworn to, which is, not to force any married man, against his will, to serve us: Now we have been at a close consultation whether we should oblige you to go with us, not as one of the company, but as a forced prisoner, in order to be our pilot on the coast of Brasile, where we are designed to cruise, and hope to make our voyage; and your mate*, continued they, *has offered to enter with us, but desires to defer it till we*

*have determined your case. Now your mate, as yet, is ignorant of
our articles, we never exposing them to any till they are going to
sign them. He was asked, Whether you was married or not?
and he said, He could not tell for certain, but believed you was not:
Upon which we spoke, and said, We had known you several years,
and had sailed with you in a frigat-built ship of three hundred
tons, or more: That you was an extraordinary good man to your
men, both for usage and payment; and that, to our knowledge
you was married, and had four children then: However, there is
one man who would fain have the company break through their
oath on that article, and tells them, They may, and ought to do it,
because it is a case of necessity, they having no possibility of getting
a pilot at present for that coast, except they take you: And in
their run along the coast of Guinea, if they should light of anybody
that was acquainted with the coast of Brasile, and no way
exempted from serving them by the articles, then they might take
him and turn you ashore, but until such offered, he did not see
but the oath might be dispensed with; but,* continued they,
*Captain Loe is very much against it, and told them, That it
would be an ill precedent, and of bad consequence; for if we once
take the liberty of breaking our articles and oath, then there is
none of us can be sure of anything: If, said Captain Loe, you can
perswade the man upon any terms to stay with us as a prisoner, or
otherwise, well and good; if not, do not let us break the laws
that we have made ourselves, and sworn to.* They went on and
told me, *That most of the company seemed to agree with Captain
Loe's opinion, but Russel,* said they, *seemed to be sadly nettled
at it, that his advice was not to be taken; and,* continued they,
*you will be asked the question, we reckon, by and by, when
Russel comes on board, and all the heads meet again; but you must
be sure to say you are married, and have five or six children; for
it is only that, that will prevent you being forced; though, you
may depend upon it, Russel will do what he can to perswade the
company to break the article, which we hope they will not, nor
shall they ever have our consent; and, indeed, there are very few
of the company but what are against it, but Russel bears a great
sway in the company, and can almost draw them any way.*

53

However, we have put you in the best method that we can, and hope it will do: But, for fear notice should be taken of our being so long together, we have told you as much as we can, and leave you to manage it; and so God bless you.

Upon this, away they went, and by and by Captain Loe turns out, and comes upon deck, and bidding me good-morrow, asked me, *How I did? and how I liked my bed?* I thanked him, and told him, *I was very well, at his service, and liked my bed very well, and was very much obliged to him for the care he had taken of me.* After which, he ordered a consultation signal to be made, which was their *Green Trumpeter*, as they called him, hoisted at the mizen-peek: It was a green silk flag, with a yellow figure of a man blowing a trumpet on it. The signal being made, away came the boats flocking on board the Commodore, and when they were all come on board, Captain Loe told them, He only wanted them to breakfast with him; so down they went into the cabbin as many as it would well hold, and the rest in the steerage, and where they could.

After breakfast, Captain Loe asked me, *If I was married? and how many children I had?* I told him, *I had been married about ten years, and had five children when I came from home, and did not know but I might have six now, one being on the stocks when I came from home.* He asked me, *Whether I had left my wife well provided for, when I came from home?* I told him, *I had left her in but very indifferent circumstances: That having met with former misfortunes, I was so low reduced, that the greatest part of my substance was in this sloop and cargo; and that if I was put by this trip, I did not know but my family might want bread before I could supply them.*

Loe then turning to Russel, said, *It will not do, Russel. What will not do?* said Russel. Loe answered, *You know who I mean; we must not, and it shall not be, by G – d. It must, and shall, by G – d,* replied Russel. *Self-preservation is the first law of Nature, and Necessity, according to the old proverb, has no law. Well,* says Loe, *It shall never be with my consent.* Hereupon most of the company said, *It was a pity, and ought to be taken into consideration, and seriously weighed amongst them, and then put to the vote.* At which Loe said, *So it ought, and there is nothing like the time present to decide the controversy, and to determine the matter.* They all answered, *Ay, it was best to end it now.*

Then Loe ordered them all to go upon deck, and bid me stay in the cabbin; so up they went all hands, and I sat still and smoaked a pipe of tobacco, wine and punch being left on the table: And though I was very impatient to know the determination, sometimes hoping it would be in my favour, and sometimes fearing the contrary; yet I durst not go out of the cabbin to hear what they said, nor make any enquiry about it.

After they had been upon deck about two hours, they came down again, and Loe asked me, *How I did? and how I liked my company since they went upon deck?* I thanked him, and said, *I was very well, at his service; and as for my company, I liked it very well, and it was company that few would dislike.* Why, said he, *I thought you had been all alone ever since we went upon deck.* I answered, *How could you think, sir, that I was alone, when you left me three such boon, jolly companions to keep me company?*

Z – ds, says Loe, and seemed a little angry, *I left nobody, and ordered nobody but the boy Jack, and him I bid stay at the cabbin-door, without-side, and not go in, nor stir from the door, until I bid him.* But, I said, *sir, my three companions were not humane bodies, but those which you left on the table, to wit, a pipe of tobacco, a bottle of French claret, and a bowl of punch;* at which they all laughed, and Loe said, *I was right:* So after some discourses had passed by way of diversion, Russel said to me, *Master, your sloop is very leaky;* I said, *Yes, she made water. Water?* says he, *I do not know what you could do with her, suppose we were to give her to you. Besides, you have no hands, for all your hands now belong to us.* I said, *Sirs, if you please to give her to me, I do not fear, with God's blessing, but to manage her well enough, if you let me have only those which are on board, which I hope you will: namely, my mate and the two boys.* Well, says he, *and suppose we did, you have no cargo, for we have taken to replenish our stores, all the rum, sugar, tobacco, rice, flower, and, in short, all your cargo and provisions.* I told him, I *would do as well as I could, and if the worst came to the worst, I could load the sloop with salt, and carry it to the Canaries, where, I knew, they were in great want of salt at present, and therefore was sure it would come to a good market there:* Ay, but, says he, *how will you do to make your cargo of salt, having no hands, and having nothing wherewith to hire the natives to help you make it, or to pay for their bringing it down on their asses; for you must believe,* said he, *I understand trade.* I told him, *If it did come to that Extremity, I had so good interest both at the Island of Bona Vist, as likewise at the Isle of May, that I was sure that the inhabitants would assist me all that they could, and trust me for their pay till I returned again; especially when they came to know the occasion that obliged me to it; and that, upon the whole, I did not fear, with God's blessing, to get a cargo of salt on board, if they would be so generous as to give me the sloop again. Well, but,* says Russel, *suppose we should let you have the sloop, and that you could do as you say, what would you do for provisions? for we shall leave you none; and I suppose I need not tell you, for, without doubt, you know it already, that all these islands to windward are in great scarcity of victuals, and especially the two islands that produce the salt, which have been oppressed for many years with a sore famine.* I told him, *I was very sensible that all he said last was true, but hoped, if they gave me the sloop, they would also be so generous as to give me some provisions, a small quantity of which would serve my little company; but if not, I could go down to the Leeward Islands, where likewise, I had some small interest, and I did not doubt but I could have a small matter of such provisions, as the islands afforded, namely, maiz, pompions, feshunes, etc., with which, by God's assistance, we would endeavour to make shift, until it pleased God we could get better.* Ay, but, says he, *perhaps your mate and boys will not be willing to run that hazard with you, nor care to endure such hardship.* I told him, *As for my boys, I did not fear their compliance, and hoped my mate would also do the same seeing I required him to undergo no other hardship but what I partook of myself.* Ay, but, says Russel, *your mate has not the same reasons as you have, to induce him to bear with all those hardships, which you must certainly be exposed to in doing what you propose; and therefore you cannot expect him to be very forward in accepting such hard terms with you (though I cannot conceive it to be so easie to go through with, in the manner you propose, as you seem to make it).* I answered, *As for the mate's inclinations, I was not able positively to judge in this affair, but I believed him to be an honest, as well as a conscientious man, and as I had been very civil to him in several respects, in my prosperity, so I did not doubt, if I had the liberty to talk with him a little on this affair, but he would be very willing to undergo as much hardship to extricate me out of this my adversity, as he could well bear, or I in reason require of him, which would be no more than I should bear myself; and when it pleased God to turn the scales, I would endeavour to make him satisfaction to the full of what, in reason, he could expect, or, at least, as far as I was able.*

Come, come, says Captain Loe, *let us drink about. Boy! how does the dinner go forward?* The boy answered, *Very well, sir.* Says Loe, *Gentlemen, you must all dine with me to-day.* They unanimously answered, *Ay.* *Come then,* says Loe, *toss the bowl about, and let us have a fresh one, and call a fresh cause.*

They all agreed to this, and then began to talk of their past transactions at Newfoundland, the Western Islands, Canary Islands, etc. What ships they had taken, and how they served them when in their possession; and how they obliged the Governor of the Island of St. Michael to send them off two boat-loads of fresh meat, greens, wine, fowls, etc., or otherwise threatned to damnifie the island, by burning some of the small villages: Of their landing on the Island of Teneriff, to the northward of Oratavo, in hopes of meeting with a booty, but got nothing but their skins full of wine; and how they had like to have been surprized by the country, which was raised upon that occasion, but got all off safe, and without any harm, except one man, who received a shot in his thigh after they were got into their boats; but, they said, they caused several of the Spaniards to drop; and, that they should have been certainly lost, if they had tarried but half a quarter of an hour longer in the house where they were drinking, and where they expected to get the booty, which they landed in quest of, according to the information given them by one of the inhabitants of the island, who was taken by them in a fishing-boat and told them, that, that gentleman had an incredible quantity of money, as well as plate, in his house: And on this occasion they threatned the poor fisherman how severely they would punish him for giving them a false information, if ever they should light of him again; but, I suppose, the fellow kept close ashore after they let him go, all the time they lay lurking about the island: They also boasted how many French ships they had taken upon the banks of Newfoundland, and what a vast quantity of wine, especially French claret, they took from them; with abundance of such like stuff; which, as it did not immediately concern me, so I shall not trouble myself with particularizing: And, indeed, my attention was so wholly taken up with the uncertainty of my own affairs, that I gave no great heed to those subjects that were foreign to me; and which, for that reason, made but a slight impression on my memory.

In this manner they passed the time away, drinking and carousing merrily, both before and after dinner, which they eat in a very disorderly manner, more like a kennel of hounds, than like men, snatching and catching the victuals from one another; which, though it was very odious to me, it seemed one of their chief diversions, and, they said, looked martial-like.

Before it was quite dark, every one repaired on board their respective vessels, and about eight o'clock at night I went to my hammock, without observing, as I remember, anything worth remarking, save, that Captain Loe, and I, and three or four more drank a couple of bottles of wine after the company were gone, before we went to sleep, in which time we had abundance of discourse concerning Church and State, as also about trade, which would be tedious to relate in that confused manner we talked of these subjects, besides the reason I just now mentioned.

58

Loe stayed up after me, and when I was in my hammock, I heard him give the necessary orders for the night, which were, that they were to lie too with their head to the north-westward, as, indeed, we had ever since I had been on board of him; to mind the top-light, and for the watch, to be sure, above all things, to keep a good look-out; and to call him if they saw anything, or if the other ships made any signals.

In the morning, about five o'clock, I turned out, and a little after, one of the three men who spoke to me the morning before, came to me, and bid me good-morrow, and asked me very courteously how I did? and told me, that they would all three as before, have come and spoke to me, but were afraid the company, especially Russel's friends, would think they held a secret correspondence with me, which was against one of their articles, it being punishable by death, to hold any secret correspondence with a prisoner; but they hoped all would be well, and that they believed I should have my sloop again; Russel being the only man who endeavoured to hinder it, and he only, on the account of having me to go with them on the coast of Brasile; but that most of the company was against it, except the meer creatures of Russel. He said, I might thank my mate for it all, who, he much feared, would prove a rogue to me, and enter with them; and then, if they should give me my sloop, I should be sadly put to it to manage her myself, with one boy, and the little child. He also said, That he, and the other two, heartily wished they could go with me in her, but that it was impossible to expect it, it being death even to motion it, by another of the articles, which says, *That if any of the company shall advise, or speak anything tending to the separating or breaking of the company, or shall by any means offer or endeavour to desert or quit the company, that person shall be shot to death by the Quarter-Master's order, without the sentence of a court-martial.* He added, That until my mate had given Russel an account of my being acquainted on the coast of Brasile, he seemed to be my best friend, and would certainly have proved so, and would have prevailed with the company to have made a gathering for me, which, perhaps, might not have come much short in value of what they had taken from me; for there was but few in the company but had several pieces of linnen cloth, pieces of silk, spare hats, shoes, stockings, gold lace, and abundance of other goods, besides the publick store, which, if Russel had continued my friend, for one word speaking, there was not one of them but would have contributed to make up my loss; it being usual for them to reserve such things for no other use but to give to any whom they should take, or that formerly was of their acquaintance, or that they took a present liking to: He said farther, That he believed Captain Loe would be my friend, and do what he could for me; but that, in opposition to Russel, he could do but little, Russel bearing twice the sway with the company that Captain Loe did; and that Russel was always more considerate to those they took, than Loe; but now I must expect no favour from him, he was so exasperated by the opposition that the company, and especially Captain Loe, made to my being forced to go with them on the coast of Brasile: He, however, bid me have a good heart, and wished it lay in his power to serve me more than it did, and bid me not to take very much notice, or shew much freedom with them, but rather a seeming indifference: Adding, That he and his two consorts wished me as well as heart could wish, and whatever service they could do me, while among them I might assure myself it should not be wanting; desiring me to excuse him, and not take amiss his withdrawing from me; concluding, with tears in his eyes, that he did not know whether he should have another opportunity of private discourse with me; neither would it be for the advantage of either of us, except some new matter offered them occasion to forewarn, or precaution me, which, if it did, one of them would not fail to acquaint me with it: And so he left me.

Some time after, Captain Loe turned out, and after the usual compliments passed, we took a dram of rum, and entered into discourse with one or another, on different subjects; for as a tavern or alehouse-keeper endeavours to promote his trade, by conforming to the humours of every customer, so was I forced to be pleasant with every one, and bear a bob with them in almost all their sorts of discourse, though never so contrary and disagreeable to my own inclinations; otherwise I should have fallen under an odium with them, and when once that happens to be the case with any poor man, the Lord have mercy upon him; for then every rascally fellow will let loose his brutal fancy upon him, and either abuse him with his tongue (which is the least hurtful) or kick or cuff him, or otherways abuse him, as they are more or less cruel, or artificially raised by drinking, passion, etc.

Captain Russel, with some more, came on board about ten or eleven o'clock in the forenoon, and seemed to be very pleasant to me, asking me how I did? telling me, that he had been considering of what I said yesterday, and could not see, how I should be able to go through with it: That it would be very difficult, if not wholly impossible, and I should run a very great hazard in what I proposed. He believed, he said, that I was a man, and a man of understanding, but in this case I rather seemed to be directed by an obstinate desperation, than by reason; and for his part, since I was so careless of myself as to determine to throw myself away, he did not think it would stand with the credit or reputation of the company, to put it into my power. He wished me well, he said, and did assure me, that the thoughts of me had taken him up the greatest part of the night; and he had hit on a way which, he was sure, would be much more to my advantage, and not expose me to so much hazard and danger, and yet would be more profitable, than I could expect by having the sloop, though everything was to fall out to exceed my expectation; and did not doubt of the company's agreeing to it: *And this*, says he, *is, to take and sink or burn your sloop, and keep you with us no otherwise than you are now, viz. a prisoner, and I promise you, and will engage to get the company to sign and agree to it, the first prize we take, if you like her; and if not, you shall stay with us till we take a prize that you like, and you shall have her with all her cargo, to dispose of how and where you please, for your own proper use.* He added, *That this, perhaps, might be the making of me, and put me in a capacity of leaving off the sea, and living ashore, if I was so inclined; protesting that he did all this purely out of respect to me, because he saw I was a man of sense, as he* said, *and was willing to take care and pains to get a living for myself and family.*

I thanked him, and told him, *I was sorry I could not accept of his kind offer; and hoped he would excuse me, and not impute it to an obstinate temper; because,* I said, *I did not perceive it would be of any advantage to me, but rather the reverse; for I could not see how I should be able to dispose of the ship, or any part of her cargo; because nobody would buy, except I had a lawful power to sell; and they all certainly knew, they had no farther right to any ship or goods that they took, than so long as such ship or goods was within the verge of their power; which, they were sensible, could not extend so far, as to reach any place where such sale could be made: Besides,* I said, *if the owners of any such ship or goods should ever come to hear of it, then should I be liable to make them restitution, to the full value of such ship and cargo, or be obliged to lie in a prison the remaining part of my days; or, perhaps, by a more rigid prosecution of the law against my person, run a hazard of my life.*

Russel said, *These were but needless and groundless scruples, and might easily be evaded: As for my having a right to make sale of the ship and cargo, which they would give me, they could easily make me a bill of sale of the ship, and such other necessary powers in writing, as were sufficient to justify my title to it beyond all possibility of suspicion; so that I should not have any reason to fear my being detected in the sale: And as for my apprehension of being discovered to the owners, that might as easily be prevented; for they should always know, by examination of the master, etc., and also by the writings taken on board such ship (which they always took care to seize upon), who were the owners and merchants concerned in both ship and cargo, as also their places of abode; by which I might be able to shun a possibility of their discovering me: Adding, That I might have the powers and writings made in another name, which I might go by until I had finished the business, and then could assume my own; which method would certainly secure me from all possibility of discovery*

I told him, *I must confess, there was not only a probability, but a seeming certainty, in what he said, and that it argued abundance of wit in the contrivance; but,* I assured him, *that were I positively certain, which I could not be, that until the hour of my death it would not be discovered, yet there was still a stronger motive to deter me from accepting it; which, though it might seem, perhaps, to them to be of no weight, and but a meer chimera, yet it had greater force with me than all the reasons I had hitherto mentioned; and that was my conscience; which would be a continual witness against me, and a constant sting, even when, perhaps, nobody would accuse me: And as there could be no hearty and unfeigned repentance, without making a full restitution, as far as I was able, to the injured person;* I asked them, *What benefit would it be to me, if I got thousands of pounds and could not be at peace with my conscience, until I had restored everything to the proper owners, and after all, remain as I was before?* A great deal more, I told them, I could say upon this head; but doubted that discourses of this nature were not very taking with some of them, and might seem of very little account; *Yet I hope,* said I, *and God forbid that there should not be some of you, who have a thought of a great and powerful God, and a consciousness of His impartial justice to punish, as well as of His unfathomable mercy to pardon offenders upon their unfeigned repentance, which would not so far extend as to encourage us to run on in sinning, thereby presuming to impose on His mercy.*

Some of them said, *I should do well to preach a sermon, and would make them a good chaplain.* Others said, *No, they wanted no Godliness to be preached there: That pirates had no God but their money, nor Saviour but their arms.* Others said, *That I had said nothing but what was very good, true, and rational, and they wished that Godliness, or at least, some humanity, were in more practice among them; which they believed, would be more to their reputation, and cause a greater esteem to be had for them, both from God and man.*

After this, a silence followed; which Captain Russel broke, saying to me again, *Master, as to your fear that you wrong your neighbour in taking a ship from us, which we first took from him; in my judgment, it is groundless and without cause; nor is it a breach of the laws of God or man, as far as I am able to apprehend; for you do not take their goods from them, nor usurp their property: That we have done without your advice, concurrence, or assistance, and therefore whatever sin or guilt follows that action, it is intirely ours, and, in my opinion, cannot extend to make any unconcerned person guilty with us. It is plain, beyond disputing,* continued he, *that you can be no way partaker with us in any capture, while you are only a constrained prisoner, neither giving your advice or consent, or any ways assisting; and therefore it may be most certainly concluded, that it is we only that have invaded the right, and usurped the property of another; and that you must be innocent, and cannot be partaker of the crime, unless concerned in that action that made it a crime. But you seem to allow, that we have a property, while we are in possession; but,* added he, *I suppose you think, that all the claim we have to the ships and goods that we take, is by an act of violence, and therefore unjust, and of no longer force than while we are capable to maintain them by the same superior strength by which we obtained them.*

I told him, *I could not express my conceptions of it better or fuller, I thought, than he had done; but hoped, neither he, not Captain Loe, nor any of the gentlemen present, would be offended at my taking so much liberty; which was rather to acquaint them with my reasons for not being able to accept of their kind offer, than to give any gentleman offence;* adding, *That I had so much confidence in their favours, that, if I could have accepted them, I verily believed, they would all have concurred with Captain Russel, in what he so kindly and friendly designed me.*

At which words they all cries, *Ay, Ay, by G – ,* and that *I was deserving of that and more.*

I told them, *I heartily thanked them all in general, and did not wish any of them so unfortunate, as to stand in need of my service; yet, if ever they did, they should find, that the uttermost of my abilities should not be wanting in retaliation of all the civilities they had shewn me, ever since it was my lot to fall into their hands; but, in a more especial manner, for this their now offered kindness, though I could not accept it with a safe and clear conscience, which I valued above anything to be enjoyed in this world.* I said, *I could add farther reasons to those I had already urged; but I would not trouble them longer, fearing I had already been too tedious or offensive to some of them; which, if I had, I heartily begged their pardon; assuring them once more, that if it was so, it was neither my design nor intent, but the reverse.*

Hereupon they all said, *They liked to hear us talk, and thought we were very well matched:* Adding, *That Captain Russel could seldom meet with a man that could stand him: But, as for their parts, they were pleased with our discourse, and were very sure Loe and Russel were so too.*

Captain Loe then said, He liked it very well; but told me, I had not returned Captain Russel an answer to what he last said, which he thought deserved one.

I answered, that since the gentlemen were so good-natured, as not only to take in good part what I had hitherto said, but also to give me free liberty to pursue my discourse, I should make use of their indulgence, and answer what Captain Russel had said last to me, in as brief and inoffensive a manner as I was capable of.

Then turning to Russel, I said, *Sir, your opinion of my notion of the right you have to any ship or goods you may take, is exactly true; and I think your right cannot extend farther than your power to maintain that right; and therefore it must follow, you can transfer no other right to any one than what you have yourselves, which will render any person who received them, as guilty for detaining them from the proper owners, as you for the taking them.*

He said, *Be it so; we will suppose* (and seemed a little angry), *for argument's sake, we have taken a ship, and are resolved to sink or burn her, unless you will accept of her: Now, pray, where is the owner's property, when the ship is sunk, or burned? I think the impossibility of his having her again, cuts off his property to*

all intents and purposes, and our power was the same, notwith-
standing our giving her to you, if we had thought fit to make use
of it.

I was loth to argue any farther, seeing him begin to be peevish; and knowing, by the information afore given me by the three men, that all his pretended kindness and arguments were only in order to detain me, without the imputation of having broken their articles; which he found the major part of the company very averse to; wherefore, to cut all short, I told him, I was very sensible of the favours designed me; and should always retain a grateful sense of them: That I knew I was absolutely in their power, and they might dispose of me as they pleased; but that having been hitherto treated so generously by them, I could not doubt of their future goodness to me; And that if they would be pleased to give me my sloop again, it was all I requested at their hands; and I doubted not, but that, by the blessing of God on my honest endeavours, I should soon be able to retrieve my present loss; at least, I said, I should have nothing to reproach myself with, whatever should befal me, as I should have, if I were to comply with the favour they had so kindly intended for me.

Upon which, Captain Loe said, *Gentlemen, the master, I must needs say, has spoke nothing but what is very reasonable, and I think he ought to have his sloop. What do you say, gentlemen?*

The greatest part of them answered aloud, *Ay, Ay, by G –, let the poor man have his sloop again, and go in God's name, and seek a living in her for his family. Ay,* said some of them, *and we ought to make something of a gathering for the poor man, since we have taken everything that he had on board his vessel.* This put an end to the dispute; and everybody talked according to their inclinations, the punch, wine, and tobacco being moving commodities all this time: And every one who had an opportunity of speaking to me, wished me much joy with, and success in, my newly obtained sloop.

Towards night, Russel told Captain Loe, that as the company had agreed to give me the sloop again, it was to be hoped they would discharge me, and let me go about my business in a short time; and therefore, with his leave, he would take me on board the scooner with him, to treat me with a sneaker of punch before parting. Accordingly, I accompanied him on board his vessel, though I had rather stayed with Loe, and he welcomed me there, and made abundance of protestations of his kindness and respect to me; but still argued, that he thought I was very much overseen in not accepting what he had so kindly, and out of pure respect, offered to me, and which, he said, would really have been the making of me. I told him, I thanked him for his favour and good-will; but was very well satisfied with the company's generosity in agreeing to give me the sloop again, which, I said, was more satisfactory to me, than the richest prize that they could take.

Well, says he, I wish it may prove according to your expectation. I thanked him; so down we went into the cabbin, and, with the officers only, diverted ourselves in talking until supper was laid on the table.

After supper, a bowl of punch, and half a dozen of claret, being set on the table, Captain Russel took a bumper, and drank success to their undertaking; which went round, I not daring to refuse it. Next health was prosperity to trade, meaning their own trade. The third health was, the King of France: After which, Russel began the King of England's health; so they all drank round, some saying, *The King of England's health*, others only *The aforesaid health*, until it came round to me; and Captain Russel having emptied two bottles of claret into the bowl, as a recruit, and there being no liquor that I have a greater aversion to, than red wine in punch, I heartily begged the captain and the company would excuse my drinking any more of that bowl, and give me leave to pledge the health in a bumper of claret.

Hereupon Russel said, *Damn you, you shall drink in your turn a full bumper of that sort of liquor that the company does. Well, gentlemen*, said I, *rather than have any words about it, I will drink it, though it is in a manner poyson to me; because I never drank any of this liquor, to the best of my remembrance, but it made me sick two or three days at least after it. And d – n you*, says Russel, *if it be in a manner, or out of a manner, or really, rank poyson, you shall drink as much, and as often, as anyone here, unless you fall down dead, dead!*

So I took the glass, which was one of your Hollands glasses, made in the form of a beaker, without a foot, holding about three quarters of a pint, and filling it to the brim, said, *Gentlemen, here is the aforesaid health. What health is that?* said Russel. *Why*, says I, *the same health you all have drank, the King of England's health. Why*, says Russel, *who is King of England?* I answered, *In my opinion, he that wears the crown, is certainly king while he keeps it. Well*, says he, *and pray who is that? Why*, says I, *King George at present wears it.* Hereupon he broke out in the most outrageous fury, damning me, and calling me rascally son of a b –; and abusing his Majesty in such a virulent manner, as is not fit to be repeated, asserting, with bitter curses, that we had no king.

I said, *I admired that he would begin and drink a health to a person who was not in being.* Upon which, he whipped one of his pistols from his sash, and I really believe would have shot me dead, if the gunner of the scooner had not snatched it out of his hand.

This rather more exasperated Russel, who continued swearing and cursing his Majesty in the most outrageous terms, and asserting the Pretender to be the lawful King of England, etc. He added, that it was a sin to suffer such a false traiterous dog as I was to live; and with that whipped out another pistol from his sash, and cocked it, and swore he would shoot me through the head, and was sure he should do God and his country good service, by ridding the world of such a traiterous villain. But the master of the scooner prevented him, by striking the pistol out of his hand.

Whether it was with the fall, or his finger being on the trigger, I cannot tell, but the pistol went off without doing any damage: At which the master, and all present, blamed Russel for being so rash and hasty; and the gunner said, I was not to blame; for that I drank the health as it was first proposed, and there being no names mentioned, and King

George, being possessed of the crown, and established by authority of parliament, he did not see but his title was the best. *But what have we to do*, continued he, *with the rights of kings or princes? Our business here, is to chuse a king for our own commonwealth; to make such laws as we think most conducive to the ends we design; and to keep ourselves from being overcome, and subjected to the penalty of those laws which are made against us.* He then intimated to Russel, That he must speak his sentiments freely, and imputed his quarrel with me, to his being hindered from breaking through their articles: Urging, that he would appear no better than an infringer of their laws, if the matter were narrowly looked into: And that it was impossible ever to have any order or rule observed, if their statutes were once broken through. He put him in mind of the penalty, which was death, to any one who should infringe their laws; and urged, that if it were once admitted that a man through passion or the like, should be excused breaking in upon them, there would be an end to their society: and concluded with telling him, that it was an extraordinary indulgence in the company, not to remind him of the penalty he had incurred.

Russel, still continuing his passion, answered, That if he had transgressed, it was not for the sake of his own private interest, but for the general good of the company; and therefore did not fear, neither in justice could he expect, any severity from the company for what he had done; and for that reason, whatever he (the gunner), or those of his sentiments, thought of it, he was resolved, whatever came of it, to pursue his present humour.

Then says the gunner to the rest, *Well, gentlemen, if you have a mind to maintain those laws made, established, and sworn to by you all, as I think we are all obligated by the strongest tyes of reason and self-interest to do, I assure you, my opinion is, that we ought to secure John Russel, so as to prevent his breaking our laws and constitutions, and thereby do ourselves, and him too, good service: Ourselves, by not suffering such an action of cruelty in cold blood, as he more than once attempted to commit, as you are eye-witnesses of, and, I believe, most on board have been ear-witnesses to the pistol's going off; and all this for no other reason in the world, but through a proud and ambitious humour, conceiting he is the man that is not to be contradicted, and that his words, though tending to our ruin, must yet be received as an oracle without any opposition.*

At which they all said, It was a pity the master should suffer, neither would they permit it; and speaking to Russel, they said, They would not allow him to be so barbarous: That they had always valued themselves upon this very thing of being civil to their prisoners, and not abusing their persons: That, until now, he himself had been always the greatest perswader to clemency, and even to the forgiving provocations, and permitting them to go from them with as little loss as could be, after they had taken what they had occasion for: *But now*, said they, *you are quite the reverse, to this poor man, and for no other reason, that we know of, but, as the gunner said just now, because we would not yield a greater power to you alone, than you with the whole company have when conjoined; that is, that you at any time, to gratify your own humour, shall have liberty, not only to dispense with our laws, but to act against the sentiments of the whole company.*

Russel answered, That he never did oppose the company before; neither could he believe any present could charge him with any cruelty in cold blood, ever since he belonged to the company; but that he had a reason for what he did, or would have done, if he had not been prevented. Hereupon the master interrupting him, said, *Captain Russel, we know of no reason for your passionate design, but what we have told you; and, as you have been told before, it reflects a revenge against the company; but not being able to effect that, you turn in on that poor man the master of the sloop, and, as it were, in despite of the company, because they have decreed him his sloop again, that he may provide a living for his family, you would barbarously, nay brutishly, as well as to the company contemptuously, murder that poor man, who has given you no occasion to induce you to such an action that we know of; and if he has given you any sufficient cause to be so offended at him, we promise you this instant, to deliver him up to you, to suffer death, or what other punishment you think fit to inflict on him.*

Russel told them, That he had been in the company almost from the first, and he challenged anyone to charge him with singularity, or opposition to the company, or of cruelty to any one prisoner before that rascal, as he called me, and that therefore they might be assured, he should not have taken up such resentments against me, if he had not a sufficient reason to provoke him to it, which he did not think proper at that time to divulge.

Then, says the gunner, *neither do we think proper that you shall take any man's life away in cold blood, until you think fit to acquaint the company with the reasons for it; and I think it was your place to satisfy the company, before you took the liberty to attempt the life of any man under the company's protection, as I think all prisoners are: And, to say the truth, I do verily believe, you have no other reasons to give than those hinted by the master and me; and therefore, I think it but reason, to use such methods as may prevent your passionate design, and secure the prisoner until morning, and then send him on board the Commodore, who, with the advice of the majority, may order the matter as he thinks best.*

This was consented to by all, and so Russel, having his arms taken from him, was ordered not to offer the least disturbance again, nor concern himself with or about me, until after I was on board the Commodore, on pain of the crew's displeasure, and also of being prosecuted as a mutineer; and the gunner, master, boatswain, etc., bid me not be discouraged; assuring me, that there should no harm come to me while I was on board of them; and that they would send me away now, but that there is, said they, an express order among us, to receive no boats on board after eight at night, or nine o'clock at farthest; but they would put me on board Captain Loe in the morning, where they were sure I should be protected and secured from the revengeful hand of Captain Russel; for they said, they were sure that Captain Loe had a great respect for me, and would

71

be a means to counter-ballance Russel; and they said they
would sit up with me all night for my greater security: Which
they did, smoaking and drinking and talking, every one
according to his inclination, and so we passed the time away
until day.

Russel went to sleep about two o'clock in the morning in
his cabbin; however, the master, the gunner, and five or six
more, did not go to bed all that night, but would have had me
gone to sleep, telling me, I need not fear, for they would take
care that Russel should not hurt me.

About eight o'clock in the morning, I was carried on board
Captain Loe, the gunner and steward going with me, who told
him all that had passed; and acquainted him, that they still
believed Russel to be so implacable against me, that he would
murder me in cold blood before I got clear of them, if he did
not interpose to protect me from his violence. Captain Loe
said, He very well knew, and he believed so did they all, what
was the reason that made Russel so inveterate and implacable
to me: He added, That Russel did not do well; and that I had
behaved myself so inoffensively, that there could be no reason
to induce the most savage monster to be such an irreconcileable
enemy to me; but that it was an easy matter to dive into the
cause of it, to wit, his being thwarted by the company in his
humour; and because they would not break through the
articles which cemented them together, and which were
signed and swore to by them all, as the standing rule of their
duty, by which only they could decide and settle controversies
and differences among themselves; the least breach of which,
would be a precedent for the like infractions, whenever
Russel, or any other, thought fit to give way either to revenge
or ambition, and that then all their counsels would be fluctuating;
and fancy, and not reason, would be the rule of their conduct;
and their resolutions would be rendered more unconstant
than the weathercock. He added, That he hoped the company
would inviolably adhere to their established laws, which, he
said, were very good; and were they not, yet, as they were
made by the unanimous consent of the whole company, so

they ought not to be altered without the same unanimous consent; concluding that, for his part, he would rather chuse to be out of the company than in it, if they did not resolve to be determined by their articles. Hereupon they answered, That what he had said was very good, and they were resolved to adhere to his advice.

After this they drank a dram, and then returned with their boat on board the scooner, and Captain Loe told me, he was sorry for Captain Russel's disgust against me, because he believed it would be a disadvantage to me; but, however, there was no remedy but patience; assuring me, that Russel should neither kill me, nor abuse my person, and I should have my sloop again, and be discharged in as short a while as possible, that I might be clear of Russel, who, he was afraid, would always continue my foe.

All the officers and men likewise spoke very friendly to me, and bid me not be daunted; so we passed the time away in several kinds of discourse until dinner; after which, Loe ordered a bowl of punch to be made, and said he wished I was well clear of them.

About four o'clock in the afternoon Captain Russel came on board, as did also Francis Spriggs, who commanded the other ship, and after a little while, says Russel to Captain Loe, *The mate of the sloop is willing to enter with us as a volunteer.*

Loe made answer, and said, *How must we do in that case? For then the master of the sloop will have nobody to help him, but one boy; for*, says he, *the little child is no help at all.*

Russel said, *He could not help that. But*, said Loe, *we must not take all the hands from the poor man, if we design to give him his sloop again;* adding, *That he thought in reason there could not be less than two boys and the mate.*

Z – ds, says Russel, *his mate is a lusty young brisk man, and has been upon the account before, and told me but even now (for*, said he, *I was on board the sloop but just before I came here, and Frank Spriggs was along with me, and heard him say), That he was fully resolved to go with us, and would not go any more in the sloop, unless forced; and when he came out of Barbadoes, he said, his design was to enter himself on board the first pirate that he met with; And will you refuse such a man, contrary to your articles, which you all so much profess to follow; and which enjoin you by all means, not repugnant to them, to encrease and fill your company? Besides,* continued he, *he spoke to me the first day, that he was resolved to enter with us.*

Loe replied, That to give the man his sloop, and no hands with him to assist him, was but putting him to a lingering death, and they had as good almost knock him on the head, as do it.

Russel answered, As to that, they might do as they pleased; what he spoke now was for the good of the whole company, and agreeable to the articles, and he would fain see or hear that man that should oppose him in it. He said, He was Quartermaster of the whole company, and, by the authority of his place, he would enter the mate directly, and had a pistol ready for the man that should oppose him in it.

Loe said, As for what was the law and custom among them (as what he now pleaded, was), he would neither oppose, nor argue against; but, if they thought fit to take the man's mate from him, then they might let him have one of his own men with him.

Russel said, No; for all the sloop's men were already enrolled in their books, and therefore none of them should go in her again. *Gentlemen,* continued he, *you must consider I am now arguing, as well for the good of the company, as for the due maintenance and execution of the laws and articles; and as I am the proper officer substituted and intrusted by this company with authority to execute the same, so (as I told you before) I have a pistol and a brace of balls ready for any one, who dare oppose me herein;* and turning to me, said, *Master, the company has decreed you your sloop, and you shall have her; you shall have your two boys, and that is all: You shall have neither provisions nor anything else, more than as she now is. And, I hear, there are some of the company design to make a gathering for you; but that also I forbid, by the authority of my place, because we are not certain but we may have occasion ourselves for those very things before we get more; and for that reason I prohibit a gathering; and I swear by all that is great and good, that if I know anything whatsoever carried, or left on board the sloop against my order, or without my knowledge, that very instant I will set her on fire and you in her.*

Upon which I said, That since it was their pleasure to order it thus, I begged that they would not put me on board the sloop in such a condition; but rather begged, if they so pleased, to do what they would with the sloop, and put me, and my two boys, ashore on one of the islands.

Russel said, No; for they were to leeward of all the islands, and should hardly come near any of them this season again.

I said, I should rather be put ashore anywhere else, either on the coast of Guinea, or on whatever coast they came at first, than be put as a victim on board the sloop; where I should have no possibility of anything but perishing, except by an extraordinary miracle.

He told me, My fate was already decreed by the company, and he, by his place, was to see all their orders put in execution; and he would accordingly see me safely put on board the sloop, in the exact condition as he had but now mentioned.

I was going to make him a reply, but casting my eye on Captain Loe, he winked at me to be silent; and taking a bumper, drank success to their proceedings. The health went round, and Loe ordered the great bowl to be filled with punch, and bottles of wine to be set on the table in the cabbin, to which we all resorted, and spent the remaining part of the evening in discourses on different subjects: Only Frank Spriggs offered to perswade me to accept of what was first offered me, which Russel swore I should not now have, I having not once, but several times already refused it. Captain Loe not being then willing to have any more of that kind of discourse, broke it off by singing a song, and enjoining every one present to do the same, except me, whom he said he would excuse till times grew better with me: And thus they diverted themselves, and passed the evening away until towards eight o'clock, and then every one repaired on board their respective ships; and, after they were gone, Loe and I, and two or three of his confidents, smoaked a pipe, and drank a bottle or two of wine; in which time he told me, He was very sorry that Jack Russel was so set against me. I said, So was I, and wondered what should be the reason of it, having given him no cause, unless by drinking that health the preceding night: I said, I had imputed to liquor, the fury he was then in, and was in hopes, that after that had worked off, his resentments also would have cooled, and was not a little concerned to find it otherwise. Loe said, The health was not the cause, but rather the effect of his anger, and a meer pretence to cloak his resentment for other disappointments: Adding, That I did right to take his hint given me by winking, to answer no more; *For*, says he, *I knew that every thing which you could speak to him, would be taken edge-ways; and the more you said to excuse yourself, the more it would add fuel to his anger, which he turned against you who could not resist him, because he could not have his will of us; but we will endeavour to draw him off by degrees; and for that reason will not discharge you, but I will keep you on board with me, where he shall not hurt nor abuse you, except with his tongue, which you must bear, until we see if we can alter his temper, so as to deal with you a little more favourable than at present he designs.*

I thanked him, and all of them present, for their favours and good-will, and it being near midnight, we parted, and every one retired to his rest, and I to my hammock; and being pretty much fatigued the night before, as well as the preceding day, soon fell asleep; and about day-dawning, I got up, and came upon deck, and walking upon the quarter deck very solitary, one of the three men, mentioned before, passed by me, and asked me how I did, and said he was very sorry for the unkindness already shewed me, and like to be shewed; but it was what they expected, as they had before hinted to me, and that still there was like to be a tough struggle about me: That Russel did design to be very barbarous to me, and that Loe, and a great part of the company, intended to oppose him in it; that there were a great many who were Russel's gang or clan, and designed to stand by him in it, and had threatened, that if there were much disturbance about it, they would shoot me, and so put an end to the controversy: That there were some, on the other hand, that threatened hard if they did, to revenge my death by some of theirs; so that it was likely to be an untoward touch, and he wished it might not prove to my disadvantage in the end; but would have me still to keep a good heart, and trust in God, and hope for the best, and by no means to speak one word, or concern myself either way, but patiently wait the issue, which he hoped would be better for me than some of them intended; and so heartily wishing me well, walked his way.

Now you must believe these accounts were not a little shocking to me; but I had no friend that I could really rely on, but God, to whom I made my petitions, and whose assistance I humbly besought, to extricate me, in His own good time, out of these difficulties and snares which were laid for me on every side, and, in the mean time, patiently so to bear them, as not to murmur and repine at His fatherly chastisements, nor, by their extremity, through desperation, wound my conscience; but that in all things, I might, through the guidance of the Holy Spirit, be directed so as to submit myself entirely to His will, who infinitely knew what was better for me than I knew myself.

After some time passed, Captain Loe came upon deck, who asked me how I had rested the preceding night? I told him, Very well, considering my present case; but, next under God, had grounded my hopes upon him, to rid me of my present fears, by dispatching me away as soon as possible he could with conveniency. He told me, He would do everything in his power to further my desires, and hoped that what he had already done on my account, would sufficiently convince me of his desire to serve me; but that things hitherto had fallen out very unluckily and cross, as I myself was able to judge by what was already passed.

I told him, I had very good reasons to return him my hearty thanks, and owned myself bound to him in the strictest ties of gratitude; and that if it ever should be in my power to serve him, I would not content myself with bare acknowledgements of his favour.

He said, His will was at present more extensive than his power; but that he still hoped to prevail with Russel, and those who were of his side, to be more compassionate to me before I parted with them, than at present they seemed to intend, and as soon as he had brought them to a better temper, he then would procure my discharge; but if Russel still continued inexorable, which he should be very sorry for, then you must endeavour, says he, to keep up a good heart, and patiently wait until Providence brings you out of your present calamities, which I hope He will.

I thanked him, and told him, I would endeavour to follow his advice, though, I said, it was with some impatience that I waited to have my doom determined in a discharge from them. He bid me be easy, it should be shortly.

By this time there were several joined with us, so we broke off that discourse, and fell into other talk.

About two or three o'clock in the afternoon, Captain Russel, Captain Spriggs, and some of their officers, came on board, and held a consultation, which I was not allowed to be a hearer of; but, understood afterwards, it was chiefly about their own affairs, in relation to the further prosecution of their intended voyage; and by the little mention that was made of me, it appeared that Russel continued still inflexible, bitterly swearing, that he would, if he had a thousand lives, lose them all, rather than miscarry in this his fixed resolution.

In this difficult situation I stood, not daring to speak freely for fear of offending, nor be silent, lest I should be thought contemptuous; not knowing how to avoid their resentments, and every resentment menacing, and often bringing death. And thus I tediously, as well as dangerously, passed my time among them, until it pleased God to put it into their hearts to discharge me; though, if seriously weighed, this my discharge seemed like sentencing me to a lingering and miserable death; yet I must needs confess, considering the whole matter, that I was in a manner miraculously befriended and supported, even in spite of malice, rage, and revenge, for which I shall always pay my humble acknowledgements to the Divine Providence.

CHAPTER FOUR

*

AFTER several efforts made by Captain Loe, and others, and abundance of arguments used to bring Russel to better temper relating to me; and finding it all to no purpose, and that some of his clan had bound themselves by oath to stand by him, even to my destruction, if the dispute continued much longer, Captain Loe, and Captain Spriggs, and others, who were my friends, resolved on sending me away as soon as possible; and for that purpose Loe, the tenth day after I was taken, made a signal for a general consultation on board of him; and as soon as the officers and leading men of the other two ships, were assembled, he made a speech to them, to let them know the reason of his calling them to a consultation, telling them, *That he thought it was time to discharge me, as they had before agreed, as also to prosecute their intended voyage, they having lain a long time driving; and that, altogether out of their way, by reason they could not expect, either here, or in this drift, to meet with any ships.*

To this they all agreeing, Captain Loe told them, *He thought it would be best to discharge me first, for several reasons, among which, my being cumbersome to them, as well as unserviceable, they being forced to sail the sloop themselves; besides, he said it was not proper that I should be made acquainted with the design of their voyage.*

They asked, *Why he did not turn me away?* Saying, *They did not know for what reason I had been kept so long, the company having settled that matter so long since.*

Captain Loe said, *Gentlemen, you all know what arguments we have had already about this matter, and how Captain Russel, and some more, were angry with the master of the sloop, and, I verily believe, without any cause by him given to any of you designedly; and therefore, I hope you have considered better of it since, and laid aside your resentments against the poor man; neither,* said he, *let us do anything now in passion, for I do not design (nor would I, if I could), to inforce any of you to comply to any thing against your will; nor would I have you think, gentlemen, that I shall ever shew so much respect to any prisoner as, on his account, to cause a difference or wrangling among ourselves; but yet, gentlemen, give me leave to say, That though we are pirates, yet we are men, and though we are deemed by some people dishonest, yet let us not wholly divest ourselves of humanity, and make ourselves more savage than brutes. If we send this poor man away from us, without provisions or hands to assist him, pray what greater cruelty can there be? I think the more lingering any death is made, the more barbarous it is accounted by all men; and therefore, gentlemen, I leave it to your own consideration.*

To this Russel made answer, *That he, in the company's name, had made the master of the sloop very good and generous offers, in the hearing of all the company; but that I had, in his opinion, after a very slighting manner, refused them: That it was my choice to be sent thus on board the sloop, rather than the compulsion of the company; and that, notwithstanding he told me what I must trust to by insisting on the sloop, and how favourable they were designed to be to me, if I would have but a little patience until they could provide for me, yet that I had refused their favours notwithstanding the pains he took to perswade me;* adding an egregious falsehood (but I durst not tell him so), *That I had petitioned and begged of the company, rather to be put in the sloop in the condition he now proposed for me, and that therefore, according to my desire, it should be so; and he hoped it could never be reckoned cruelty in them to give a person his free choice. And, gentlemen,* says he, *we have had a great many more words about this matter already, than ever we had in the like case before; but I hope you all have so much value and respect for one another, and for the general peace, as that we shall have no more debate on this head, but determine at once the time when he is to be discharged, the manner of it being already settled by the major part, and I as your Quarter-master, as my office requires, will see it executed, and, perhaps, in a more favourable manner than at first I designed, or he really deserves at mine or your hands either; but let that rest there.*

Then Captain Loe said, *Mr. Russel hath spoke to you, gentle-*

*men, his sentiments, which, in the main, are reasonable and true,
and I am glad he is reconciled to the master of the sloop before their
parting; and, I cannot say, but I always believed Jack Russel to
be a man of so much sense, as well as good-nature, that he would
scorn to take revenge on one whose condition rendered him uncapable of helping himself. And I think, gentlemen, we may
discharge him as soon as you please, and this afternoon, if you are
agreed to it.* They all said, *Ay.* Upon which Russel told them,
it should be done that afternoon; telling Loe, *That after
dinner he would take me on board the scooner with him, and,
from thence, send me on board the sloop, and see what could be
done for me.*

Some of Loe's company said, *They would look out some things,
and give me along with me when I was going away;* but Russel
told them, *They should not, for he would toss them all into Davy
Jones's locker if they did; for I was the scooner's prize, and she
had all my cargo and plunder on board of her, and therefore
what was given to me should be given to me out of her:* And
turning to me, said, *Well, Master, I will this evening put you
on board your own sloop, and will be a better friend to you,
perhaps, than them that pretended a great deal more; but I am
above being led by passion, etc.* They all dined on board of
Loe, who, after dinner, ordered a bowl of punch to be made
in the great silver bowl, and set a dozen of claret on the
table, and that they said was for me to take my leave of them,
and part sailor-like. I thanked them; so they drank round to
my good success, and then to their own fortunate proceedings
and good success; and Loe told me, *He wished me very well, and
hoped to meet with me again, at some time when they had a good
prize of rich goods, and he would not fail to make me a retaliation
with good advantage for my present loss.* And they all present
said, *I need not fear meeting with a friend, whenever I met with
them again.*

About duskish, they began to prepare to go on board their
ships, and I took my leave of Captain Loe, and all his ship's
company, and in particular of the three men, who, I believe,
were my hearty friends, and returned them all thanks for their

kindness, as well as good humour, shewed to me since my first coming on board of them. I also took my leave of Captain Spriggs, and those of his company who were present, wished me well, but not one of them, I believe, dared to give me any lumber[1] with me, nor durst I have accepted of it had they offered it, for fear of angering my newly and seemingly reconciled enemy, who, in all likelihood, would have taken from me whatever they would have given me: And for that reason I believe it was, that none of them offered to give me a farthing, notwithstanding all their professions of kindness to me though this generosity is very usual with them, to people that they profess much less favour for, than they did to me.

Russel being ready, I was ordered to go in his boat, which I did; and, as soon as we were come on board the scooner, he ordered a supper to be got ready, and, in the meantime, there was a bowl of punch made, and some wine set on the table. Russel invited me down into the cabbin, as also his officers, and we drank and smoaked until supper was brought, and then he told me I was very welcome, and bid me eat and drink heartily; *For*, he said, *I had as tedious a voyage to go through, as Elijah's forty days' journey was to Mount Horeb, and, as far as he knew, without a miracle, it must only be by the strength of what I eat now; for I should have neither eatables nor drinkables with me in the sloop.*

I told him, *I hoped not so:* He rapt out a great oath, *That I should find it certainly true.* I told him, *That rather than be put on board the sloop, in that manner, where there was no possibility to escape perishing, without a miracle, I would submit to tarry on board, until an opportunity offered to put me ashore where they pleased; or would yield to anything else they should think fit to do with me, excepting to enter into their service.*

He said, *It was once in my power to have been my own friend; but my slighting their proffered favours, and my own chusing what I now must certainly accept, had rendered me uncapable of any other choice; and that therefore all apologies were but in vain; and he thought he shewed himself more my friend than I could well*

[1] Strictly, money due for goods in pawn.

expect, or than I had deserved at his hands, having caused him to have a great deal of difference with the company, more than ever he had in his life before, or ever should have again, he hoped.

I told him, *I was very sorry that I was so unfortunate as to be the unhappy occasion of it; but could from my heart aver, that it was not only undesigned, but also sorely against my inclinations;* and begged of him, and all the gentlemen then present, *to consider me as an object rather of their pity, than of their revenge.*

He told me, *All my arguments and perswasions now were in vain, it being too late: I had not only refused their commiseration when I was offered it, but ungratefully despised it: Therefore,* says he, *as I told you before, it's in vain for you to plead any more: Your lot is cast, and you have nothing now to do, but to go through with your chance as well as you can, and fill your belly with good victuals and good drink, to strengthen you to hold it as long as you can: It may be, and is very probable to be, the last meal that ever you may eat in this world: However, perhaps such a conscientious man as you would fain seem, or it may be are, may have a supernatural, or, at least, a natural means wrought by a supernatural Power, in a miraculous manner, to deliver you. However, I cannot say but I pity the two boys, and have a great mind to take them on board, and let the miraculous deliverance be wrought on you alone.*

The master and gunner said, *They heard the boys say, they were willing to take their chance with their master, let it be what it would. Nay, then,* says Russel, *it is fit they should. I suppose their master has made them as religious and as conscientious as himself. However, Master,* says Russel (speaking to me), *I would have you eat and drink heartily, and talk no more about changing your allotted chance; because, as I told you before, it is all in vain; besides, it may be a means of provocation to serve you worse.*

Gentlemen, says I, *I have done: I will say no more; you can do no more than God is pleased to permit you; and I own, for that reason, I ought to take it patiently.*

Well, well, says Russel, *if it be done by God's permission, you need not fear that He will permit anything hurtful to befall so good a man as you are.*

About ten o'clock at night, he ordered to call the sloop's boat, which was brought by some of the pirates of his own clan, who were stationed on board of her, and asked them, *If they had done as he had ordered them, viz. to clear the sloop of everything?* And they said, *Yes*, rapping out a great oath or two, adding, *She had nothing on board except ballast and water. Z – ds*, said Russel, *did not I bid you stave all the casks that had water in them on board? So we did*, said they, *but the water that we spoke of was salt-water, leaked in by the vessel, and is now above the ballast; for we have not pumped her we do not know when.*

Said Russel, *Have you brought away the sails I told you of?* They said, *All but the mainsail that was bent*, for the other old mainsail that he had ordered to be left, was good enough for nothing but to cut up for parceling, and hardly for that, it was so rotten; besides, it was so torn, that it could not be brought too, and was past mending, and for that reason they let it lie, and would not unbend the other mainsail.

Z – ds, says Russel, *we must have it, for I want it to make us a mainsail. D – n it*, said the men, *then you must turn the man adrift in the sloop without a mainsail.*

Pish, said Russel, *the same miraculous Power that is to bring him provisions, can also bring him a sail.*

What a devil; is he a conjuror? said one of them.

No, no, says Russel, *but he expects miracles to be wrought for him, or he never would have chosen what he hath.*

Nay, nay, said they, *if he be such a one, he will do well enough; but I doubt*, says one of them, *he will fall short of his expectation; for if he be such a mighty conjuror, how the devil was it that he did not conjure himself clear of us?*

Pish, said another, *it may be his conjuring books were shut up. Ay, but*, said another, *now we have hove all his conjuration books over board, I doubt he will be hard put to it to find them again.*

Come, come, says the gunner, *gentlemen, the poor man is like to go through hardship enough, and very probably may perish; yet it is not impossible but he may meet with some ship, or other*

*timely succour, to prevent his perishing, and I heartily wish he
may; but, however, you ought not to add affliction to the afflicted;
You have sentenced him to a very dangerous chance, which I think
is sufficient to stop your mouths from making a droll and game of
him. I would have you consider,* added he, *if any of you were at
Tyburn, or any other place to be executed, as many better and
stouter men than some of you, have been, and the spectators, or
Jack Catch should make a droll and May-game of you, you
would think them a very hard-hearted, as well as an inconsiderate
sort of people: And pray, gentlemen, consider the sentence which
you are now going to execute on this poor man, will be as bad, or
rather worse, than one of our cases would be there; because,
unless Providence stand his friend in an extraordinary manner,
his death must as certainly ensue or be the consequence of this your
sentence, as it would there be to any of us by the sentence of a
judge, and so much the more miserable, by how much it is more
lingering.*

Damn it, said Russel, *we have had enough, and too much of
this already.*

Ay, said the gunner, *and take care, Russel, you have not this
to answer for one day, when perhaps you will then, but too late,
wish you had never done it. But you have got the company's
assent in this, I cannot tell how, and therefore I shall say no more,
only that I, as I believe most of the company, came here to get
money, but not to kill, except in fight, and not in cold blood, or
for private revenge. And I tell you, John Russel, if ever such
cases as these be any more practised, my endeavour shall be to
leave this company as soon as I possibly can.*

To which Russel said nothing in answer; but bid the men that
came on board in the boat, to leave the sloop's boat on board the
scooner, and take the scooner's boat with them on board the
sloop; and, as soon as they saw the lights upon deck on board
of the scooner, to come away from the sloop with the scooner's
boat, and bring the master of the sloop's biggest boy with them;
and to take their hands out of the sloop's boat, and put the
master's boy on board of the sloop's boat with his master, and
let them go on board themselves with their boat, and to be

sure to bring the sloop's mainsail with them, and also the mate of the sloop. All which they said they would do; so away they went; and then Russel told me, *He would give me something with me to remember him;* which was an old musket, and a cartridge of powder, but for what reason he made me that present, I cannot tell; and then ordered the candles to be lighted in the lanthorns and carried upon deck, and ordered two hands to step into the sloop's boat to carry me away, and to execute his former orders; and then shaking hands with me, he wished me a good voyage. I told him I hoped I should.

The gunner, master, and several of the crew, shook hands with me also, and heartily wished me success, and hoped I should meet with a speedy and safe deliverance. I thanked them for their good wishes; and told them I was now forced into a necessity of going through it, whether I would or not; but thanked God I was very easy at present, not doubting in God's mercy to me, though I was not deserving of it: And that if I was permitted to perish, I knew the worst; and doubted not but He would graciously pardon my sins, and receive me to His everlasting rest; and, in this respect, what they had intended for my misfortune, would be the beginning of my happiness; and that in the meantime, I had nothing to do but to resign myself to His blessed will and protection, and bear my lot with patience. And so bidding them farewell, I went over the side into the boat, which was directly put off; and about half-way between the scooner and sloop, we met the scooner's boat, and, according to their orders from Russell, they put my boy on board of me, and so put away again to get on board their own vessel.

After their boat put away from us, I thought I heard the voice of my mate, but was not certain, because he spoke so low, his conscience checking him, I suppose, for his leaving me so basely. I called to him, and said, *Arthur, what! are you going to leave me?* He answered, *Ay. What*, said I, *do you do it voluntary, or are you forced?* He answered faintly, *I am forced, I think.* I said, *It was very well.* He called to me again, and said, *He would desire me to write to his brother, and give him an account where he was, if ever I should have an opportunity.* I told him, *I did not know where his brother lived.* He called and said, *He lived in Carlingford.* I told him, *I did not know where that was.* He said, *It was in Ireland. Why,* said I, *you told me in Barbadoes that you was a Scotchman, and that all your friends lived in Scotland.* But he made me no further answer; but away they rowed towards their vessel, and I towards the sloop, and it being a very dark, as well as a close night, it was as much as ever I could do to see her; this being the last time that I spoke to, or saw any of them, nor do I ever more desire to see them, except at some place of execution.

I shipped this man at Barbadoes, and he told me then, that he had been mate of a sloop belonging to some part of New England, but was shipwrecked, and lost everything; and was almost naked when I first met with him, not having a shirt, or anything else of cloathing, to shift in the room of what he had on, until they were washed; neither had he any money, but he was out of debt there I believe, because I never heard of anybody's coming after him for any demands that way, as is usual for landlords, etc., in those parts in such cases; for as soon as any of their lodgers or debtors are shipped on board any vessel, they make it their business to find out the master, and acquaint him with their being creditor to such a person; and in presence of the said person procure a promise, if they can, from the master to keep their wages, as they shall become due, in his hands, or, at least, so much as amounts to the debt, until his return there, obliging the debtor to assign over to the master an order to authorise him so to do, otherwise they will not suffer him to go off the island. I bought him cloaths and instruments, with such other necessaries as I thought might be absolutely requisite for him to the performance of the voyage. I observed nothing in him tending to any of the common vices, too common among seafareing men, especially those who have frequented these parts; to wit, swearing, drunkenness, debauchery, etc. He was a pretended rigid Presbyterian, and seemed mighty averse to the Church of England, as established by law, about which we had several arguments. I do not remember, all the time that he was with me, to have heard him swear; and yet, as my biggest boy told me, after he had acquainted the pirates of his resolution (or rather returned to be a pirate again, as he by his own discourse to them manifested), then, it seems, he far exceeded the most profligate of them, both in the frequency and horribleness of them; and, as my boys told me, was almost constantly drunk, while on board the sloop, after the pirates had taken me.

But to proceed: My boy and I got on board the sloop, and found neither fire, nor candle, nor anything that we knew of on board to make the one or the other. I could hear the water which the sloop had in her, by her motion with the sea, rowl from one side to the other, as if she had been almost full of water; I asked the boys when she had been last pumped, and whether she had been then sucked dry; they told me, She had not been pumped these three days past, and that she had then been sucked dry, and they said they would have pumped her several times since, but the pirates swore at them, and would not let them, saying, Damn her, let her sink and be damned, they had a boat on board sufficient to carry them all to their own ships; and agreed to have cut a hole through her, or fire several shot through her bottom as that night, in order to sink her, and with the boat to go all on board their own vessel; and were consulting about the manner of doing it, just as the scooner called for them to send the sloop's boat on board; and they verily believed she had been quitted, if not sunk by this time, if they had been let alone.

I made fast a rope to the mast for a mainrope, and went down in the hold to see what quantity of water was in the sloop, and finding it not above a foot above the ballast, I was a little encouraged, though that was dismal enough, but yet nothing nigh so bad as at first I thought it was; for, indeed, by the noise that the water made, with the motion the sea gave the vessel, I thought she had been half full at least; but finding it better than I expected, I was in hopes to free her; and when once freed, we had little reason of doubting, but what we should be able, while our strength held out, to keep her so, until it pleased God to send us some succour.

I came upon deck, and asked Potter, my biggest boy, if the pumps were in order, or whether the pirates had broke or put them out of order? He said, he thought not; so I went to work with them, being the only way to know; I put the two boys to one pump, and I exercised the other; I bid them not strike with the pump, but to draw a long drawing stroke, which in a manner delivers as much water as striking, especially when there are not hands to spell (that is, to take turns while the others recover breath): besides, it doth not tire so soon, and consequently would not make them so drowsy as striking would. I inquired what drinking water they had on board. Potter told me, he believed there was not one drop of fresh water on board, because, he said, all that was in the sloop, except one hogshead, was sent on board the pirates; and after they came from on board the scooner, the two men that went in the boat said, Captain Russel ordered them to stave that, and not leave one drop of fresh water on board the sloop. *But, sir,* said he, *I think they have done as barbarously by us in another respect, as in leaving us without provisions. Ay,* said I, *What is that? Why,* said he, *they have taken all our sails, except the jib and the old foresail that is bent, and that old mainsail that is good for nothing, it is so rotten. What,* said I, *have they served us so* (making as though I had known nothing of the matter, neither did I but of the mainsail, which Russel ordered them to unbend, and bring away with them when they came away from the sloop). *Well,* says I, *never fear, boy, I trust in God we shall do well enough still, in despight of all their malice. Ay ay, sir,* says the boy, *I do not fear it, and am heartily glad we are got clear of them. They often asked me to enter, and go along with them, but I would rather chuse to go with a Turk or Infidel: besides, was I sure to perish, I could not leave you, when I consider how kind you have been to me, and shall never forget it while I live: And I wonder,* says he, *that Mr. Hunter* (i.e. *the mate*) *should be so barbarous as to leave you in this extremity, as some of the pirates here on board told him, for he had acquainted them how kind you had been to him, and they refused at first to enter him; and I believe they would not have let him enter, if it had not been for Captain Russel.*

I shall take leave briefly to mention in this place some account of this boy: His name is Potter, and he had served his time to a potter at Kingston-upon-Thames, and after, in a youthful frolick, inconsiderately took a fancy to go to sea, and in order thereto spoke to a man who pretended to be a crimp, *i.e.* one that used to provide sailors with voyages, boys to masters, etc., and who undertook to help him to one. This fellow so managed the matter, as to bind him to a plantation-servant for America for the term of five years; and after the boy was put on board the ship, and found how he had been trapanned, he began to repent of his voyage; but they made him believe they were at very great charges for the crimp's trouble and pains, and for his lodging, diet, etc., which they enhanced to such a sum, as they thought was above his purse, and demanded to be reimbursed of, before his acquittal; so that for want of friends, or through shame to apply himself to them, he was forced to acquiesce, and was carried to Barbadoes, where he was to be sold; and I understanding the lad's unhappy case, upon his prayers, and promises what a good and faithful servant he would be, I bought his time, and paid twelve pounds for him of that country money: And, indeed, I always found him, not only true and faithful to my interest, but affectionate to my person, insomuch that it raised my value for him, so that I looked upon him rather as a child or relation, than as a bare servant.

But to return: In this manner we pumped and talked, sometimes the one, and sometimes the other, and gained upon the vessel apace, insomuch, that before daylight we had sucked her dry, and then we gave over. I forgot to mention, that Russel, when he gave me the old musket and the cartridge of powder, gave me also two half pound papers of tobacco, and Potter finding a short broken pipe in the cabbin, I smoaked a pipe, and lying too under my foresail all night, when day appeared I looked all about me, but lost sight of the pirates, who, I suppose, made sail in the night, not caring I should know or see which way they bent their course, for fear of giving an information of them; for they were prodigiously afraid of meeting with any of His Majesty's ships, nor could they endure to hear any talk of them: Though as secret as they thought they had kept the design of their intended voyage from me, yet I perfectly knew it to be to go directly for the coast of Guinea, and to fetch as far to windward as they could, and then to cruise along that coast, and then stretch over on the coast of Brasile, where they promised themselves mountains of treasure; from thence along the coast of Guana, and so down among the islands, and to be at the latter end of the spring on the coast of North America, namely, Carolina, Virginia, New York, New England, and so by the summer, to be on the coast of Newfoundland; Russel being the chief scheme projector.

As soon as the day broke out clear, I went to work, to find out, whether, by chance or design, they had left on board anything fitting to eat or drink. I made my first search in the cabbin, and swept out of all the bread-lockers, near the crown of my hat full of dust and crumbs together, of bisket, which I secured very safe; and, in another locker, I found four or five hands of tobacco, which, with the pound given me by Russel, made up a good stock of that commodity. I found also, four or five short broken pipes about the cabbin, and they left my forestaff,[1] with only the thirty-cross, having, as I suppose, flung the other crosses overboard. They left me also my bedding, that being useless to them, there being not above three or four in any of the ships, that lay either in a cabbin or hammock, namely, the captain, master, steward, and gunner, the rest kennelling like hounds on deck, or where they could.

From the cabbin, I went into the hold, and rummaged there, and found in one hogshead, about the quantity of ten gallons, as near as I could guess, of rum, and, in a rice cask, between twenty and thirty pounds of rice; and, searching farther, I found a small remnant of flower in the bottom of a flower cask. I tried, and drained all the water casks, and found that to be

---

[1] An instrument for taking the altitude of a star.

our scarcest commodity, not being able to drain out of all of them, above two or three pints.

Having seen all my store of provisions, and what I had, under God, to trust to of that kind, I proceeded next to examine what condition my sails were in; and, I cannot say, but I took it more barbarous of them, to take my sails from me, than their turning me away without water or provisions; at least, I verily believe, Russel thought I had not one mouthful of any sort of eatable, nor one drop of water; they left me the same jibb that was bent, and an old foresail, and an old mainsail that was much rent, torn, and rotten: I haled it upon deck, and spread it, but was at a sad loss, how to contrive to mend it. I went down into the cabbin, to see whether they had left any needles or twine, and found in the twine-locker, half a dozen skeins of twine, but not one sail-needle. Potter, in the mean-time, was hunting in the men's chests and lockers in the steerage, and found in one of them six needles, and about a pound and a half of twine, and two pawms; at which, I was very glad, and we went to work to mend the mainsail, but not having stuff enough on board, I cut off the first reef, and tabled down the foot of it again, and sowed on the bolt-rope, and, with what I cut off, I mended it as far as it would go, and what more was wanting, we mended with some old canvas, which lay in the mate's cabbin, underneath his bed which, by good luck, was neither taken away, nor hove overboard.

We were three days fixing and mending the mainsail, before we could fit it so as to bend it; during which time, we had light winds, calms, with variable airs of wind, cloudy, and mostly overcast by day, but clear and starlight commonly by night, but saw nothing of a vessel all this time, which was the chief and principal thing we looked out for.

The fourth day in the morning, we bent the mainsail, but it proving calm, did not set it, but lay driving and rowling in the sea, with only the foresail up, and had been so ever since we were left by the pirates; our daily food was raw flower, or rice, with a dram of rum: laying up safe, our little stock of water, till I had a little idle time, and then I got some flower up, and made as much dough as my water would, of which I made cakes, and baked them on the bottom of an iron pot, which I had on board, and, after I had baked all, which was four little cakes, I took one, and divided it among us three, but Potter was very unwilling to eat any, desiring me, to keep the bread all for myself, to take a dram with, and said, he and the little boy could eat raw rice and flower well enough, and that it agreed very well with him, and so little Jack said too, and that they had not suffered any thing as yet, either as to hunger or thirst. I told them, they must take but a very little rum to get down their flower or rice, for too much would make them dry; they said, they would not: so we eat our cake; and each of us took a small dram of rum, and so had the best meal that I made, since I came last on board of the sloop.

This night, I took two several observations, one by the North Star, the other, by the Cock's Foot, and found myself in seventeen degrees of north latitude, there being six minutes' difference between the two observations, but whether this happened by the sett of the current, the eye, horizon, or declination of the stars, I shall not now examine or determine. I had asked the master of the scooner, that night I came away from them, what distance he reckoned he was from the Island of St. Antonia? And he told me, about sixty-five or seventy leagues, and the island bore east, half a point southerly.

Next day we had a fresh trade, and I began to be in a doubt which way to endeavour for; Guinea being the nighest and easiest land to fetch, especially with a trade, or even most winds; but I thought to myself, What can I do when I come there? I can neither have credit, nor, if I had, could I, but by a meer chance, except on board a ship, meet with anything there to refit me.

To go for Barbadoes was a long run, and the season being then so subject to calms, and mostly light winds, it might be a very tedious and long run thither. If I endeavoured to run for the Islands of the Cape de Verd, I must beat it up to windward, if a trade wind continued, which would also be a long time effecting; and besides, my sails, all but the jib, were so bad, that it would be hazardous, if not impossible, to make them hold out to beat up sixty or seventy leagues right in the wind's eye; but those Islands of the Cape de Verd being the nighest land by far, the coast of Guinea, which probably I might fetch, being the distance of about two hundred leagues, and Barbadoes, the nighest island of America to us, being little less than six hundred leagues distant from us; whereas the Cape de Verd Islands, as I said before, were not above seventy leagues distant at most, and the winds inclinable to shifting, I concluded with myself, to endeavour for any one of those islands, but chiefly that of St. Nicholas.

The trade blowing now about the north-north-east point, I set sail, and stood to the eastward with my larboard tack on board, by which I shortened my way to both the nighest lands to me at once, namely the Islands, and the coast of Guinea; so that if the trade held fresh, in about a week's time, I should be upon the coast of Guinea; and if I run three or four days as we now lay up, and then, if the wind should veer to the eastward or east-southerly, then I should have a fair chance, if not to fetch them, yet to fetch very nigh them; and I must own, that only the sight of land would have been at this time very pleasant and reviving to our hopes, which I cannot say as yet were anything faintish.

So steering east-and-by-north, east, east-and-by-south, and east-south-east, according as the winds would suffer us, I kept my luff as nigh as with a full fair standing sail she would lie, being obliged not to touch or hank her up in the wind, because of my mainsail's being lessened, as I mentioned before, by reason I could not get canvas to mend it withal, and therefore it may easily be conceived, that she neither did hold the wind, nor make the way through, which she would have done had not her sails been lessened.

We sailed with a steady, fresh, moderate gale of wind, from ten o'clock in the morning until about eleven that night, and then the wind began to die away, insomuch, that between two and three in the morning, it fell flat calm, and so continued all the day following until about six in the afternoon; after which time, we had sometimes light airs of wind, variable from the north-west, round to the westward, and so to the southward, and to the south-south-east, with thunder and lightning, and it looked as if there was a turnado brewing; but we had none, neither had we any rain, though it looked very likely, and we very much hoped and longed for it, but in vain. Those variable light airs of wind would hold sometimes half an hour, other some less; some of them would be gone before we could get the sloop's head the right way to make use of them; and between those airs be flat calm, one hour between, some two hours, others two and a half, three, four, five, or six hours' calm; and this sort of weather held us better than two days. We made the best advantage we could to get as much as possible to the eastward; and in these two or three days we got about twenty-five leagues, according to my judgment, to the eastward; and, by observation, I found myself in sixteen degrees and fifty-six minutes of north latitude, and, by computation, the Island of St. Anthony bore about forty-six leagues' distance.

I ought before to have acquainted the reader, That it was October the 19th, 1722, that I was taken by the pirates, and the 29th day of the same month, they discharged me, and I have brought down my relation to the 7th of November; in the afternoon of which it falling calm, I lowered all my sails, and let her lie.

The night following we had one smart shower of rain, which made us fall to work to save every drop we could, with as much care and caution, as an alchymist would use in preparing his grand arcanum; and, by that means, saved about a gallon, besides some draughts which we drank, and eat some rice with it.

We had two or three other small showers, but scarce enough thoroughly to wet the deck, and therefore could save no water from them. We had also a great deal of thunder and lightning, but especially in the great shower.

About four o'clock in the morning, which was the 8th day of November, it cleared up, but continued calm, and the sea very smooth: When day broke out I spread the mainsail, and dried that and the foresail, both which wanted mending again; and as soon as the mainsail was dry enough to sow, I began upon that first, which took me up the most part of the day: In the meantime, I ordered a fire to be made, and boiling some flower in some of the water which we had saved, we made a little pap, which we eat, and it went down most sweetly, taking a dram of rum after it, and were very thankful to Providence for this delicious meal, it being very warm to our stomachs. I resolved to save the rest of the water for the like occasion, that we might refresh our spirits with so comfortable a recruit when we might be grown faint by eating of the raw rice or flower.

It still continued calm, with light cat-skins, as we commonly term them in the sea dialect, which are light airs of wind, not spreading perhaps above half a mile, or some of them above the quantity of an acre of ground on the water.

After I had mended up the mainsail, I fixed the foresail as well as I could, and about five o'clock in the afternoon, 10th November, a moderate gale sprung up at east, and freshened up, and veered to the east-south-east, and about ten or eleven at night to the south-east.

I stretched away to the south-eastward until the 16th day, and about ten in the forenoon we saw St. Anthony, which then bore from us east, half a point northerly, and I judged we were about eighteen or nineteen leagues distant from it, and it falling calm, we lay with our sails all down, to save them from flapping.

CHAPTER FIVE

*

THE calm continuing all day, and the sea being very smooth, about one or two in the afternoon Potter saw a shark, a voracious fish, the description of which is so common, that I shall not trouble my reader with it. I looked about, and saw four more, but one swindging one, swam close up alongside, and almost even with the water's edge. *Come, come,* said I, *we will, with God's leave, have him by and by. Ay, sir,* said the boy, *if we had our shark-hook, and a piece of beef or pork. No matter,* said I, *we will have him presently.* So I got some rags of several colours, and made them fast together, being about the bulk of a three or four pound piece of meat, knowing that there is hardly anything but what the sharks will snap at, and having made it fast to the end of a rope, hove it overboard, and ordered the boy to tend it as a bait, or decoy, and as the shark came nigh it, to hale it up, and only play with him, to keep him about the vessel, while I got ready another rope, at the end of which I made a running bowling knot, and the noose so as to keep it open with one hand, lowering the under part beneath the surface of the water about two or three foot, which was easily done, by reason it was flat calm, and the vessel had no way at all, holding with my other hand the single part of the rope, ready when the shark had wholly got his head through the noose, to hale, and thereby jam the running knot taut about him, the boy all the time playing with the bait before the noose.

This fell out according to our desire; for the shark coming up, and endeavouring to get the bait, entered his head through the snare; but I, being over-eager with a sudden jirk, jammed the noose close, before the neck fins were got through, and haled his head above water as high as we could, making fast the rope; but in two or three plunges, he slipped his head out, and immediately darted, as it were, out of sight, after whom all the other sharks pursued, thinking, as I suppose, he had got some prize.

I was not a little concerned at his escape, and blamed myself for being so hasty, as not to wait until his head and throat fin had passed through the snare before I had jammed it; but my concern was dissipated by the fresh appearance of the same sharks, as I supposed, being the same number, and, as nigh as I could guess, of the same size; upon which I hove the bait overboard again, and fixed my snare as at first, and, as I supposed by his bigness, the same shark again made to the bait, but shunned the snare, and so continued playing about it near three quarters of an hour, and then he darted at the bait with such swiftness, as if he had a design, either to pass the noose, or to make sure of the bait, which he had been deluded with so long. I had as much eagerness to catch him, as he had to catch the bait, and my former oversight made me more wary and dextrous, and as soon as I judged him entered far enough in the noose, I jammed the snare by a sudden jirk of the rope, and haled him up so high, that his head, with about a quarter of his body, was above water, and finding him well secured, I let him hang so, and gave him time to tire himself by beating against the vessel, which he did now and then pretty hard.

When he had lain so about an hour, he began to be pretty quiet, now and then striking and flouncing, but very weak and faint, so that I thought I might venture to get him in, or, at least take him wholly out of the water, and making a running bowling knot on the end of another rope, I cast it over his tail fin; I jammed it close, and haled his tail also above water, and made it fast. He lay as if he had been dead, for about three or four minutes, and then began to strike so hard with his tail, that at every stroke he made, the vessel shook, and fearing it would do it harm, I lowered his tail down in the water again, and clapped a tackle on the rope that was about his throat, he being so heavy, we could not hale him by hands any higher, and hoisted him up so, that about a foot and a half of the tail part, was in the water, and let him hang till he seemed to be almost dead, and then I hoisted him first by one end, and then by the other, with the tackle, till we got him in upon deck, and then he began again to strike so hard with his tail, as if he would have beat the deck down, which I soon put a stop to, by cutting off about a foot of his tail part, in which lies most of this fish's strength: He then lay pretty quiet, and I put an end of a boat-hook staff into his mouth, which he crushed to splinters, with as much ease as one could squeeze an eggshell.

On cutting the belly open, I found five young ones, all alive, about the bigness of a small whiting; though I have hitherto called it he, according to an old rule I had been taught at school, to reckon any nouns whose gender, by the rules of grammar, I could not find one, masculine.

She had a very fine liver, not blackish, nor dark reddish, as most large sharks have, but of a fair gray colour, which I preserved. The whole length of the shark, was something more than eleven foot and a half, and it must needs be near upon three hundredweight. I struck a light by help of the old gun that Russel gave me at parting, which I then thought a useless present, and accepted it only, because I durst do no otherwise; but having neither tinder-box, nor steel left me, it would have been impossible for us to get fire without it; and though they left me the two compasses that were in the beetacle,[1] there was not one inch of candle; which, however, in failing upon a wind I did not much matter, except when any light air, breeze, or catskin, came in the night, and the sky was overcast, and no stars to be seen, more especially if it was large, as any way from the western hank, in which case I was forced to supply the want of candle, by blowing a coal of fire, whereby I could discern the compass so, as to get her head the right way.

Having, as I said, struck a light, and caused a fire to be made; the pot was put on, with sea water, and, as soon as our fish was boiled, we eat heartily of it. After which, I cut the greatest part of the shark into thin long slices, and dried it in the sun to preserve it, having no salt on board.

About midnight it began to thunder, and rained a smart shower, of which, we saved about three gallons; and about four o'clock in the morning, it cleared up, and the stars shewed

[1] Binnacle.

themselves, which saved me the trouble of blowing a coal to see the compass.

It continuing a fine pleasant fresh gale, veering to the north-west; as soon as it was day, I set the Island of St. Anthony, which bore from me south-south-east, about ten leagues, the gale continuing still; but dying away by degrees, about eleven in the forenoon, 17th November, it fell flat calm again, at which time, St. Anthony bore south-and-by-west, about eight leagues distant.

I broiled some of the fish for breakfast, and eat of it pretty heartily, which made us all very dry, but thank God we had a good stock of water, so that now we could venture to drink a little. I made them put the pot on, with some fresh water, and a little rice to boil, and when the rice was a little soft, I had it thickened with flower, and then put a piece of the shark's liver into it, shred small, which soon dissolved in it mostly to oil, as fish livers generally do; and this served us in the room of butter in our hasty-pudding, which we sailors usually call pap, of which, we made a hearty and pleasant meal; and, as we had the sight of land, our hopes were much revived. I lowered down all my sails, and overhaled them, and mended what was amiss, the calm continuing till two o'clock the morning following, and it being a clear, serene, star-light night.

Afterwards a gale sprung up at south-south-west, and veered to the west-north-west, I still steering east-north-east; and about eight o'clock in the morning, 18th November, it fell calm, and continued so all that day, and until nine o'clock at night, intermixt with light insignificant airs and catskins. The wind freshened up to a gale about ten at night, with thunder and lightning from the north-north-west board, as was the wind also. We had several small showers of rain, but so small, that we could not save any water from them; and as it thundered pretty much, and looked very black and thick over the Island of St. Anthony, we judged that there fell abundance of rain that night there, which we heartily grudged them, and had rather it had fallen where we were, though we had undergone a wet jacket for it, and had no cloaths to shift us.

In the morning of 19th November, when the day cleared, we could very plainly see, St. Anthony, St. Vincent, St. Lucia, Terra Branca, and the Monte Gourda, which is the highest mountain of the Island of St. Nicholas, lying on the north-west side of it, but a good way up in the land, and may be seen from any side of the island, at about nine or ten leagues'distance, in the form of a flattish sugar-loaf; it bore from us south-south-east about ten leagues distant.

About four in the afternoon sprung up a light gale at north-north-east, and it looked hazy to windward, and very like a true trade; and I was the rather induced to think it so, because it was the time of year for the true trades to blow, and for the most part to hold strong, from their first coming, until towards the latter part of March; and not knowing but the wind might, as is very usual, veer to the north-east, east-north-east, or perhaps further, and being desirous to fetch the Island of St. Nicholas, rather than any of the other islands, because I was well acquainted there, and it was the likeliest place to get a mainsail at, by reason they spin the best there; I therefore kept my luff, and steered away east, which I was sure would carry me a good distance to windward of the island; so that if the true trade held, I should not fear going to windward of it, and be thereby enabled to chuse, as well as to make a large wind to which road I liked best to anchor in.

Besides, as I knew that the pirates had taken the Priest's sloop, I was sure, if I could get there, I should not want for freight I could in reason desire, as soon as I could refit, and put myself into a posture to go to the Isle of Sal; for I was sure the Priest, for his own interest, would do all that lay in his power to assist me; there being hardly a family on the island, but what had a relation then on the Island of Sal, where they all apprehended they might probably perish before another occasion offered, if I did not go.

The gale continuing all night, about four o'clock in the morning I edged away more to the southward, and about eight it fell calm until noon, but was very hazy, insomuch, that I could see no land. Between twelve and one in the afternoon,

20th November, sprung up a gale at north-east, which increasing, soon cleared the air, so that I saw the Island of St. Nicholas, the east point bearing west-south-west, and, by supposition, about eight or nine leagues distant. I crowded all the sail that I could make to get in to an anchor before night, the wind still increasing. About five in the evening I doubled the east point of the island; after which, when I came to luff up to keep the land aboard, I found the wind more northerly, with very hard flaws coming down the deep gullies.

It being late in the evening, and likely to prove, as indeed it did, a close night, and not having daylight enough to gain, as I intended, the road of Paragheesi, but fearing I might miss it in the night, the high lands being so very like one another, I resolved to anchor in Currisal Road, it being nigher, as likewise to get off some water, there being none to be had within two miles of Paragheesi.

I was forced to make a board or two, to fetch into the anchoring place, and anchored in sixteen fathom water, about a quarter of a mile from the shore, just about duskish; and saw a fire and some people on the shore.

After we had stowed our sails, I hoisted the boat out to get in the end of the cable which the pirates had slipt, and put a buoy on the cable end, having discerned it and the buoy on the anchor before I anchored, and for that reason let go my anchor nigh enough to it to get the end of it on board. In order to which, I took a quoil or two of small rope with me in the boat, to make one end fast to the cable end, and to bring the other on board; and so by the small rope to hale or heave the cable on board the sloop, and ride moored until I thought proper to move from thence; but being so few hands, we were so long a getting the boat out, that night came on, and it was so dark, that I could not, with all my diligence, find the buoy; and so was forced to come on board again with the boat, without effecting my design.

Potter then requested me to let him scull the boat ashore to get a cag of water, which I consented to, but bid him be sure not to make any stay at all ashore, but come off as soon as he had got his cask filled, which could not be long, the water being close to the sea-side.

Soon after he was gone with the boat, I was taken very ill with faintness and trembling at heart, insomuch, that I had much ado to get down to my cabbin, which I attributed to my overwatching and working to get the vessel in, and to our drowthiness the preceding day, which was more excessive than I had experienced ever since we parted with the pirates. I bid the little boy Jack keep a good look-out for the boat, and have a rope ready to heave to her when she came off; and to be sure not to fall asleep: All which he promised to observe. I had not long lain down on my bed, before I fell fast asleep; and, waking in a surprize, I called out to the little boy, who not answering, I turned out, and came upon deck, and found him asleep in the gangway. I awakened him, and asked him, If the boat was come on board? He told me No, and looking about me, I could but just see the island. This was as nigh as I could guess between twelve and one o'clock, and I was not a little surprized to see myself thus again exposed to the sea, and that in a much worse condition than before; my help gone; the sloop daily growing more leaky; deprived of my boat, and my thirst very great, which perhaps was increased by the hopes I had of getting some water, as well as owing to the great fatigue of the preceding day; but knowing it in vain to despair, I resolved to do what I could, and depend upon Providence for the rest: However, I had two tough jobs to manage, to wit, to heave the anchor up, there being a whole cable out to the better end; and to pump the water out, which was in some places above the ballast: And the latter being the more dangerous, I concluded to begin with that first, knowing, that if I could suck her dry, I should be in hopes to keep her so. Accordingly I went to work, and pumped about half an hour, in which time I gained upon her considerably, and resting a while, took the other half hour's spell; after which I rested again, and smoaked a pipe of tobacco, and took a dram of rum with a little raw rice, and then fell to my work of pumping, and in five or six good spells more, I sucked her;

and then immediately applied myself to heave in the cable; and to enable the little boy to hold on, I made him a jigger with a block fixed to the cable. and a rope reeved through it, so that having a double purchase, he made shift to hold on; though it was very tedious and slow. I hove up till about half the cable was in, and then I went and took a spell at the pump, and pumped her out dry; after which I rested, took a dram, and smoaked half a pipe of tobacco, and then went to heaving up the anchor again, then to the pump again, and the next spell I got the anchor up, and stowed it with the pawm over the gunnel; after which I set sail. and the trade wind continuing to blow, I stretched to the north-west, finding that I was able to keep the sloop free, though she made a great deal of water; and I think I never found myself heartier or stronger in all my life. It was a great concern to me to think of leaving my boy and boat at St. Nicholas, besides the hopes of supplying myself with a sail, which I could not expect at any of the other islands; neither could I propose anything at any of the other islands, but the saving mine and the boy's life, by running the sloop on shore in some convenient place; having no boat to go ashore for water, or to get any of the natives to go with me; for I could not expect that any of them would venture to swim off to me, without some previous conversation, or acquaintance, for fear I should be lurking there to steal some of them away: Wherefore being determined to get to the Island of St. Nicholas, I stretched, as I said before, to the north-west, and stood till I brought the south-west point of the island north-north-east from me about the distance of six leagues, and then I tacked and stood to the eastward till I came abreast of Currisal, it being then about six in the evening, and bearing north, distant about seven leagues; and falling calm in a little time after, I lowered down all the sails, and let her lie while that held, which was all night, and till between eight and nine o'clock the next day.

I was tedious dry, but had no help nor means to quench it; and durst not eat any of the dried fish, because it made me more thirsty, as I thought, than if it had been salted.

This seemed to me the most irksome situation I had yet been in; for I was now, as it were, alone, having little or no help in the little boy, unless to hold the helm while I was at the pump, which was every half hour, or oftener, or while I was doing any other business; not daring to lie down to take a nap, except a short one which I ventured to take during the calm.

I smoaked a pipe of tobacco or two, and also took a dram, with a little rice; and about nine o'clock in the morning, 22nd November, some small catskins came on, and towards noon sprung up a breeze at north-east; I then made sail, and stood to the north-north-west, and hoped to fetch Paragheesi with that board; but the lee-tide being made, I fell short by half a league, and fearing to be put again to leeward of the island, and the boy and I not being able to work the sloop as we ought, I was resolved to fetch in with any anchoring-place I could fetch, and stretching in till I got the shore close on board, I then edged away to a sandy bay, called by the natives Puttacko, where I anchored in six fathom water, in clear sandy ground.

I had hardly been at anchor an hour, when a black came down to the waterside, and called to me. I answered him again. He said something, and waved a long pole, which he had with him; but the wind blowing fresh, I could hear nothing that he said to understand it, only Logo, which, in their language, is as much as to say, presently, or by and by. He went away; and in about half an hour, another black came down to the waterside, and waving his long staff, as the other had done, said something, but I could hear only, Logo, Presto; and away he went.

I gave God thanks for His mercy, that I was once more got to an anchor; and hoped my boy would get some of the inhabitants to help him to bring the boat from Currisal; but not expecting him till the next morning, I tended the pump, in the intervals smoaking a pipe of tobacco, etc. About sunset I saw a small boat come from Paragheesi, with several blacks in her, rowing towards us, at which I was not a little rejoiced.

They came on board to the number of seven, all lusty stout

young fellows, and brought with them two ten gallon casks full of water, and bid me drink heartily of it. I drank twice; and they urging me to drink again, I told them, I had enough; at which they seemed to admire; and one of them said, If he had been so long without water, he could drink one of those ten gallon casks of water himself before he should be satisfied. They told me, *That the Priest and Governor of St. Nicholas had sent them on board with that little boat, which was the Priest's, to assist me to get my sloop up to Paragheesi, in order to secure her, this being a very foul road, and open to the easterly winds, which were very frequent at this time of the year, and always made such a sea in this bay, that it would be next to impossible for the vessel to be safe there; and that the sunken rocks (which lay a large stone's-cast from the shore) were so sharp, that the best swimmer on that island could have no hopes to save himself if the vessel should be put from her anchor.* I told them, *I would stay till my servant came to me from Currisal with the boat.*

They told me, *That could not be this fortnight or three weeks, the wind being set in a strong trade, which commonly at this time of the year, blew hard, and continued long: That they were sent by the Priest and Governor to help me, and they thought it a very good opportunity to get up to Paragheesi, as soon as the windward current was made, which would be in an hour or two: That they were "Homo's de Mare"* (i.e. seamen) *and two of them understood the sea very well, and were pilots.* Which is a title they give to any of their own people that can steer or take charge of any of their little boats that go a fishing. They told me, *I need not be concerned at my boy's not being on board, for they were bred up seamen from their infancy, and could work the sloop up to the Port of Paragheesi, or anywhere to the other islands, and would not have me trouble myself about it, but smoak my pipe, or go and take my rest, for they would take charge of the vessel, and get her into the port, and moor her safe; For,* said they, *we have been very much used to take charge of strangers;* an Appellation which they give to all Europeans, except Portuguese, whom they call Branca's (*i.e.* white's, or white people), I suppose because they were the first white people they ever saw; and, from whom, it's probable, they learnt, after the manner of that nation, to call all other people strangers. I told them, *I thought it was much better to stay till the day tide, when they would be better able to see the ropes, and stand by the work, than they could in the night, they being strangers to the vessel; and besides, perhaps the rest of their company might not be such good seamen, or be used to working in vessels, as they were.*

They told me, *The rest of their company were not pilots, as they two were, and could not work a vessel as they could; but that they were good sailors, and could endure hardships, and do anything that they were commanded, as well as any white sailor whatsoever.*

I said, *If they could do that, it was sufficient: but I had another reason to offer, which might, I thought, sway with them, to tarry till the day tide, which was, That my sails were very bad, and would not hold in anything of a taut wind, and, if anything gave way, we could better mend it, and set it to rights by day than by night.*

They said, *No, it was much better to try for it in the night tide, by reason it was always less wind under the land by night, than by day, neither did the strong flaws come down through the gulleys, as they generally do in the day.*

I still insisting in my opinion, they told me, *If my sails were so bad, as I represented them, they would certainly not hold out to beat up in the day time; for I should not fail of having taut winds blow off the land, as well as hard flaws come down the deep gulleys; and if I was not resolved to weigh the next windward tide coming on, they would all go on shore, and not stay on board to run the hazard of losing their lives, or being drove out to sea; which might chance to happen on a lee tide, where they might have no possibility of fetching any part of the island.*

I considered with myself a while, and found some reason in what they said, and promised to weigh the next spring tide, if they were sure that we could get to Paragheesi.

They told me, *That if they had not been very certain of that, I might be sure they would not venture to weigh from thence, and bid me not to trouble myself about such thoughts; they would*

*to get her safe up and moored, long enough before the
*ward current was spent, even without one knot of sail, if we
k the advantage of the whole tide.

I told them, I was glad to hear it was so easy to get up to
the road, and wished it to fall out as they said.

They said, I need not at all doubt that; and about eight at
night, they told me the current was set to windward, and that
it was time to weigh.

I said, *That, according to the best observations that I had made
among these islands, the current should not set to windward, till
near ten o'clock.* They said, *As for the time, or hours, they were
ignorant of them, as being not used to reckon that way, but they
could tell by the rising of the moon, or by the rising and height of
several stars; and they perfectly well knew, that the tide was
already made up to windward, and, if I did not think fit to weigh
now, they would all hands go ashore with their boat, and believed
I should have no more help from the island; if I did not lay hold
of such a fair opportunity as now offered.* So I told them, *If
they were sure the tide was made to windward, they might go to
work, and heave up the anchor as soon as they pleased.* At which,
they went to work, but would not let me heave at the windlace,
because they said, *they were hands enough, and I need do no
more, but order what I would have done, etc.*

We got the anchor up, and stowed it, and set the sails, and
made a trip off to the south-east, with a moderate gale, and
the wind increasing, we stood along shore, and off withal, till
we reckoned (as well as we could discern the land to know it)
to be abreast of a place called Porto Ghuy; and then putting
her a stays, the mainsail split so in the staying, that I was forced
to lower it down, for fear it would blow all to pieces; which
so daunted them, that they resolved to quit the sloop, and take
to the little boat which they came off in. This put me into as
great a streight, as any I had been in yet: We being then about
two leagues from the shore, an ugly chopping sea running,
the wind blowing fresh, and it looking very black to windward.

I then observed, to add to the misfortune, that the blacks
were almost all drunk; for when they first came on board, I

made the little boy fetch them a bottle of rum, and they observing where he brought it from, were so impudent, seeing none but the boy and I (notwithstanding I forbad them), to fetch it themselves, telling me, *That the least they could expect, was to participate of what was in the sloop, and that I shewed myself very ungrateful, as well as nigardly, to think much at anything they could eat or drink that was on board the vessel.*

I told them, *I did not begrudge them, but would have them only forbear drinking, till we had secured the sloop, and then they should be very welcome to it all.*

They had the impudence to tell me, *The sloop was as much theirs as she was mine, and also everything that was in her; that I was in distress, and must have certainly perished, if they had not come off, and brought me and the boy some water.*

I told them, *That it was a kindness, I owned; but that I was in no evident danger of perishing, when they came on board, the sloop being well at an anchor, and the pump sucked dry; and, thanks be to God, I was in good health, and therefore able enough, with God's blessing, to keep her free, till my boy could come to me from Currisal with my boat.* They said, *That if I had waited there, till the boy came to me with my boat, I might wait long enough, for they did not believe, that any of the islanders would venture to come down in the boat with him, till the blowing weather was over, which they did not expect to be, this two or three months.*

I told them, *If they left me now with the boat they would leave me in a much worse condition than they found me in, when they came on board; for they had drank all the water that they brought on board, and though I was destitute of it when they came, yet I was at an anchor nigh the shore, and should always have been in hopes of a supply; and, at worst, could put the sloop on shore, and so escape perishing that way.*

They said, *They could not see what I could do with the sloop now, having no sails to work her with; and to lie, and drive to leeward all night, and the next day, till we got the sail mended, we should be so far to leeward of the island, that it would be impossible to fetch any part of the island, and then we must either perish at sea, or be forced to some place, from whence they might never be able to get to their families, or homes, any more; and therefore, they were resolved not to run that hazard, but endeavour to get thither in the small boat, which they had brought with them.*

I told them, *I thought the hazard to be so great by venturing in the boat, the sea running so high, and the wind blowing so hard, and right off the shore, that it was next to an impossibility to row to the shore.*

They replied, *They were satisfied it was a great risque, but to abide in the sloop, in their judgment, was a greater; and, if they must perish, would rather choose it in sight of their native land, than anywhere else; and if I thought fit to take my chance with them, and they found we were too many for the boat to carry, there were several among them that could, in case of necessity, depend on swimming ashore, and if necessity required it, they would, for the security of the rest, take to the water and swim;* and one of them, who reckoned himself the best pilot, said, *That if the boat should be overturned by the waves, he would not have me to doubt, but he could, and would, carry me safe to the shore.*

I told him, *That was a very ticklish chance to trust to, and that he would soon be tired in the water with such a load as I should be, not being able to strike one stroke; and that I could expect no less, than to be quitted by him, rather than perish himself.*

He said, *That if I relied upon him, he would sooner die with me, than leave me; besides, there were others in the company,* he said, *that could swim as well as he, and they would take turns, and did not fear getting me and the little boy safe ashore, though there was no boat at all.*

I considered, that all, or most of this, proceeded from the rum, the fumes of which had got in their brains; and that it would have been as desperate an action to go with them, as to cast myself headlong into the sea; the boat being so small, that nine or ten hands were as many as she could conveniently carry in smooth water, and what else could be expected, but to perish in such a sea as then run?

Whereupon I told them, *I was resolved to trust to Providence, and continue in the sloop; and if they would do so too, I doubted not, with God's blessing, but they would by far, stand the better chance.*

They replied, *That if they must perish, they would perish in sight of their own land, and not be driven to an unknown place to perish, where they should never be heard of.*

I said, *That if they were to perish in endeavouring to get ashore in the boat, there could no account be given of them, nor could their friends know any more what was become of them, than if they had been lost in the farthest part of the world.* They answered, *They were sure that some of them should be able to get safe ashore, were both the sloop and boat to go to the bottom ; and, if but one of them got safe ashore, it would be sufficient to give an account, where, when, and how they were lost, which would be a great satisfaction to their friends; and it would be more pleasing to themselves, to think they should die so near their own homes.*

I repeated to them the danger they would expose themselves to, and that there was hardly any possibility of their escaping, if they ventured all of them to take to the boat, whatever chance might befal some of them; but it was all in vain. They said, *Their chance could be no better, if they staid in a leaky sloop, without sails, water, provisions, etc.* And often repeated, *That it would be better for them to perish in sight of their homes, than in a far, or strange place.*

Besides, says one of them, *if you should get to any land, you would want for nothing, but we could expect nothing but to be killed, or made slaves of, during our lives, which, to us, would be worse than death itself; and therefore,* continued he, *I am resolved, come what will, to trust myself to the boat and St. Anthony, and doubt not, but he will prevail with God, to carry me safe; and so,* says he to the rest, *let us be gone, for the longer we delay, the farther off we drive, and the farther we have to row before we can get to the shore: and let us, moreover, make a vow to St. Anthony, that if he will bring us safe to our homes, we will join and pay for a sung Mass in his church, the first Sunday after our safe arrival: and let us also,* said he, *give the blessed Virgin Mary, the Mother of God, a sung Mass in her chapel, that she may command her Son to assist St. Anthony to conduct us safe to the shore.*

Now you must know, there is a vast difference, betwixt a sung Mass, and a said Mass, as well in the price, as the efficacy; it being, according to those people's opinion, the way of the Church of Rome, to raise their prices, in proportion to the pretended merit, or efficacy of the thing; now a sung Mass, which they call *Missa Cantado*, is sung by the priest and the whole choir, by note, and is so common in this island, that there are very few males, but what are taught, though I don't know, that ever I heard that the females learned to sing. They are taught by the head singer, who is titled *Meastre Musica* (*i.e.* master of musick), and is chosen to that office, for the goodness of his voice, etc. This *Missa Cantado*, costs ten *testoons*, that is, between five and six shillings, and is paid to the priest, out of which he pays the singers; but a said Mass, is only called *Missa*, for which they pay to the priest, two *testoons;* so that it is not so efficacious as a *Missa Cantado*, but in the same proportion, as two is to ten; and it is reckoned almost scandalous, for any but the poorer sort, to have a said Mass, either for the living or the dead.

But to return, they concluded to take to the boat, and accordingly, it was haled up alongside, and the water hove out, oars got in (which were more like paddles for a canoo, than oars for a boat), and everything being got ready, the head pilot, who took upon him to be the spokesman for the rest, told me, *They were just upon departing, and, if I thought fit to take my chance along with them, I should fare as they fared, and no otherwise.*

I told them, *I was resolved to abide in the sloop, and desired them, to tell my boy on the island, if all, or any of them, should get safe to the shore, that I would endeavour to get to the island if I could; but if I should not come soon, and he could light of an opportunity, by any ship's touching there, to be sure not to slip it, but make use of it to get off the island as soon as he could; and also desired them to give my thanks and service to the Priest and Governor, for their care in sending assistance: but could wish they had not come on board at all, since it happened as it did; for then I had still been lying safe at an anchor.* Into the boat they stepped, being all, or most of them, very drunk, the night very dark, and a brisk gale of wind; and, what with my concern at my present case, and the darkness of the night, I did not count them, nor mind whether all they that came on board, went in the boat or no.

After they were gone, I began to consider what a comfortless plight I was in, and repented that I let them weigh my anchor, and heartily wished that the boy and I were safe ashore with the other boy, on the Island of St. Nicholas: I should willingly have gone in the boat, and quitted the sloop, but that it was so small, that I could not but think it would be a great presumption to venture to do so, especially as they were all so drunk.

But, however, recollecting myself, that there was now no remedy but patience, I began to consider, what course to take to extricate myself out of this my present, and indeed hitherto, greatest misfortune; for my mainsail was very much torn, my twine almost expended, and I had no help, nor anybody to consult with.

The wind also, was now veering to the eastern trade, so that it seemed a hazard, whether I should be able to fetch my head-sails, the Isle of May, or even St. Jago, which was the leewardmost island that I was acquainted with of the Cape de Verd Islands: the Islands of St. Philip, and that also of St. John, I was utterly unacquainted with, they being very little, or not at all used by our shipping, the sea-draughts giving but a very imperfect description of them, and the waggoners and pilots of those parts, being every whit as much, or more defective, making them both to be very dangerous; the Island of St. Philip, to have few or no inhabitants, the roads, or anchoring-places, very bad; the island of St. John, to have one good road, but very difficult for one unacquainted to enter, by reason of the abundance of rocks both sunken, and otherways; though most of these descriptions I found to be false.

I passed the remainder of the night, very solitarily, lying with my head to the north-north-west. It blew a fresh gale at north-east, cloudy, and sometimes overcast, hazy and windy-like to windward.

In the morning, as soon as the day broke out clear, I could see from me east-north-east, the Terra Vermilia, as it is called by the inhabitants, and the Punte de Vermilharee, north-east and by north. I wore the sloop, and put her head away to the east-south-east, and made the boy steer her, the wind being then about the north-east and by north. I kept her away one point from the wind, because, having none by the head-sails, she would make no way through the water if I kept her hankering up in the wind; and then I went to work, to overhale the mainsail, which I found so torn, that it was past mending, neither had I twine enough to do it, if it had not; wherefore I lashed the upper reef cringle down to the boom, and tore, or cut the sail, even at the foot, all along the upper reef; and where it wanted, I mended it as well as I could, and then set it; by which time, it was as nigh as I could guess, three or four o'clock in the afternoon, when, to my great surprize, I heard the voice of men in the hold. I went to the hatchway, and looking down, I saw three blacks, who called to me, and asked me, *If we were at an anchor?* I told them, *We were at sea.* They asked me, *If I could see any land?* I told them, *I could not.* They asked, *Where I was designed to go to?* I told them, *I could not tell, it must be where God pleased, and was resolved for the first land that I could make, and was in hopes, we should fetch St. Jago.*

At which they seemed to rejoice, and got upon deck, and one of them told me, *That he was very well acquainted at the Islands of St. Jago, St. Philip, and St. John, and that he had been at all of them, and round them also. That he had been three years an inhabitant on the Island of St. John: that he was carried there from St. Nicholas, in a French pirate, who left him at the Island of St. John, where he remained three years; and that the same pirate came again, with whom he returned to St. Nicholas. The pirate captain's name,* he said, *was Maring-*

win, a French-Briton; and the black that told me all this, was
called Nicholau Verd.

I asked them, *How it came, that they did not go with their
countrymen when they went away with the boat?*

They told me, *They were afraid the boat would sink before
they could get to the land; besides, the rest of their consorts
were very much in liquor, which made them the more afraid,
and thought I might know better than they, and therefore believed
they chose the least danger, by staying with me, and hoped if we
should be put to any strange land, that I would neither sell them
for slaves myself, nor suffer anybody else to do so.*

I told them, *They might depend upon it, that they that made
slaves of them, should make one of me also.*

They told me, *They came first on board, with an intention to
serve me, in assisting me to gain the port of Paragheesi, which my
want of sails, and other necessaries,* they said, *had prevented;
but that now they would gladly do anything that I bid them, and
desired, that I would accept them as servants.*

They added, *That they were very sorry their comrades went
away and left me, after they had drank off my rum,* though,
by the way, they themselves, as they afterwards told me,
when they had got safe on shore, had also drank plentifully
of it, and that was the chief reason of their staying behind,
having drank in the hold till they fell dead drunk asleep,
though now they pretended it was out of pure love and respect
to me, and they would never leave me, but continue with me
always servants, etc.

They asked me, *What I thought of the boat? and whether those
that went in her, were got safe ashore or no?* I was willing to
encourage them, and told them, *I believed not, and was much
afraid they were all perished.*

They said, *They did believe as much, and reckoned themselves
happy in not accompanying them in their rash folly; for they
thought it could not be right, because I was so averse to it, and
they were all sure, that I knew a thousand times better then any
of them,* and abundance of such parlavers.

They also said, *They had relations, some on this island,*

*some on the other; and if we could but arrive at this, or that
island, oh! I should want for nothing, but should be plentifully
supplied with everything the island afforded.*

Night coming on (which proved clear overhead, but very
hazy all round the horizon) and it continuing a taut fresh
gale at north-east, I steered east-south-east, and south-east-
and-by-east all night, and the next morning, when the day
broke out clear, we saw the peek of the Island of St. Philip,
in the form of a sugar-loaf above the haze. We could not see
any of the other parts of the island, though very high land, the
haze seeming to be elevated above the imaginary horizon,
about twenty degrees; and the peek seemed to have its head
elevated to thirty degrees or more.[1]

The blacks were very much rejoiced at this discovery of
land, but could not thoroughly give credit to their own eyes,
and used every now and then, to distrust and fear, it was not
certainly land that we saw, and then they would come and
ask me to remove their distrust: and so often repeated their
questions, that I was thoroughly tired with their interrogations.

I was in hopes of seeing St. Jago, but it was so hazy, that I
could not, though if it had been anything clear, we might have
seen it very plain; the peek of St. Philip bore, when we saw it,
from us south-east-and-by-south; and, as the sun rose, the
haze was more elevated by his attractive rays, that the peek
was altogether obfuscated, and hid from our sight; which
increased the blacks' doubting and confirmed their opinion,
that it was not real, but imaginary land we had seen, neither
could I perswade them, though I was as certain as was possible
to be by the sense of seeing; but they were very much down in
the mouth.

I encouraged them all that I could, by telling them we should
be in with the land before night, to which they gave little
credit, supposing, as they told me afterwards, that I only told
them so, that they might not be cast down.

I found, by the bearing of the land from me, with consideration to the course I had steered, that the current set

[1] The volcano of Fogo (St. Philip's) is 10,500 feet high.

strong to the westward, and therefore, notwithstanding the island bore south-east-and-by-south, I resolved to steer south-east-and-by-east, being assured that the current must needs set us down very near the island, before we could run the length of it; however, I knew we could not run so far wide of it, as not to see it, let it be never so hazy, and was resolved, if possible, to come in with it on the weather side, as being then capable of running down along the shore at my leisure, and view the coast narrowly, to find some convenient road or bay to anchor in, or, at least, to run the sloop on shore in, to save our lives, if we saw no way or prospect of doing better.

The blacks tended the pump, and told me, if the boy and I would but steer, they would do that, or anything else I bid them do, that they were able; which was a great help, as well as encouragement to me, to what it was when the boat, and, as I then thought, all the blacks had left me and the boy to shift for ourselves.

However, they continued very uneasy, and continually one or other of them was asking me, *Whether I thought that was land that we had seen? Whether I was sure of it? And how long I thought it might be before we should get sight of it again, etc.?* But to their great satisfaction, as well as mine, we saw it again, and seemed to be very near it, the top of the peek being, as I supposed, forty-five degrees, or thereabouts, elevated above the horizon; and we could see the top of the great mountain, which lies on the north-west side of the peek, which is the highest, excepting the peek on that island.

The land still continued discernible when the haze was thin, which we could perceive to fly very fast over it, and this was about four in the afternoon, and the peek then bore south-south-east, a little southerly, and I then steered right down for the island.

The blacks were exceedingly rejoiced at this sight, and mighty inquisitive to know, *How long it would be before they could get ashore?* I told them, *I was afraid it would be very diffi-cult to get ashore on this island, having no boat; besides, I thought there were but very few inhabitants there, and therefore probably we might be in danger of faring hard, or, perhaps, famishing; and that I was informed the Island of St. John was better; for that there were more inhabitants on it, and probably we should there have a better chance to find necessaries to sustain nature, till it pleased God an opportunity offered for us to get off the island; and that, besides, there was in it a good harbour, if we should be so fortunate as to find it.*

To which Nicholau Verde answered, *That my informer gave me a very wrong description of those two islands; for the Island of St. Philip was one of the most plentiful of the Cape de Verd Islands, for maiz, feshoons, pumkins, man-d'-yoaks, as also for cows, horses, goats, mules, etc., for the latter of which,* he said, *they used to have formerly a great trade with the French; and that it had three or four times the number of people on it that St. John's had; but the harbours or roads were indeed very bad, and a great sea always tumbled in upon the shore; and that it was dangerous even for one that could swim very well, to venture to swim ashore there, the surf breaking in so heavy on the shore, except at particular times, as, namely, in the months of July and August, when the northern trade blew very weak.*

He added, *That he was at that island when a French ship was there trading for mules, etc., and he observed that the sea run so high for several days together, that they were not able to send their boat ashore sometimes for three or four days successively, and used to curse the island very often, because the roads were so bad.*

The Island of St. John, he said, *was indifferently plenty, and had a hundred or more inhabitants on it when he was there, which, as nigh as he could guess, was about twenty years past, and had a very good harbour, which he was positive he could direct me into as well as to any part of the Island of St. Nicholas, where he was born, and had lived all his life, except that time that he was carried off by the French pirate, Maringwin, who left him at St. John's about three years; and that he had been round both the islands, and had been several times, at several places of these two islands, as well as St. Jago, ashore with the said pirates' boat, who always took him with them as a linguist for them, by which means he was very well acquainted, both with the people and landing-places of all the three islands.*

I told him, *If he thought he could find the way, and direct me into that road without running foul of the sunken rocks, it would do well for us all.*

He said, *He would engage his life to do it;* whereupon I told him, *I would lie by all night to windward of the Island of St. Philip, and a little before day would bear away for the Island of St. John, that we might have daylight to get into the harbour and be the better able to shun the rocks, etc.*

They seemed very much dissatisfied at this, fearing, if they did not directly get there, when night came on they should lose sight of the land, and never attain it more, and had a great cabal and murmuring amongst themselves; after which, Nicholau Verde told me, *That he thought I had better run for the Island of St. John directly, being sure we should get sight of it before night, and that then he would engage his life to carry the vessel safe into the harbour let it be never so dark.*

I told him, *I did not think it proper, neither would it be safe; for the weather being hazy, and it being almost night, it would be impossible for us to get sight of St. John's before night, and so perchance we might, by the uncertainty of the current, miss the island, especially as we had no candle on board to see how to steer a direct course by the compass. Besides,* I told them, *the night was likely to prove very dark and hazy, and we might be on the rocks before we could see them, and so perish all together.*

Upon his insisting, *That he was sure, if he could once see the island, if it was never so dark he could find the way into the harbour;* I told him, *I would not venture in the night; but if he was so positive he knew the way into the harbour in the night, I could the better depend upon him to find the way in by day.*

Whereupon they all said, *That if I would not run in now directly, they were sure we should lose sight of the land before the next morning, and then what could they or I either expect but to perish.*

I told them, *They need not fear that; for I would engage my life to bring them to the Island of St. John, with God's assistance, by the next day noon at farthest, and did not fear but we should be much better off than their consorts (who, in all likelihood, had rashly perished with the boat) if Nicholau could but direct me into the harbour.*

So about half an hour past six in the evening, it being then duskish, I laid the sloop a-try under her foresail, with her head to the north-westward, the peek then bearing south-south-east, a little easterly, and the north-east point of the island south-south-west, a little westerly; the vessel came up to north-and-by-west, and fell off to the north-west-and-by-north.

The blacks were so disheartened, for fear we should lose the land, that they went down in the hold, and there lay upon the ballast, resolving not to see themselves perish; nor could I perswade any of them once to come up and take a spell at the pump all the night, but were so dispirited, that they lay like dead people, not caring to stir, nor even to speak; so that the boy and I were forced to look out, and tend the pump, which I was the better able to do, because they had eased me of that labour all the day before.

I now and then catched a nod as I sat on the deck, and then took a spell at the pump, and then a pipe of tobacco, and so I passed the night away till about four o'clock the next morning; at which time I set the north point of the island, and it then bore south, a little easterly, distant, according to my estimation, about four or five leagues.

I then called to the blacks to come up and help me to hoist the mainsail, for that it was time to make sail, and bear away for St. John's; but they would neither come up, nor answer, supposing, as afterwards they told me, that I did it only to get them to pump, concluding, that we were out of sight of all land, and should ever remain so: So I was forced to bring the main haliards to the windlace, and make the boy hold on, while I hove the mainsail up, as much as we had of it, which was not above half a sail, it being shortened three reeves.

After I had got the mainsail up, I made the boy put the

helm a weather, and hoisted the jib, and steered away for the north point of the Island of St. Philip, keeping it a point or better open upon the larboard bow.

After we had been under sail about an hour, or something better, they hearing me cun the boy at the helm, began to have a mind to see or hear what I was doing; Nicholau called to me, and asked, *Whether I saw the land?* I told him, *Yes; and that we were very near the point of the island (which was under our lee-bow) when they went down, and were now sailing directly for the Island of St. John.*

Upon this good news they all started up, and came upon deck, and as soon as they saw we were so near the land, contrary to what they expected, and even contrary to what they all thought was possible, they were very much rejoiced and revived, and immediately went to the pumps and pumped the vessel out dry; though there was not much water then to pump out of her; for I seldom let her stand half an hour without pumping, dreading to let too much water be in her at a time, for fear a large spell would make me thirsty; and having nothing to quench my thirst on board, and very little to allay hunger, the rice and the rum being almost gone, and the dried shark I dared not eat of, it always making me very thirsty whenever I eat any of it.

By this time it was day, and doubling the point of the island, I haled more southerly along the coast of the island, till we got abreast of that part of St. Philip's, called by the inhabitants the Ghors, which is very much noted for the exceeding hard and sudden gusts of winds that come off there, the nearer to which, the harder they are, and reach off the shore about four leagues, and then lose their fierce violence. These gusts are but weak in the night, and rather weaker in the morning, till about ten in the forenoon, at which time the sun rising above the mountains, they blow prodigious hard till about four or five in the afternoon.

We were, when abreast of it, about two leagues from the shore, and it being so early in the morning, had not much of them, though it could not well have damaged us for the quantity of our sails that we had spread; but the rottenness of them rendered them unable to have held out the force or violence of such of them, as might be counted very moderate in respect of the more violent flaws.

We could see the Island of St. John very plain, and I steered directly for it; and, in a little time, raised the little islands which lie on the north-east point of the island, and by the natives called Ghuys; within which lies the best road or harbour in the island, called by the inhabitants Fuurno, which in their language signifies an oven; so called, I suppose, from the several caves which are thereabouts.

As soon as we made the little islands, I, by the direction of my pilot, Nicholau, steered directly for the eastermost of them, which was the highest, and kept it a little open on the starboard bow, and so run till we were got within about half a league of the east end of it, and then kept along the island till we were abreast of the west end, which hath a high rocky point, almost like a sugar-loaf, with the top broke off, not flat, but a little rounding. When we were got abreast of the last mentioned point, we then steered for the north-east point of St. John's, by the natives called Ghelungo, which bears from the west point of the eastwardmost of the little islands about south-west-and-by-south, distant about a large league and a half, or two leagues.

Then I began to ask my pilot Nicholau, *Whereabouts the harbour was?* who very readily shewed me, as he thought; but when we had sailed a little farther, then he shewed another place, and as we ran along, he still was shewing me a new place for the harbour; insomuch, that I plainly saw he was utterly ignorant: for every new point of land that we raised, still that was the point he said, that made the harbour; insomuch that the other blacks began to chide at him, and tell him, *That they believed he knew nothing of it; and that either he never had been at the Island of St. John, or else this that we now saw must be some other land that he had never seen.*

I told them, *I was positive this was the Island of St. John, and that they might certainly credit me; for I could not b mistaken in the island, whatever was the matter that Nicholau could not remember which, or where the harbour was.*

They said, *They could not tell the meaning of it, for the land was so remarkable, that anybody, that ever had seen it but once, might know it again.*

Nicholau said, *He was sure it was the Island of St. John, but it was so long since he had been there, that he could not, he saw plainly, know the harbour at a distance; yet he was sure he should know it when he came to it.*

I asked him, *If he was certain we were not past it already?* He said, *He was sure we were not,* and so I kept on all along the island, within about a mile or less, of the shore, that I might be sure not to miss it; and, at last, we discovered it; but then we were got to leeward, for the harbour lies round a point and turning up to windward, so that you cannot perceive its opening till you are past it; and under the land, the wind is always light, though it blows never so hard a trade in the offin, which makes a short popling sea, and in a light wind, makes it very difficult, for any vessel to turn up under the shore; but impossible to us, our sails being so small, that the vessel would scarce answer her helm, in that popling short sea; and besides a strong lee current, which we perceived to horse us down to leeward apace.

I asked my pilot Nicholau, *Whether there was no place to leeward, that we might anchor at?* He told me, *No, and that if I did not put the sloop ashore before I drove to leeward of Punta de Sal, I should not be able to get ashore, but we must all of us certainly perish.* I asked him, *What he would advise me to do?* He said, *He would have me put the sloop ashore upon the rocks, and every one make their escape as they could.*

I told him, *Neither I nor the boy could swim, and we should run as great a hazard that way, having no boat, as by driving to sea again.*

He said, *As for his part, since he was got so nigh the shore, if I would not put the sloop ashore myself, they could, and would, whether I would or no.*

I told him, *I had a gun ready loaden for any, or all of them, that should offer to do anything on board of my vessel against my will.* Upon which words, he jumped overboard, saying, *He wished me well, and the rest that were with me, but would endeavour not to perish himself;* and away he swam ashore.

The other blacks told me, *They could not swim well, and dared not to venture; but if they were sure they could safely swim ashore, they would not leave me, till I could also secure myself; but withal, they hoped I did not design to carry them away to sea without any water or provisions.*

I told them, *I cared as little for starving, or perishing at sea, as they could; neither did I design to go in this condition any farther, than to find a convenient place to anchor the sloop in; and, if not, to put the sloop ashore in the best manner, and at the most convenient place I could find for our safe escaping ashore.*

But, said they, *Nicholau said, If you did not put the sloop ashore, before you drove past that point (*pointing to Punta de Sal*), you cannot get ashore at all.*

I told them, *Nicholau knew nothing of the matter, as they might easily perceive, by his not knowing the harbour before they were past it, and too late; for,* continued I, *had he known it, we had now, with God's blessing, been safe in and moored; and, perhaps, I might have so recruited here, as to have been able to put you all ashore at St. Nicholas again.*

At which, they began bitterly to curse Nicholau, and to wish that he might be drowned before he got ashore; or, if he did get thither safe, that he might break his neck down the rocks before he got quite up.

I told them, *I was not out of hopes yet, and was almost sure I should find an anchoring-place about Punto de Sal, and, with God's assistance, would get them all safe ashore, if they would pump the water out of the sloop;* for our eagerness of looking out for the harbour, and disappointment in missing it, had made me neglect the pump, and she had a great deal of water in her, insomuch, that with her rowling in the sea, the water washed over the ballast.

However, my black shipmates told me flat and plain, *They would not pump, nor do anything else, till they saw whether they should live or die; and, as soon as the sloop was safe at an anchor, they would then pump, or do anything that I would desire them.*

Ay, said I, *I suppose to get ashore, and leave me as Nicholau has done.*

Hereupon they made bitter imprecations upon themselves, if ever they would leave me, or the sloop, till I thought fit myself; but all that I could do, could not perswade them to pump one stroke.

I run down along shore, and haled in close to Punto de Sal, insomuch, that haling about the point, a man might almost have jumped ashore.

It may, perhaps, be thought that I was foolhardy for venturing so nigh the rocks, without being acquainted with them; but if the necessity I lay under, and the reasons that induced me to do so, be considered, I think I may be cleared on that head; for that point being the leewardmost land of the island that I could see, I did not know how the land might trench away on the other side of it: So, that, as far as I knew, I might not be able to hale in with the land on the other side of the point. I also observed it to be a smooth steep rock, yet not so smooth but what it seemed possible to get up it, and generally such sort of rocks are steep too; so that my intention was, as soon as I had opened the land beyond the point, if I had no prospect either to hold the shore on board, or of an anchoring-place, to run her so nigh the point, if necessity so required, that with the way that the vessel had, I could steer her to the rock, so that the boy and I might jump ashore; for to drive to sea as now we were, if we could any ways avoid it, would be too great a presumption.

As soon as I opened the land on the other side of the point, I discovered a small deep little bay, and luffing in about it, having my lead ready upon deck, I hove a cast, and had thirteen fathom water: I hove again, and had twelve fathoms, the northern stream being made, which set strong into the bay, and round the point, checked me in mainly. I hove the lead again, and had ten fathoms, the next cast I had nine, and then I cockbilled my anchor, and heaving one cast more, I had eight fathoms and a half. I not liking the shore well, which to me looked very ragged, which most-an-end denotes foul ground, though, by the lead, it seemed to be both even and clear, I let go my anchor in eight fathom water; and as soon as I had veered cable enough to hold the sloop, and stowed the sails, I took and rigged both pumps, and took hold of one pump-break myself, and bid them take hold of the other, and we should soon pump her out: But they said, *They wanted water, and were very dry, faint, and hungry, and unable to pump; but they would swim ashore, and see for some water, and come on board again.*

I told them, *There was no place nigh us, I believed, that had any water; neither did it look as if there were any; and therefore desired them to wait with patience till the morning, and to be sure some of the inhabitants would come down to us, and perhaps might bring some provisions too, since they must needs know and hear of our necessity by Nicholau, who I was sure would not fail to give them an account who we were, and of our necessities.*

They told me, *They did not know but Nicholau might be drowned, or devoured by some fish before he got ashore, and that they would not trust to that: That it might be, the sloop would drive to sea again in the night.*

I told them, *They need not fear that; and if we found no relief before the next noon, I myself would hale the sloop in, and go with them ashore.*

They said, *They would go ashore and get some water, and would come off to me in the morning betimes, and bring me some, if I did not go away with the sloop in the night.*

So away they went overboard, and swam ashore, which was not far, being about a large stone's-cast, and never came to me more.

It was evening, and almost duskish, when they went away; but I could see some of the natives up aloft on the tops of the rocks, but they did not come down that night.

So the little boy and I were again left alone to shift for ourselves as well as we could; and after I had put some service in the hawse, I fell to work at my old trade of pumping, and was heartily tired before I got her sucked; for being nigh the shore, so that I could have made shift to have saved the boy and myself, I was not so much afraid as when I was at sea; which fear, I found now, had made me so vigorous, and, I thought, strong, that I was not then tired, as I could perceive, at all; but now it seemed not only tiresome, but tedious and irksome, insomuch, that I began almost to despair of being able to hold out without some of her assistance; however, with much to do, I, after a long and tedious pumping, got her to suck. She had as much, or more water in her, than she had when the pirates first left me; but then I had my biggest boy to help me, who could pump as much as I could, and then I was more strong and vigorous, being pretty much fatigued, emaciated and debilitated since then.

However, I resolved with myself to keep her, if I could possible, till I could find, whether there was hopes to get anything at this island, so as to recruit, and enable me to run down to Barbadoes; for I hoped, if I could get a little provisions, and perswade two or three of the blacks to go with me to help me at the pump, which, now she became so leaky, was the principal part of the work, the sails, with a small matter of mending, would serve to run down.

CHAPTER SIX

*

As soon as it was day, three of the inhabitants of the island came down to the seaside, and haled the sloop. I answered them. They asked me, *How I did?* and welcomed me to their island. I thanked them. They asked, *Whether they might come on board?* I told them, *They might if they pleased, or knew how, for I had no boat.* They said, *They had a boat of their own:* At which they jumped into the sea, and swam off to me. As soon as they were come on board, they asked me, *Whether I was not an Englishman?* I told them, *Yea.* They said, *They loved the English the best of any nation,* and asked me, *Where the rest of my company were?*

I told them, *The pirates had taken all my men from me.*

They said, *They knew that, for Nicholau Verd had told them of that the day before.*

Then, said I, *Nicholau is got ashore? Yes,* said they, *and he would have come down to you with us, but that he has hurt his thigh and hip against the rocks as he was landing, insomuch, that if we had not been there when he came ashore, to help him out of the water, he would have certainly perished; but,* said they, *we asked not for your men, that is the Englishmen, but the blacks which Nicholau told us he had left on board when he swam ashore.* I told them, *They went ashore the preceding night; and told me when they swam ashore that they would come again on board this morning, and bring me some water off with them; but I had not heard of them since.*

They asked me, *If I had any water on board, for Nicholau Verd,* they said, *had told them, that I had had no water when he came ashore, nor for a long time before.*

I told them I had not one drop. They said, *If I would go ashore, they had some pompion*[1] *there, and would make a fire and dress some of it, and get me some water.*

I told them, *I could not swim;* at which they much admired, that any man should venture to go to sea without knowing how to swim.

[1] Pumpkin.

128

I told them, *That abundance of our countrymen did; and that swimming was not so common amongst us, as it was amongst them.*

They said, *It was very strange, that we using the sea more than any nation, yea, even more than the Portuguese, who had taught all the world to be sailors, as they were informed, should not practise swimming: It was what they practised,* they said, *even from their infancy, not excepting their very women; and that they should be afraid to go down upon the rocks to fish, unless they could swim; for fear they should at any time happen to fall into the sea; in which case, if they could not swim, they could expect nothing less than to be drowned.*

I asked them, *If there was any water nigh hand?* They said, *Yes,* and shewed me whereabouts it was, and told me, *If I would give them a large calabash, they would swim over the bay, and fetch some; for the rocks were so steep, that if a man went ashore on one side of the bay, he could not go round to the other side, without swimming.*

I thanked them, and told them, *I had no calabashes, but I had a small cask;* and bid the boy hand up a half anchor which was in the hold.

When the boy brought it up, they said, *It was too cumbersome to swim with, and they would therefore go ashore, and take their own calabashes:* Which are gourds, that after all the pulp and seeds are taken out, are set to dry, and so become hard, and serve them to carry their water to their houses, as also when they go a fishing or hunting; for they never go abroad from their huts without a calabash of water with them; and for their more easy carriage of that, and their provisions, when they go a journey, as also to bring home the fish or venison that they catch, they have every one of them a goatskin, stripped off without cutting the skin open, something like a soldier's knapsack; and the hide of the legs being stripped down to the hoofs, and the hoofs cut off with the skin, serves to sling them for their more easy carriage, which they do by making fast the feet of one side together, and putting their arms through, by which means they hang over their backs with little or no trouble to them, as they are so used to them.

They accordingly swam ashore; and by that time they had reached it, there appeared in sight aloft on the rocks, some more of them, who hallowed and hooped much after the manner of the Mandingo negroes; from whom, I believe, they might take their origin, being very like them in gesture, manners, and physiognomy, and using a great deal of the Mandingo dialect in their speech.

They were answered by the blacks who swam ashore; at which they descended down the rocks, and the others below waited for them till they came down, and, I suppose, told them of their being on board, etc., after which, these newcome blacks swam off, being three in number, and came on board, and asked me, *How I did, etc.?* and told me, *They had brought nothing from the town with them, because they did not know of my necessity; saving two pompions, which belonged to those blacks who were gone to fetch me water, who had desired them to bring them off with them: That they also had met with the blacks who came ashore last night, and who, as they told them, were going to the Governor to get him to send me down some men to pump the water out of the ship, for that there was a great deal of water came in through her bottom, and if the Governor did not send me down some help, the ship would sink; and that they were so tired with the pump, that they were almost dead; but had said nothing of my want of water and provisions.*

I asked them, *Whether the Governor was a good man or not?* They told me, *He was an extraordinary good man, and they believed he would have been down with me before now, but that he was very sick of a fever and cough, which he had had a long time, insomuch, that he had not been out a hunting for several months; but they were sure I should have some help down that day; and desired me to shew them the pump, that they might see what it was;* which I did: And then they desired me *to let them see how I worked with it, that they might help me.* Which I did very willingly, and they pumped till it sucked, and then I made them leave off.

In about two hours, the blacks who went for the water returned, and brought two calabashes full with them, which I believed might be about six quarts: I then went to work to make a fire, and the blacks were so obliging, they would not let me make it, but made it themselves. I made the boy get up a little rice, and sliced a pompion into the pot with it, of which we made some good pap, and, as soon as boiled, we all eat heartily; after which, I gave them a small dram of rum apiece, for which they were very thankful.

I would have dressed some of my dried shark; but as soon as they saw it, they asked me, *If that was not fish called Sarde?* I told them, *I did not know.*

They asked me, *Where I got it.* I told them, *I catched it at sea;* and when I told them after what manner, they lifted up their hands and eyes, and much admired my ingenuity in the contrivance of catching it, and that any English should eat it; and were sure it was that kind of fish which they called Sarde, asking me, *If it would not seize and devour an human creature, if it should light on one in the water?*

I told them, *It would, and was a very voracious fish.* Then they said, *It was the same;* and directly, without asking my consent, tossed it all overboard, and said, *They thought that no man of any nation would eat any fish that fed upon human flesh; but especially the English, whom they took to be the nicest and cleanliest people in the world.*

I told them, *We did not use it commonly for food, and that where necessity did not enforce us, we always abhorred such food; but I catched it to keep me from starving, and yet, notwithstanding I had it so long on board, and was reduced to such want, I was sure there was not three pound weight of it eaten.*

Some said, *It was better to eat anything than starve;* others, *That they would sooner starve than eat anything that lived upon human kind.*

After we had eaten and talked a while in this manner, they began to talk among themselves about going to their town, and told me, *They wondered that the Governor had not sent some men down to me, and believed that they who went from me to town, had not spoke with the Governor, or perhaps they might be weary, or not find the way to it; but they would go ashore, and make the best of their way to town, and speak to the Governor that night, to send me some help betimes in the morning, and likewise to order me some venison and other provisions; and did not know but some of themselves might come on the morrow, if they were not too much tired;* for, they said, *it was an ugly difficult way to town, as well as long and dangerous, the rocks being very apt to fall; but some of them would stay to help me to do what I wanted to be done, that was in their power to do, and also go and catch me some fresh fish.*

I thanked them, and desired them *to give my service to the Governor, and desire him to send me ten or a dozen men down, to hale my vessel further into the bay, to make her fast, and I would pay to his satisfaction with anything I had on board the vessel.*

They said, *I need not fear having twenty, or more men down on the morrow;* and so went ashore all together, two of them having concluded to stay, but went ashore with the rest to catch some fish for my supper. They also pumped the vessel dry before they went ashore, as they had done all the time that they were on board.

Now I began to be a little up in my spirits, seeing the people were so affable, and was in hopes that the danger of perishing by famine was over. About duskish, the two men who went a fishing returned on board, and brought a good handsome dish of fish, and a cabalash of water with them, which we dressed, with some pompion; and after we had taken the fish up out of the pot, at their desire, I made the boy bring up a little flower, and with it and the fish-broth we made some pap, which by the blacks was accounted a most savoury dish, as also it was to me and the boy, not having eat any hot or dressed victuals a long time before.

They told me, *They would not have me trouble myself with the pump, but the boy and I might go to sleep, and take a whole night's rest, which they did believe,* they said, *I very much stood in need of.*

I thanked them, and said, *I would accept of their kind offer, but desired, if I should chance to fall asleep, and it should blow*

*or fall calm, or the wind should shift, that they would not fail to
call me; for,* said I, *if it should fall calm, the vessel, by the turning
of the tide, might take a turn with the cable round the anchor,
and when the anchor was foul with the cable, it would not hold,
but let the vessel drive either on the rocks, or else out to sea,
according as the wind blew.*

They said, *They would be sure to call me if occasion required,
or any alteration happened different from what it was when I
lay down.*

So I smoaked a pipe of tobacco which they had brought
with them, and gave to each of them a short junk of pipe, for
I had no other left by the pirates, and considering I could not
employ or make use of my rum better, than to entertain such
guests as they were with it, I gave each of them a small dram
apiece, and told them, *I had but very little of it now; but had a
great deal of it when the pirates took me, who had robbed me of it
all, except a little that lay in the bottom of a cask, which I believed
they knew nothing of, or they had not left me that; but since I
saw they were so kind to me, I could wish I had something better
to give them.*

They thanked me, and told me, *They would rather have me
keep it for myself, because, perhaps, I being used to drink it,
might not so well be able to live without it; but as for their parts
they could do very well without it, though it was the best liquor
that ever they had tasted; having often heard of it, and several
of their islanders had drank pretty much of it, especially when the
pirates used to come thither; but for their parts they never before
tasted any Aqua ardenta (which is the general name they give to
all hot spirits, not knowing the difference, or how to distinguish rum
from brandy, etc.). But they would not,* they said, *have me own
that I had any on board, for there were some of the inhabitants
who knew what Aqua ardenta was; and if once they came to
know I had it, they would drink it all away from me, and then I
should be destitute of something to comfort me, and perhaps die
for want of it; for they had heard that their food was so different
and ordinary to what ours was, that an Englishman could not
live upon it. Besides, their people not being used to any such,*

could not have any want of it, water being their only drink, and therefore more natural to them. They also had heard it related, they said, *That a certain pirate called Maringwir, a Frenchman, which country they did not know but might be in England, having landed on this island* (which as my unlucky pilot Nicholau Verde told me, was about twenty years before, and these two blacks, by their countenance, I judged to be about twenty-four years of age), *had abundance of that strong water on board, and was very free of it among the black people of this island, who drank plentifully of it, and not being used to it, were mad for some time after, and some of them fell sick, and died of mad fevers: notwithstanding which, many that were now on this island, were almost every day wishing, that a pirate, or any other ship, would come and take them with them to some country, where they might have enough of that hot liquor to drink; and that they had often declared, they would certainly go with them.*

Hearing this, made me in hopes, that if I could recruit myself with a small matter of provisions and water, it would be an easy matter, if what they said but now was true, to get three or four of them to go with me, to help to carry the sloop down to Barbadoes.

I asked them, *If there was good store of cotton on the island.*

They said, *There was cotton enough, but nothing nigh so much as had been, because the seasons had not been so kindly, for want of rain, as they used to be, nor their island so plenty as formerly; but still,* they said, *they did not want, there being more by one half than they gathered and made use of.*

I asked them, *If they did not make cotton cloths to sell.*

They said, *There was few or none on the island but what had cotton cloths, and some had a great many; but no ships coming to buy them, they generally made no more than they had occasion for, for their own use: But that, however, some women had six or eight cloths; of which number,* says one of them, *my mother is one; but they wore them so seldom, that a cloth would last some years.*

I asked them, *Whether I could not get some cotton thread to mend my sails?*

SHIPWRECK ON THE ISLAND OF ST. JOHN

They said, *I need not fear that, they were sure nobody would refuse to give me a skein or two of thread for asking*.

I told them, *I would buy it;* for I had some glass beads, and some old cloths, etc., than which you cannot have a more acceptable commodity to traffick with those people.

It growing late (I believe near or about the hour of ten), they said, *They would have me go lie down and sleep, and they would look out for me, and call whenever there was occasion, and would keep the sloop always pumping dry.*

Being pretty sleepy, and much fatigued by sitting up all the night before, I was willing to accept their kindness, and gave them a half-hour glass, and shewed them, that in a certain space of time, all the sand would run out of the upper glass into the lower, and then, by turning the end which had the sand in it, uppermost, in the same space the sand would run again into the other end; and so by turning the glass as soon as the upper end was empty, they might know how the time passed; and that it would be enough to pump the vessel every time they turned the glass, and when they had sucked her, to let the pump stand till the upper end of the glass was empty; and then to turn the glass and pump again.

They said, *They would;* and asked, *How many times the glass must run out, and be turned again, to make that space of time which I called an hour?* Having told them, *Twice*, they asked me, *Whether the glass would run the sand in that time if every one went to sleep, as exactly as if it was watched?*

I told them, *It was all the same;* and they asked me, *If I knew how many glasses would run out before the day appeared.*

I said, *I could, if they took care to turn the glass again as soon as the upper end was empty, and not before, provided I could know exactly what hour of the night it was when the glass was first turned.*

But how will you do to know that, said they.

I have a thing, said I, *by which I could tell by the stars, if the north side of the sky were clear to the water; but now I cannot, because the land hinders me.*

They said, *They believed all white men were fittaseers[1] (i.e.* conjurers).

I told them, *We utterly detested having any correspondence with the devil, and in our country when anyone was found guilty of sorcery, he or she was by the law of the land immediately burned.*

They said, *It was a very good law, and they wished they would do so there also; But,* said they, *we do not mean, when we say all white men are fittaseers, that they are such evil persons, or committ such mischievousness as our fittaseers do, or that you are beholden to the devil for your skill, as ours are: We rather think you are more ingenious, and know more than the devil himself does; and therefore we do believe, that it is not in the power of our fittaseers, with all their skill and assistance of the devil, to hurt a white man, especially if he be a scholastico (i.e.* an artist, or man of learning), *as they believed most strangers to be, who were piloto's, and therefore when I went up to town, they hoped I would do something to affright them, so as to make them forbear hurting them and their cattle, and especially little children, as against whom they had such a spite, especially if their parents had any ways offended them; that in some families they would not suffer a child to live, but would so bewitch it, that in a little time it would pine away, and die.*

I was willing to keep up their esteem of me, and told them, *I would see what was to be done in that matter when I went up to their town, which I designed should be as soon as the Governor sent me down some men to help me, and that I had got the sloop a little better made fast, and farther into the bay.*

They said, *I should have hands enough by the morrow;* and asked, *How many glasses they must turn to make it the middle of the night? And how many more to bring day? And if I could not guess this, within two, three, or four glasses, by any of the other sides of the sky besides the north?*

I told them, *I did believe I could;* and so guessing the time of the night to be about ten, I bid them, *turn the glass then, and let it run out, and turn it thrice more, and that would bring*

[1] *Feiticeiros,* the Portuguese word for witch-doctors.

midnight; and then turn it eleven times more, and that would very near, or quite bring day; asking them, If they could be sure to keep a true account of the number of glasses which they turned?

They said, *Yea: Then,* said I, *you can reckon well, I suppose.* They said, *Yes, yes, they would have me to think they were not like the terra firma Preato's (i.e.* mainland blacks), *for although they were black, yet they believed there was a God and a Christ, and they thanked St. Antonio, and were beholden to him above all the saints, even more than to St. John, who was the guardian saint of their island, and under whose care they had been put by the Portuguese, when they first brought their forefathers from the terra firma, and placed them on this island. Yet,* said they, *we are more obligated to St. Antonio, because it was he that directed the Portuguese, and conducted them with us to this island, through whom we not only came to the knowledge of himself, but also of God, Christ, St. John, and also of all the other saints that we know; and of the Virgin Mary, who is God's Mother, and can command her Son to do anything she pleases; and we are sure that God cannot deny His Mother, which is the reason that we oftner pray to her than to God, or Christ; because she being a woman, is more easily perswaded, as are almost all women, than men.*

They added, *That a great many of them could both read, write, and cast accompt, though they owned they had not the use of figures like the English, who, as they had been informed, exceeded all people in the world, for navigation, physick, conjuration, and arithmetick; even the Portuguese themselves, from whom they had learned all that they knew; and, therefore, as we exceeded the Portuguese, who were their teachers, so it could not be otherwise but we must abundantly exceed them.*

They then repeated their desire, that I would go to sleep; whereupon I bid them good night, charging them to be sure to call me if they saw any alteration; which they promised, and I went to my cabbin, and mused and contemplated on my present condition, as well as what means I could use to extricate me out of it, with a hearty desire that the Almighty would direct me in the best way and method; and seeing it a fine night, and a steady, fresh, yet moderate wind, blowing the right trade, and likely so to continue, I at last fell asleep, and held it till about four or five in the morning; at which time awaking in a sort of surprise, as not being a long time used to such long and undisturbed sleeps, I arose, and came upon deck, and found my two new shipmates sitting forward, talking together.

I bid them a good morning, and asked them, *How they had passed the night?*

They said, *Very well;* and asked me, *How I had slept?*

I told them, *Very well.* They said, *They got forward to talk, because they would not wake or disturb me; and thought, considering the watching and fatigue I had had, that I should not have waked before the sun was up.*

I told them, *I had not had such a long or sound sleep in a great while before;* and asked them, *How long it was since they pumped?* They said, *They pumped when they turned the glass, which was about half out, and I took the sounding rod and sounded, and found the sloop had not above eight inches water in her.*

They told me, *That the last time they pumped, for fear they should not do right, they called the little boy, who told them, that she was dry enough, and then they made him go to sleep again; but were loth to wake me, lest I should not go to sleep again presently, which they knew the boy would presently do.*

I asked them, *How many glasses they had got out? or, whether they had not let them stand?*

They said, *They had not let them stand at all; after it was out of one end, they immediately turned it; and that this glass that was now running, was the tenth; and that they had watched it the narrower, to see if it could tell them when day came.*

I told them, *That it would be day, I believed, before two glasses more ran out, besides that which was then running.*

Well, they said, *if it was so, that would be just as I had told them before I went to sleep; and if it so fell out, they should think it one of the most ingenious things that ever they had seen in their lives; and that as I had told them in the beginning of the night, that I could not tell the exact time of the night, being hindered by the land, so if the day came in the thirteenth glass, they thought it was exact enough.* They asked me, *Whether I would not go and take another nap of sleep?* I told them, *No; but they might, and I would look out and tend the pump.* They said, *No; they had rather watch and count the glasses till day; and as for the pump, they would not have me trouble myself with that any more, for I should always have men enough while I was here, that would come of their own accord, and take turns on board.*

I told them, *By what I had already seen of them, I had no reason to believe that I should want help, or anything else that the island afforded.*

They asked me, *If I would smoak a pipe of tobacco.* I thanked them and told them, *Yea.* So they rummaged their pouches, but betwixt them could hardly make a pipe full, they having expended the stock which they had brought from home: Whereupon I told them, I had some tobacco yet, which the pirates had left me, and offered each of them a pipe, which they thankfully accepted; and so we passed the time till day, which broke out a little after they had turned the twelfth glass; at which they much wondered, that such an inanimate thing should measure and keep time so exactly, and that they who had life and sense in them, could nothing nigh measure or guess the time as that did; and sometimes they said there was something of magick in it.

About sun-rise there was a great noise, and calling from the tops of the lower rocks, as if there had been a hundred people. The blacks which were with me on board, told me, they believed these that I heard whooping upon the rocks, were the forerunners of the company which the Governor had sent. I said, I wished it might be so; and that by the noise they made, there seemed to be a great many: But they said it was only the sounding of the rocks, which made me think so; but they knew there were but two men.

The reader will perhaps wonder how I came to be so perfect in their language so soon, it being the first time I came among them: But I must acquaint him, that the ground or original of their language is the same with that of their stock, which was, as I hinted before, from the Mandingo negroes; from which they retain a dialect, as well as a great many of the primitive words of that large nation, and far extended language; and the rest of it is made up of a corrupted Portuguese, and some other words, which seem to be coined or invented since their settlement here, and incorporated by use with their hodge-podge language.

Now I had a tolerable smatch of the Portuguese language, which is the most significant part of their dialect: Besides, they have so many motions (as indeed most of the inhabitants of the Cape de Verd Islands have, especially those of this, and the Island of St. Philip) that thereby, and by the accent, which gives life and force to their meaning, of which I had some notion before, that they served very much to explain what they said. I also understood something of the general barbarous language of the Windward Island, which comes so nigh to the language of the Leeward Islands, as in a great measure enabled me to apprehend the purport of what they said in the general, and to make us understand one another; but yet so obscurely and confusedly, and with so much difficulty, as would have rendered an interpreter necessary, could such a one have been had; though perhaps he could not express himself with the emphasis or force that I could; however, he might be a better master of the tongue. But to return: The blacks waited a while to see if they would come down; but seeing they did not, they said they would go ashore and meet them, and send them on board, and they themselves would go a fishing, and bring some on board for dinner: So away they swam on shore.

Some time after, two men came down, and swam on board, being the same who had whooped in the morning, and brought with them a pompion; and told me, that the other two, who had been on board all night, were gone a fishing, and would be back about noon, and had given them a great charge to mind the pump; and desired me to shew them what they must do.

This I very readily did, and they as readily wrought as they were taught; and about twelve or one o'clock, the other two returned with a handsome dish of fish, which we dressed with some pompion, and, as before, made some pap with the fish-broth, and made a hearty meal thereon; but my mess-mates desired me not to use my flower, but keep it for myself and boy; which they all took to be my son, and still believed to be so.

They told me, *I should not get any such food here, as my flower was; and that if the Priest heard that I had any, he would, they believed, expect me to give him some.*

I told them, *That I had but a very little; but the Priest, Governor, or anybody else on the island, was very welcome to that, or anything else that I had on board.*

I waited and expected to have some help down, but none came; and in the afternoon it began to blow, and looked dark, cloudy, and heavy to windward, over the land, which is a certain sign of a gale of wind, so that I began to fear, if it should blow hard, and my ground tackle give way, I should drive out to sea, and then should be in a worse condition than ever I had been yet: I proposed therefore to them, to swim with the end of a small rope ashore, and by that to hale a cable-end, and make it fast to the rocks; which they did, but so slightly, that it slipt; and all the arguments that I could use to persuade them, could not prevail with them to try once more, and to carry a fast ashore: Which made me very disconsolate, the wind increasing still: They seeing me dissatisfied, and asking the reason, I told them, *That I could expect nothing but to perish, if I and the boy should drive again out to sea;* and told them, *how safely that might be prevented, if I had a cable well made fast ashore.*

They said, *They had tried already, and the evening now grew cold; besides, they were so spent and tired with what they had done, that they could not pretend to get it ashore again: besides, they knew that they could never make it well fast; but they were sure there were some men would come down the next day from the town without fail, that could make fast my cable to the rocks, or do anything else that I had occasion to have done.*

I told them, *I did not know what sort of ground we had in the bottom, and did not know but it might be rocky, and would cut my cable; which, if it did, I could expect nothing but to drive to sea, and perish, having no way to escape to the land, and no boat, and neither the boy nor I being able to swim one stroke.*

They bid me not be disheartened, *For they would manage that well enough; And,* said they, *we two that tarried with you on board last night, will go up to town to-night; and will go to the Governor as soon as we come up, and speak to him to order men down to help you, and will come down with them ourselves; and the other two men who came down to-day, will stay on board with you, to pump, or do anything you desire them, that they can, till we come back again; and if the vessel should drive away, you need not fear but what we would safely and securely get you ashore, and the boy also;* and pointing to the cross-jeck-yard which lay upon deck, they said, *With that they could carry me a hundred times farther than from thence to the shore, with ease.*

I thanked them, and desired them to take a little flower up with them for the Priest and Governor, and with it to give my service to them, and desire them to send some people down to me, and to be sure to get Nicholau Verd to come with them, because he would be more serviceable than they, by reason he could make fast a rope, or do anything else much more handy than any of them could.

They told me, it was better to let the flower alone; because they had a long, as well as a dangerous way to climb up the rocks, and that it was now so late, that were it not that my necessity required it, they should not care to climb up those steep, as well as rotten rocks; but they would tell both the Priest and Governor of it, with the reasons of their not bringing it up with them, and desire them to send somebody down for it themselves: So away they went ashore.

It continued to blow at night, as it had done in the afternoon; but towards day it was a little moderate, and the sun rose pretty clear; only, before his rising, it shewed very hazy and fiery to the north-east and east-north-east board, which the two blacks that were on board with me, said, was a great and sure sign of very hard gales of wind, as the day increased, and the sun rose up higher; but more especially after the sun began to fall. All which came to pass very exactly, though I could see nothing that portended anything of a hard gale.

After the sun had mounted about thirty degrees of altitude, it began to blow very hard, and the flaws came down the rocks with an incredible force, even beyond what I could believe to have been in the wind, if I had not felt it: Sometimes they would come right off the high rocky land, and sometimes a counter flaw would blow right counter to that on the land, and raise up the water beyond what I ever saw a whale or grampus do, to an almost incredible degree; and if they took the sloop at any time on the bow, quarter, or broadside, she would heel to it, more than anybody would believe that had not seen it. Indeed they did not hold long, some a minute, or half a minute, some came with a sudden puff, and would be gone again before she brought her cable taut.

I could not tell what to do; but often wished that the boy and I were safe ashore, and frequently looked out, to see if I could perceive any of the blacks coming down the rocks to us; but all in vain.

About two in the afternoon it ceased a little, but still continued to blow very hard, though not in such strong flaws as it did, and I began to hope the heart of the gale was broke; and about three in the afternoon, the two blacks who went up the evening before, came down, and swam off on board, and was glad to see that we were not drove out to sea. *They were afraid*, they said, *they should have blown off the rocks, as they were a coming down;* and told me, *They had been with the Priest and the Governor, who had told them, they had both of them spoke to the people, and had ordered so many to come down to assist me, that they thought I had had help before them: That thereupon they went to speak to the people; but found them all unwilling to come down, nor did they care to give them any reason wherefore: That they went also to find Nicholau Verd, to get him to come with them, as I had desired them, but they could not find him: That at last one told them the reason that none of them would venture to come down; which was, that Nicholau was afraid to come on board, for fear I should carry him to sea again, and had prepossessed the rest with the like fear.*

They said, *They did all that they could to persuade them that their fears were groundless, but all in vain; wherefore, seeing they could not prevail with any of them, they came down themselves to let me know it, and to do me any service they could.*

I thanked them, and told them, *The only and best service they could do me, was to get the rope ashore, as they did the day before, and make it well fast; and then, if the cable at the anchor gave way, I could always hale or heave the sloop to the rock, and by that means the boy and I should have a fair chance to save our lives.*

They said, *If that was all, they would carry me and the boy ashore now, and they would stay in the sloop.*

I thanked them, and told them, *I would rather stay on board, while I had any hopes of saving her; and wished they would carry a rope ashore, which would be a means to prevent the anchor-cable being cut with the rocks, which otherways I could expect no less, by her ranging and sweeping the ground so with the cable, with the uncertain and variable flaws.*

They said they would; so I bid them carry the small rope ashore, and make it fast to the rock, and then we would hale the sloop to the rock, and I would go ashore myself and make fast the cable; which accordingly they agreed to; so I unreeved the topping lift, the main haliards, and jibb haliards, and bent them, and three of the blacks jumped into the sea, one of them taking the end of the rope, the other two taking the bite at a distance, the one from the other, as I directed them, and got the end ashore, and made it fast; and then they came on board again, and I unbent the main sheet, and unreeved it, which was a new rope, that I had bought at Barbadoes, and bent it to the cable that was at the anchor, to lengthen it, to veer the sloop to the rock; which we did, by veering the cable, and heaving in the shore-fast, till we hove the sloop on the rock side, which was as steep up and down as a key, and about two fathom water at the rock side.

I then jumped ashore, and made fast an end of a cable to the rock, and casting off the rope from the shore, I veered off by the cable made fast ashore, and hove in upon the anchor-cable, until I got her off in her birth again; but still being dubious of the anchor cable sweeping and ranging the ground, I was willing to see whether it was rubbed, chafed, or stranded anywhere, and bending the main sheet to the shore cable, to lengthen that, I hove a peek on the anchor, and found it rubbed in several places, and in one place, better than a whole strand cut through.

My design was, as the wind then blew off shore, and not now extraordinary hard, though still a taut gale, and the sloop riding altogether by the shore-shaft, to have hove the anchor up, and to cut the cable off where it was stranded, and bend it again to the anchor, and let it go under foot, and then veer upon the anchor cable, and heave in upon the other cable that was fast ashore, and so ride moored: But all of a sudden, the blacks laid down their hand-spikes, and told me I was going to carry them away to sea, and looked very angry: I told them, no, and shewed them the cable where it was cut, and did all that I could to persuade them out of their opinion, and urged my necessity for what I was going to do, and that the sloop could not be saved without doing it; and also, that I dared not do it, until I had got a cable fast on the shore.

They told me, I had made it fast, so that it would loose whensoever I had a mind it should, and that it was only to amuse them, the better to decoy them away: That if I had served some of them that was upon the island, as I intended to serve them, they would kill me directly; but they would not do me any harm, but would run no more hazard, by assisting me, to be carried away to any place, where they should never see their friends or home any more.

I endeavoured all I could to pacify them, not knowing what danger such a notion might bring me into; and, perhaps, fix an odium on me from those, who, in all likelihood, were to be my neighbours, during a long time; at least, longer than I desired, if not for all my life; and at last persuaded them to lend me a hand to hale in again the shore-fast, and moor her again between that and the anchor, which they did, and then began to talk to one another about going ashore.

I did all I could to persuade them to stay on board, not so much for their assistance, as for fear they should spread a notion, that I was going to carry them away from the island; for I had a good cable end ashore, and well made fast, so that the boy and I could, at any time, heave her in to the rock side, when the anchor-cable gave way, and, without any danger, in a manner step ashore.

I much importuned them to tarry with me this night, and not to go ashore until the morning.

They told me, *I might endeavour to persuade them to this, in order to have the better opportunity to carry them to sea in the night.*

I represented *how unprovided I was, both for sails, provisions, and water, which was the only reason that brought me there: That they all knew very well, I had not recruited in the least with anything since I came there: Besides, they were four strong, lusty men, and I but one, and weak, and half famished; and that the boy could be reckoned as nobody.*

They told me, *That I had a Spring Guarda (i.e. a musket), and with it, could kill twenty or thirty of them, and therefore they were sure, if they resisted, to be killed; but would rather perish here, than be compelled by force to go with me; and, that that was the reason which made Nicholau Verd jump overboard from me into the sea, and make his escape to them, because he knew, that as long as I had the Spring Guarda, I could make him, and a hundred more, if they should oppose me, die, or submit to what I required of them.*

I told them, *If that was what they were afraid of, I would bring it up, and put it into their hands, for their satisfaction and security, and thereby give them an occasion to see, that I was not at all afraid to venture my life into their power, and that voluntarily, without any compulsion, more than the desire to satisfy them.*

Hereupon, I went down into the cabbin and brought it up,

and it being loaden, I fired it off, which a little surprised them; but I told them, it was only to clear it, so that it should not harm them.

They took it, and seemed to be better satisfied, and concluded, all four of them, to stay on board all night, which they did; during which, it continued to blow a taut gale, with hard squalls off the land, but nothing so hard as those which we had the preceding day.

We passed the night as well as we could, and they would have had me gone to sleep; but I could not all the night, though, to please them, I went and lay down, but had too many thoughts to let me rest.

In the morning it looked as it did the day before, and, I thought, more fiery and red; and the blacks told me, it would blow very hard as soon as the sun was risen up above the mountains, and, they believed, harder than it did the day before.

I told them, That I hoped their fears which they had of me the evening before, were over, and that therefore they would assist me to weigh the anchor, to cut the cable where I shewed them, the day before, it was stranded, in order to secure the sloop.

They said, They would not meddle with it yet, until some more men came down, which they did expect.

I said, I believed nobody would come down, until some of them went up to town.

They said, Yes, there would, for they were sure some of them would come down on the rocks to see whether the sloop was gone or no, and as soon as they saw any of them, they would call to them, and they were sure they would venture to come on board, when they had spoke to them; so I was forced to be easy, and wait their leisure.

About nine or ten o'clock it began again to blow much harder, if it was possible, than it did the day before, and we were all as wet, as if we had been thrown into the sea, with the spray, or what else you please to call it, which the sea hove up into the air like a water-spout; insomuch, that sometimes we could not see the land, though it was so nigh and so high.

We saw several people on the rocks, but it blew so hard, that they could not hear us, and sometimes could not see us, when the spray was whirled up by the fierce gusts encountering one another.

About twelve or one o'clock in the day, which was the 29th of November 1722, the anchor-cable parted with a counter-flaw on the land, and drove us on a point of broken rocks, which lay in the bay. We did all we could to heave in upon the cable that was fast on the south-east point of the bay, to clear the sloop of that point of broken rocks, over which the sea broke very much; but all in vain, for the fierce gust blowing right on, carried us upon them, maugre all the art and diligence we could use to the contrary, and sticking there, the sea struck so forcibly, that it soon made way for the water to come in through her bottom, and, in a very short time, the water was almost as high within, as without, and the sea being raised like a water-spout, with the violence of the winds encountering one another, something like the whirlwinds raising the light sands on the desarts of Africa, insomuch, that we could not see the high lands over us, only the shore underneath, and the violence of the sea and weather, struck so upon the sloop, that I expected, at every stroke, the mast would have jumped out, and could hardly tell which way to stand, to be clear of the fall of it.

This frightful situation made all the blacks get ashore, and leave the boy and I alone; but as the sloop did not heave nor strike so much when the bottom was broke and opened, so that the sea had a free passage in and out, as it did before, and the boy crying and making a pitiful lamentation, and the violence of the flaw of wind being a little abated, two of them came off, their fright being a little over, and one of them took the boy and carried him ashore: The other asked me, if I would go, which I consenting to, he advised me to tarry until he went ashore and got some more of them to help him, because, the sunken rocks were so very sharp, and, in some places, the water so shallow, that one of the blacks was very much cut by them, as he was getting ashore; but if I had any cloaths to send ashore, he said, he would carry them with him now, and then would come with some of his consorts to help me off.

Upon this, I gave him what things I could find swimming about the cabbin, and he went down and fished all the old cloaths and rags he could find, and went ashore with them, and afterwards came off with two more, to carry me likewise thither.

I would have taken the cross-jeck-yard, which lay lashed to the side upon deck, to have swam upon, and they to guide it; but they said, That would be the way to lose my life and theirs too, because of the shallow water over the sunken rocks; adding, That if the sea-breaks should drive us against another rock, it would, probably, beat them all to pieces, and wash me off the yard; but when they had only me to take care of, they should do much better.

I proposed sometime to help buoy me up, for fear I should be too heavy for them, as I could not swim at all; but they said, They did not doubt in the least, to convey me safe, with the help of St. Anthonio, who, they were sure, would assist them, because they had said a *padre nos* before they came off.

Upon my telling them, I trusted in God and Christ to help me, they said, *So did they; but as they had desired St. Anthonio, it was the same as if they had asked God, or Christ, he being God's friend, who would not therefore deny him anything; and they always chose to ask him, or any of the saints, because, as they were formerly men, they had a thorough sense of their wants, and were always compassionate, and ready to help them.*

So two of them getting into the water, the other staid to ease me down to them, and calling upon St. Anthonio to help them, and bidding me call upon my saint to help me, after they had settled themselves in the water, they bid me come in, which I did, and one took me under one arm, and the other under the other, bidding me lie still in the water, and to be sure to keep my feet together, that they might not impede theirs in their swimming, while the third, leaning over the sloop's gunnel, held me by the head till they fixed and settled themselves, and then they launched off, bidding me not to fear, but trust in St. Anthonio, which was all one as to trust in Christ: To which I made no answer, it not being a time to argue, but commended myself to the Almighty, who alone is able to deliver out of dangers.

About midway, they swam with me over a shallow rock, which I touched with my feet, and just as we got over it, a sea came up with us, and breaking upon us, one of the blacks dived down with me under water, and then let me go, which frightened me pretty much; but the other held me fast, and brought me up again, and the third black, who swam close after us, as soon as he saw that I was quitted by one of them, darted up alongside of me like a fish, and supplied the place of him who had forsook me, and, through the assistance of a merciful God, we got safe to shore.

He that had slipped me in the water, seeing the other had taken hold of me, swam back again to the sloop, to see if there was anything to be got, worth having for me; and took down the looking-glass, which was fixed up in the afterpart of the cabbin, and found three stockings, and a pair of old shoes; all which he brought ashore with him; and before he had well reached it, the stern, with the after-part of the deck, parted, and drove away; and presently after came two terrible gusts off the high lands, tumbling down through gullies in the rocks, as though they would overturn the rocks and mountains, and encountering one another on the surface of the sea, raised the water to a great height; and the counter-gust overcoming the other, brought down upon us such a heavy shower, like a deluge, that we could not tell where to get out of the way of it, and, indeed, I began to fear we should perish, notwithstanding we were got safe to the land; for where we were come ashore, there was no passage for me to get up, hardly high enough to keep clear of the water, when it was full sea.

The squall being over, and the air cleared a little (after the water raised up was fallen), the figure of the sloop was gone, her stern, and a piece of the deck, driving away; the off-side of her was broke from the bottom, and the mast was down, which, however, the rigging kept fast to the inner-side, which, as yet, was not parted from the bottom.

The natives who were on the top of the rocks, saw the sloop come on the ledge of the rocks, and likewise beheld us take to the water, but could not see whether we got ashore or not; whereupon they made all the haste down that they could, to see what was become of us; and about two hours, or more, after we got ashore, came to us to the number of five or six, and were very glad we were all got safe to the shore, and seemed to take abundance of notice of the boy, seeing him so young and little, and pitied him very much.

The blacks who had been with me in the sloop, asked the others why they had not brought them down something to eat?

They told them, That as soon as they saw the sea wash over the sloop, and us take to the water, they made the best of their way down to assist, if there was occasion, to get the captain of the sloop, and his child, ashore, because they knew that white people were not so hardy, nor used to the water like the blacks; and that there were a great many people coming (that could not clamber down the rocks so well as they) who, they believed, had something with them to eat.

Accordingly, in about half an hour, came another parcel of them down, and cursed the way, saying, They would not have ventured to come down, if they had known it had been so bad; and soon after, came another parcel, who brought with them some pompions, and some milk in a calabash, and asked, Whether we could not make a fire? They said, They had nothing to strike a fire with, neither had they any fewel to make it with; one said, He had steel, tinder, and cotton, and some of the others asked me, If the wood of the wreck would not burn? I told them, Yes, very well; at which, an elderly man bid some of the young men swim off, and bring some of the smallest and lightest pieces of boards which were swimming about in the water, which they did, the weather being something abated, and the sun beginning to shine; notwithstanding which, I shook with cold, as also did my wet companions.

But when the wood was brought ashore, we had no convenient place to kindle a fire there, the beach being wet; and though the water, by this time, was low, yet, some of them said, when the sea filled again, it would overflow all the beach up to the rocks; others said not; However, they hunted about, and at last found a place in the rock, that was about sixteen or eighteen foot above the flowing of the sea, and about seven or eight foot broad, with the rock over-hanging: There they concluded to make the fire, and said, That we that were cold and wet, would have room enough to sit down and warm ourselves, and for the rest, they might do well enough without; and asked, Whether we could not boil some pompion, to have something hot to warm us within?

I told them, There were two pots in the sloop, but I believed they could not be got now the sloop was broke, though they were left on the deck, which was whole, and fastened to that part of the sloop that stuck on the rock; but that it was probable the sea had washed them off, and that they were sunk to the bottom.

They said, That signified nothing; and that as soon as it was moderate weather, which, they hoped, would be towards the evening, some of the young men should swim off and get them, if the sea had not carried them too far, or drove them under the hollow of the rocks, beyond their discovery. Nor did they fear, they said, getting them, or anything else that would sink, and not drive away too far.

They then made me and the boy drink some of the milk they had brought in the calabash; and seeing my feather-bed swimming about on the sea, two of them swam off, and saved it, and laid it upon the rock to dry.

After this, some of the blacks went in quest of wood to make a fire with, and some grass, etc., to sleep on; while others staid with us below all night, which we passed as well as we could, it proving moderate weather, clear, and starlight.

CHAPTER SEVEN

*

THE next day also proved fine weather, and the sun rising clear and pleasant, and it growing warm, some of my companions swam off to seek for what they could find, the bottom of the wreck still lying on the ledge of rocks, and the mast, and some of the rigging being entangled there.

They brought some small pieces of small ropes ashore, and all the bits and pieces of boards on which they found any paint, esteeming them the richest stuff of all, and told me, There were the sails fast to the mast, and asked me, Whether they should save them? I told them, If they could, I should be very glad, and bid them save that, or anything else that could be saved; at which they swam off again, a dozen or fourteen of them, and disentangled the mast, sails, and ropes, from the wreck, casting off or cutting with their knives, where it was fast, and brought the mast, boom, and boltsprit, all entangled and fast together, to the shore, and we haled them as far on as we could; and what ropes we could get, we laid up as secure as possible in the clefts and hollows of the rocks. The mainsail was also washed to lint, in a manner, there not being a piece to be found of it good for anything; and the foresail was not in much better condition; for being so rotten, the sea had washed them almost away, excepting a few good-for-nothing jags which hung to the bolt ropes. The jibb was pretty much torn, but being a sound, as well as strong sail, there was a pretty deal of that fit to serve for several uses, as indeed it afterwards did.

The blacks said, If we could any way fasten and secure the mast, boom, boltsprit, etc., till they could have a calm day, they could tow them up to the harbour called the Ovens, and it might be, they might be serviceable to me one way or another.

I told them, They would, and if any ship happened to put in there, that should want them, I could sell them for something, which should be for their benefit, to help make them amends for this their kindness to me, and the great trouble they had been at to serve me.

They said, They were glad they had been of service to me, and thought it their duty to serve any stranger that was in distress, as I was, notwithstanding they were of different colours, and by us, they believed, accounted different creatures: Yet they thought we were all of one species, and they were all men, as we were, though they allowed themselves to be much inferior to us in everything.

I told them, As for that, I did not see any difference, only in the colour, which I did not know whether it was in their nature, or whether it might be occasioned by the excessive heat of the sun, and could not tell but that if a white man and woman were to come and live with them, and go naked, and be exposed to the scorching sun as they were, in three or four generations, they might be changed to their complexion.

They said, No; for they had heard, that notwithstanding their skin might lose its whiteness, and change to a reddish or brown colour, yet their hair would always hold its nature, and not be frisled like theirs, which they took to be an infallible sign to know a stranger, let his colour be what it would, from one of them. They said, moreover, That there was a curse laid on them, that they should always be subjects and servants to the whites.

I told them, I had heard something of it (being willing to continue them in their esteem for us).

They said, They were convinced that I knew it, and believed there was no white but knew that the blacks were by God destined to be their servants, which was plainly manifest by the white men coming, as they have been told, every year to Guinea, and carrying away a great many thousands to be their slaves; and if they had not been by the whites (*i.e.* Portuguese), brought away from Guinea, and, as it were, privileged, or rather a freedom indulged to them, as well by the Brancas who brought them first hither, as also by all other strangers, to whose power they lie open, they might carry them away, and makes slaves of them, as well as those of their first native country, whenever they pleased.

They said, They did not know whether it were a favour

voluntarily given to them by all nations, or procured for them by the Brancas, who first placed them there; but in gratitude, they thought themselves obligated to do all the good they could to strangers, and to assist them in whatsoever they were able, and in a more especial manner Englishmen, who were always accounted the best friends to the Portuguese, and one of whose kings, they had been told, had married the King of Portugal's daughter. This I confirmed to them; and they professed abundance of love, value, and respect to Englishmen, whom, they said, they esteemed as much as they did the Portuguese: Which pleased me very well, hoping to have friendly neighbours of them.

They continued, one or other of them, swimming about the wreck all day, bringing pieces of boards, especially those that had any paint on them; and filled all the clefts of the rocks adjacent, with pieces of wood, boards, etc., and found both the iron pots, and brought them ashore; also an iron crow, a pair of stilliards, the gun that the pirates had given me, though the stock was broke, also a small cooper's adz, which I had found one day ashore on the beach at Barbadoes, and several other things; all which they put up in the clefts, etc., of the rocks, high enough out of the reach of the sea.

They all seemed overjoyed that the pots were found, and said, That now I might dress my victuals my own way (as though I could dress it a jot the more my way in the iron pot, than I could in one of their earthen pots). They found several other things, as the cook's tormenters,[1] a pair of brass compasses, and a pair of brass dividers, a tin kettle and sawce-pan, a chissel, a caulking iron, and several other trifling things.

The manner of their finding them was thus: several places about the wreck, to and from the water, were so shallow, that they could stand upon the tops of the sunken rocks with the water up to their breasts, their navels, and in some places not so high, and the sea being pretty smooth, as it always is here in fine weather (this little bay of Punta de Sal, lying on the

[1] Long-handled forks used for taking meat out of the coppers.

lee-side of the island), they could look all round about them on the bottom, which they could see very plain, in four, five, or six fathom water, especially where the bottom is stony or rocky, and I myself have seen little shells, etc., from a rock down to the bottom, in six, seven, and even in ten, or twelve fathom water: And it is a common practice with the blacks, for their diversion, when they have done fishing, to stand on the rocks and heave stones into the water, and for others to dive and bring them up, at which exercise they are very expert, and account it no piece of dexterity to dive to the bottom in four or five fathom, and when there, to search and creep along for a minute, or better.

We put on one of the pots with some pompion, and some of those who went in the morning to fish, came back about noon with a good mess, which we boiled with the pompion, and made a hearty meal.

The place of the bay where we came ashore, was the worst place that we could possibly land at; for they were forced to swim from thence to the fishing-places, and also for water; though at low water, a man might have made shift to crawl along the rocks to where the water was, which came out of a rock stilling down into a hollow place like a cistern; but that way was so troublesome, as well as dangerous, by reason of the rocks and stones tumbling very frequently down from the mountains overhead; that they chose rather to swim always for the water than to go that way for it.

About one or two o'clock, the Governor sent a man down to me, to tell me he was very sorry for my misfortune, and gave his service to me, and desired, that when I came up to town, I would make use of his house as my own, and that I should not want for anything which their poor island afforded while I remained on it: and withal, sent me down some pompion and three or four potatoes; declaring, That his illness had prevented his coming down to me, and hoped I would not take it amiss; and also, that he had sent some men out that morning to hunt for some wild goats; but they were not returned, the messenger said, when he came from home; but if they came time enough, he would send me some that night; if not, I should have some venison on the morrow, without fail.

I told him, I was obliged to the Signor Governador, and thanked him; and a little while after, came a black from the Priest, with the same compliment from him; but brought nothing to eat, as the Governor's black did, and told me, that his master desired to know, Whether I had saved any flower, and if I had, he requested me to send him some by him; and that if I had saved any Aqua ardenta also, his master would be no less glad of it, though he had not bid him ask for any.

I told him, We had very little of either on board; but our distress was so great, that if there had been never so great a quantity, we should not have been able to save any, when the sloop run on that ledge of rocks; adding, That all we had been able to save from the wreck, was the pieces of board, etc., which he saw about us, and those iron pots.

He said, His master was more able to do me service than even the Governor himself; and he believed, if I presented him one of those pots, it would be very acceptable; and that it would be nothing in comparison to the benefit he was capable of doing me in return.

I told him, That I was sorry I had nothing to oblige his master with, worthy his acceptance: but should be proud he would receive from me anything that had been left me by my hard fortune.

About four in the afternoon, he and the Governor's black went away; I bid them present my humble service to their masters, hoping I should have the happiness of always continuing in their favour and esteem, and it should be my constant study and endeavour to deserve it.

They said, I need not doubt it; for their masters professed abundance of concern for my misfortune, as well as a great affection for my person, though unknown to them by sight; and they both had heard their masters say, That I should want for nothing that the island afforded, while I remained on it; so away they went.

Some time after, among other blacks that came down, came

one called Domingo Gumms, who was son to Antonio Gumms, who had formerly been Governor of the island; who, together with his brother, brought down some pompions, bananas, a pappai, and a cake of bread, made of bananas and maiz, which was the first bread I had eat or seen, since I came among them: Domingo told me, That his father sent me the pompion and fruit, and his mother the cake, and if I liked it, she would make me some more, and send me; and likewise desired to know if I loved milk; and if I did, I should have some sent down.

I thanked them very kindly, and told them, That milk was what I often used to eat in my own country; and tasting the bread, at his desire, told him I liked it very well; and he said, He was glad of it, and assured me, that I should have more.

I thanked him, and told them, I gave them all abundance of trouble, and had received many favours from them, but was not in a capacity of making any suitable returns, otherways, than by a grateful acknowledgement of their kindness at present; and a resolution, that if ever God Almighty should be pleased to make me able hereafter, I would make them, as far as in me lay, a grateful satisfaction.

They said, They did not desire anything in return, but to continue in my good esteem, and to let my countrymen know, how kindly I had been used among them; and that no other return would be required by them, or any of the islanders, unless the Priest, who they heard was always very craving, as well from strangers, as also from the natives; and therefore, he thought it was convenient to give me this caution, for fear he might be begging anything of me according to his usual wont.

I told him, I had nothing in the world left me here, that would be worth anybody's asking, or my giving.

He said, That if I had never so much, he was sure nobody would desire anything from me, but would rather give me, if they had anything that would be of service to me, and that the utmost of what they desired, was, as he had told me before, to be noted, and to be had in esteem by strangers; and were sorry that their island afforded nothing worth the stranger's while to come and traffick for.

I told them, That I believed, when it pleased God, that I returned to my country, and gave them an account of their civility to strangers, I did not doubt, but some of our shipping would come and visit them.

He said, If their island had any production that was worth their while to come and traffick for, it might be so; but that, as far as he could learn, by what he heard from his father and other old men, who could remember the coming of several strangers to it, most of whom were of that nation which had robbed me (viz., pirates, for they thought it was a particular nation so called); who, though they used me so hardly, he said, were very civil to them, making large requitals for every little favour they were able to shew them; and who would often tell them, that their island was very poor, and that they lived exceeding miserable, in comparison of what the white men did, in their own country; and that their not having any production that was good for any thing, was the reason so few ships came to visit them.

I told him, It was very true, that our ships seldom or never came there, because it was not known to us, that they had any commodities worth trafficking for; but, that, perhaps, their island might yield valuable commodities, but they and we both, might be ignorant of them, or what might be produced in them by art.

I then instanced how ignorant the Portuguese were of the rich productions of Guinea, at their first discovery of that coast, and how little the inhabitants thereof regarded those rich commodities, which it almost everywhere afforded, by reason they knew not the value of them, nor the manifold uses to which they contributed, both for pleasure and profit to mankind; and that in those times, the blacks set a very considerable value on gold, and ambergrease, and less on teeth, wax, etc., and that they were intirely ignorant of any other use for their woods, which now were a considerable part of the trade, but for firing.

All the time that I was talking thus, I observed, that one man of the company, listened, with more than ordinary attention, to our discourse; and eyed me constantly, whose complexion was very different from any of those I had yet seen; for all the rest were black, and had coal-black frizled hair, unless changed by age to grey, like the blacks on the coast of the main continent of Guinea, but he was of a ruddy, copper, or tawny colour, something resembling the Moors or Arabs on the southernmost parts of Barbary, and had strait, though short hair, and of a light brown colour.

This man, as soon as I had finished my talk, to my exceeding surprize, as well as joy, answered me in the English tongue, That what I had said was very true, and that there were many rich commodities, to his knowledge, produced in the northernmost part of Guinea, which as well the English as the natives were utterly ignorant of; they of their use and value, and we of their being produced in that part; and therefore, what might be as plentiful and as easy got, and perhaps cost less there, if sought for in other more distant places, with greater difficulty, danger, and charge, as he experimently knew, having been an inhabitant in those parts some considerable time, occasioned by misfortunes, as I might now be here; by which means he had an opportunity to observe the commodities produced in the inland places of that part of the continent.

Upon my asking him, What country-man he was? he told me, 'He was a Welshman born, and had been master of several ships out of Bristol: That he had been taken by Bartholomew Roberts, as he was going to the West Indies, and by him was detained, and brought on the coast of Guinea, from whom he there made his escape, and having formerly traded to those parts, as well as to most parts of Guinea, he was acquainted with almost all the coast along: That it was at Sierra Leon that he had made his escape, from Captain Roberts the pirate, and got to a black king up the river, whom he formerly in his trading had been acquainted with, who entertained him very courteously, and promised him his protection and assistance, against all that should oppose or offer to molest him:

'That although Roberts used all his endeavours to get him again, through the interest of those blacks whom he had won by his presents, by whom he had offered to the said king several presents, of considerable value, as the said black king told him, yet the king would not except any, but sent Roberts word by the said blacks, that he was not of so base a principle, as to betray any distressed person who had fled to him for succour, especially to such cruel enemies to all manner of honest trade and traffick, as he understood they were; and withal gave him to understand, that he neither stood in want of his money, cloaths, arms, or ammunition, having enough of every sort, and a thousand stout men, that understood how to use arms, as well as his men did, for all they were black; and who were always ready to receive him, if he dared presume to come within his territories, to offer the least incivility; and that if a thousand would not be sufficient to make him sensible of his folly, he would give him the diversion of being entertained with double, treble, or quadruple the number.

'That this answer so daunted Roberts, that he strove no more about it, but endeavoured to supply himself with water, wood, and what other refreshments he could get; and having obtained them, he sailed from thence, and prosecuted his intended voyage of cruising down along the coast of Guinea, as far as St. Thoma, or Princes Island.'

I asked him his name? He said, '*It was Charles Franklin, and that he was born within two miles of Carleon, upon Usk, in Wales, and that his father was a Justice of Peace, etc.*'

I asked him, How he came here in this bye and unfrequented island? He said, *He would inform me of the whole, if I would please to hear him;* which, I told him, I would very gladly: Whereupon he proceeded and said:

'That after Captain Roberts, the pirate, was sailed, he took the liberty to range about in the country, to see and observe what was curious or remarkable, either in the manners, customs, and constitutions of the people, or in the productions of the country, and, by one means or other, Captain Plunket, who was Governor of the English factory, heard, there was a man who had belonged to Roberts's company left behind, and entertained by King Thome, to whom he sent to deliver him up to him, to punish him according to justice, and the custom of the English nation.

'That as soon as the king received this message he sent for him (*i.e.* Franklin), to whom he communicated it, declaring, That he was loth to disoblige Governor Plunket, because he might thereby disoblige all the English nation; but withal told him, That if he thought the English Governor would do him any harm, he would by no means deliver him up; but bid him consider and advise him what answer to send, assuring him, that let his case be how it would, he was resolved to protect him, but withal thought it best, if he was guilty of any action which would render him obnoxious to danger, to acquaint him with it, that he might take the best measures, both to secure him from any harm, and to give the Governor as little dissatisfaction as might be.

'That he told the king, that he never had been guilty of any ill action that might make him liable to punishment; but, perhaps, the Governor might suppose he had been one of Captain Roberts's company, and left behind by chance, and therefore might think he deserved to be punished as such; but he could assure him he was not, but was forced and kept a prisoner on board of them, till he made his escape; but yet told the king, he did not care to be put into the hands of the English factory, being a stranger to Governor Plunket, as well as to the rest of the gentlemen of the factory, who perhaps might conceit him to be one of the pirates' company, and disbelieve what he said, and therefore, though undeservedly, punish him, as though he had been actually or willingly a pirate; for which reason, if his majesty pleased, he would rather still continue to be under his protection, till some ship came thither to trade, the captain or company of which might know his character or family, of which he was very certain few ships that came from England to these parts to trade, but what the commanders, or some body belonging to them, must be acquainted with him.

'That the king upon this gave him his word, and swore by his darling god, he should not be delivered into the power of any body, but by his own choice; and accordingly sent word to Governor Plunket, *That the white, under his protection, was not of the pirates' company, but by compulsion, having been taken by force, and detained a prisoner, and escaped from them, when they arrived there, and in order to avoid being taken by them again, had thrown himself upon his protection, not being acquainted that there was an English factory there, which if he had known, without doubt, he would have applied to for protection: That upon these considerations, he could do no less than succour and defend him, as a stranger in distress; which he had the rather done, as he was one of the Governor's countrymen, between whom and him there had always been a good understanding.*

'That the king also acquainted the Governor, *that he (Franklin) had a mind to continue with him, to inform himself of the custom and trade of his country: That he approved his deportment and conversation, and therefore gave him leave to do so; but that, if he thought fit to go to the Governor, or the Governor would send to his town, to inform himself farther concerning him, they were equally at liberty to do so; disclaiming all thoughts of keeping Franklin against his will, or in breach of the friendship which had always subsisted between himself and the English factory.*

'That hereupon Governor Plunket sent up a white servant of his, with two blacks, to inquire into the matter, and to know Franklin's name; which as soon as they had been informed of, they returned. The Governor taking him for one of that name who was a notorious pirate, he sent word again to the king, *That he was certainly one of the pirates, and not what he represented himself to be, and therefore desired that the king would deliver him into his hands; by which means he would not only manifest himself to be a friend to the whole English nation, but to the honest traders of all nations.*

'That hereupon the king sent for him again, and acquainted him with the message, and told him, that he was very unwilling to give the English factory of Sierra Leon any distaste; but was still firm in his resolution, not to put him into their hands, if he thought it would be any ways prejudicial to him, or if it was contrary to his inclination; and, therefore, desired him to order it so, that the English might not be disobliged on one hand, nor his safety endangered on the other.'

Franklin then continued to tell us, 'That having acknowledged the king's goodness to him, he desired to be sent farther into the country, to some neighbouring king of his acquaintance, out of Governor Plunket's knowledge, and consequently out of his reach or influence.'

Upon which I interrupted him, and said, *I do not see what danger or hazard you could be in, by being in Governor Plunket's hands; but rather I should think it would have been the best method you could have taken; for they would not have hurt you, if your case had been as you say.*

He replied, 'It was very true; neither was he afraid that they could do him any harm, but that there was one of his name, who had been a pirate, and a very noted one too; and asked me, If I never had seen the name of Charles Franklin, notified in the *London Gazette*?' I told him, I could not then call to mind that I had. He said, 'It was possible I might forget to have seen it; but he had read it several times, and his name being the same, he did not care to run himself into the danger of a long confinement, and to be obliged to take his tryal as a criminal, being descended of an ancient and worshipful family, none of whom were ever tainted with the least imputation of guilt either to their king or country; though it was morally impossible but he should be acquitted of pyracy, upon a fair tryal: Besides, he said, he had another reason to induce him to be sent up the country, which was a curiosity natural to his temper, to search and discover unknown places; and being sensible that this coast of Africa in general abounded with gold, beyond any continent in the world, and having also learnt from his conversation with the natives, that the parts far within land abounded with gold, and from whence what of that metal they had, proceeded, it made him desirous to see into it, now that so plausible an occasion offered, which, perhaps, no European ever had before: And this enquiry, he said, was the more pleasing to him, because having served an apprenticeship in Bristol, to the goldsmith's trade, and wrought at it in several places, he had attained to a tolerable knowledge of the nature of metals and minerals, and had endeavoured as much as he could, to inform himself in some of the greatest mysteries of fusing as well as separating metals from minerals, as well as one metal from another; and that in his trading on the coast of Guiney, he had made the nicest experiments on the mineral earths, stones, sands, etc., and had collected, with the greatest exactness he was capable of, the value and quantity of metal contained in them, which experiments and observations he had taken down memorandums in writing of.'

I told him, I hoped to have a farther and better opportunity to renew our discourse on this subject; but wished at present he would give me some account of the production of this island, and of the temper of the inhabitants; that I might, since it was my lot to be cast among them, so comport myself, as to win their favour, and avoid any occasion of disgusting them. He said, It was the greatest happiness he could have hoped for, to have a countryman to converse with; and would very readily comply with that, and every other request I should make him, which he was able to satisfy. 'As for this island, he said, I might easily, at first sight, discover, that it was exceeding barren, being nothing but one continued rock, as it were, and only here and there in the clefts and vallies, covered over with a thin crust of earth, which produced nothing that would be thought fit aliment for the human species by an European, who had never been used to these barren rocky mountains: That, however, bananas grew pretty well in some of the vallies, but were nothing near so large as on the continent: That in several places at the foot of the mountains, where there is any earth, pompions and potatoes grow pretty well; that they had likewise a large quantity of feshoons,[1] and wild figs, which were generally eaten by the natives for

[1] Beans.

food; as also a pretty many papais; and that those who would take the pains to plant it, had maiz enough; but that the natives were generally so slothful and lazy, that in a great measure it was the cause of their poverty: That there was store of very good fish about the island; and that there had been considerable numbers of good wild goats; but that most of them had been destroyed: That some of the inhabitants had cows, horses, asses, and hogs, of which last sort they had the most plenty; but seldom made use of any of them, except at their publick feasts.'

I asked him, How they caught their fish? He told me, 'That some of them had fish-hooks left yet, which they had got when ships had been there, and others had preserved nails, pieces of iron, wire, and the like, which they were very eager to procure at all opportunities, and very chary of when procured: That there was an old man on the island, a native of St. Philip, who had a hammer and three or four files, who made charcoal out of the wood of the wild fig-tree, by help of which, he made shift to bungle up a hook out of an old nail, for doing of which he had another nail; and the party for whom he made the hook, was always obliged, as often as he got a mess of fish, to make him a present of some; so that, said he, the old farrier, as they call him, seldom wants fish, and often supplies his neighbours with some, when they stand in need thereof.' He added, 'That the fish about this island were so voracious, that a bended nail would take them; so that there was no fear of catching fish enough.'

I said, I was glad there was no apprehension of starving; and that I could save so many nails out of the pieces of the wreck which the blacks brought ashore, that I should not grudge to give the old farrier three or four of them for fixing me one, or for lending me his hammer and files to make them myself; for I had made a great many fishing-hooks in my time with a file. He said, It would be an easy matter for me to exceed the black; for he himself made all the hooks that he fished with, and likewise for the family that he lived among; and that everybody knew them from those made by the old man, and preferred them to his: But, said he, you will have no occasion to go a fishing; for I will engage, they will supply you with fish, or anything else which the island affords, without your seeking for it.

He added, That they would have been equally civil to him; but that he chose to fish for himself, to divert his melancholy hours; and that it was principally to this diversion, and hunting, that he owned the preservation of his life, or at least his senses, in his great misfortunes. But that, as for hunting, I should find very little pleasure in it, and that it would be even impracticable for me, till my feet were hardened, as his were, because of the clambering up the broken and rotten rocks, which were equally difficult and dangerous.

I asked him, How long he had been on this island? He said, Something above three years; but he had been on the Island of St. Philip some time before he came hither; and when I was disposed to hear it, he would continue the relation of his misfortunes to the time of his coming upon this island.

I said, I should be very much obliged to him for the favour of such a relation; and took notice, that the two blacks who came down in company with him, seemed, as I thought, by the extraordinary attention which they paid to our discourse, to understand what we said. He said, No, they were ignorant of every word we said, excepting two, which he had taught them, to wit, Ay and No.

However, turning to Domingo Gumms, I asked him, How he did? and whether he understood our language? He said, No; he wished he did; and that he would give anything in his power to be master of it; but that he was glad we could understand one another.

Hereupon Franklin told them, That I was his countryman; which seemed to surprize Domingo, who said, He thought him to be a Gualego (*i.e.* a Welshman), and that I was an Englishman.

I told him, That the place where Signior Carolos (which they pronounce Singore, and was the name that he went by among the natives) was born, was a part of England, called

Gualego, as the bay we were then in was called the Bay of the Salt Point, and yet still was a part of the Island of St. John.

It soon passed about among the blacks there present, that Singore Carolos was an Englishman; and they all severally asked me, Whether it was so or no? it being their manner always to trace any relation to the source or fountain-head, before they will give credit to it, and not take any hearsay account, if they can get any other.

I satisfied their curiosity; and asked Franklin, What sort of a way it was up to their town? He said, It was so bad, that I should never be able to get up it; and the more dangerous because the stones and rocks were so loose and rotten, that a man could not be secure, either in what he rested on with his feet, or any hold he could take with his hands.

I asked him, How so many of them came down, if the way was so hazardous? He said, It was hazardous enough for them; and he heard several of them complain of the dangerousness of the way, and say, If they had known it had been so perilous, they would not have ventured to come down; For, said he, it is to be questioned, whether there be one person living on the island, that ever has been down to this place before now; and it is probable, if it had not been on this occasion, there might never any of them have come here, where we are now. It's true, said he, they often come down to that black point that you came round before you anchored, to gather salt for their necessary occasions, from whence, I believe, it took the name of the Salt Point; but then the rocks where they come down to that, are sound and firm, and though very steep, yet not so steep, by a great deal, as the way that comes down here.

I objected, That I thought I was able to get up, as several ancient men that I saw, and as he himself, who was more corpulent than I: But he said, That use was a great matter in that case; and he had been on this island, and St. Philip's (which was as bad or worse), nigh six years, and yet, for all that, there were several of the natives, who were very ancient, as well as corpulent, and seemingly decrepid through age, in comparison of him, yet could climb up rocks without either fear or apprehension of danger, which he neither could, nor dared to attempt; and besides, he was forced, he said, to swim near half a mile, or he should not have been able to have come hither to me.

How must I do then, said I, if I can proceed no farther, and yet at high water have not here so much room to stand, or walk upon, as half a ship's quarter deck? I shall be worse than a person pent up in a solitary close prison all his days.

He said, He would ask the blacks; who were most of them standing round about us, listning as attentively to what we had been discoursing all this time, as though they had understood every word we had said. He accordingly asked them their opinions, who confirmed all he said as to the difficulty; especially, as they said, that they supposed I could not go without shoes among such sharp-pointed ragged rocks, as I should meet with in the way. I told them, That was very true; but I supposed, that when once a man had climbed up to the top of the rocks, the way was something better, and more level.

They said it was; but that it was a great way to get to the top; and asked me, Whether I took as far as I could see to be the top. I told them, Yea. They said, That which I saw now, and took to be the top of the rocks, was not the hundredth part of that height that I must climb to, before I could come to the top; For, said one, for my part, I can hardly tell which is the top. Another said, The middle of the island is the top; for the rocks and ground rose continually till one came to the middle of the island. Franklin hereupon proposed to them to give me a more intelligible account of the difficult situation of the island: This disgusted the blacks, who thought he pretended to know the country better than they; and one of them resented it accordingly, raising his voice, and contracting his brow, and wondered he should pretend to give a better account than they could do, who were used to travel to such unfrequented paths on account of fishing, which he dared not attempt to go in, were he to starve for want of food. He excused himself very submissively, professing he did not mean it so, and that he could not pretend to know the island near so well as they; and that all he could mean was, That being able to discourse me in my own language, he was the more capable to make me understand what he said: And he hoped they would not be offended, at the liberty he took to discourse me in my own tongue.

They seeing me a little surprized and concerned at their resentment, softened their tone, and told him, They were heartily glad he could talk with and divert the captain, and that they would have him talk with me in that language that pleased him best; but as I could very well talk their language, they should rather we would, because they should then have the advantage of hearing some things, which they never knew or heard of before; but, however, they desired I would please myself, and they would dispense with their own satisfaction, for the sake of adding to mine.

I told them, I was much obliged to them; but finding Franklin was of my own opinion, that he had half angered them, which he said was owing to the jealousy they had, that he should stand better in my graces than they; I told him, We should have, I doubted, but too many opportunities to discourse together, and so would forbear at present to say anything more which might augment their suspicions.

By this time, night approaching, some of the men thought it best to go seek for a place more convenient to take up their abode, before it was too late: But Domingo and Franklin, and two or three more, staid with me. Some of them, as they were going away, asked Franklin to go with them; for that they should fare much better than they could below, as hardly having there room to lie clear of the sea, nor any shelter from the wind. Franklin seemed inclinable to go; but upon Domingo's telling them, That he thought Singore Carolos had more good manners in him, as well as good nature, than to leave his countryman the first night; he told them, That he could not well leave the captain to-night, and bid them that went, not to forget to go and catch a dish of fish, and bring it to me in the morning for my breakfast. They said, That enow of them would stay till the morning to catch a dish of fish. I thanked them, and asked them, How far up the rocks they designed to go? They told me, They should not go very high that night; but they had a long way to swim from the point, over the other bay (pointing towards the westward) to the point called Piscarree Pickyeana, and then a little ways up.

I told them, I thought it would be cold swimming now in the evening. They said, *No Force* (which is a very common word with these people, as well as among the Portuguese, from whom probably they learned it), and that after they had swam across the bay, they had then but a little way to go, before they came at a fuurno, or cave, large enough to shelter a hundred persons or more from rain or wind; and there was always wood enough there, or thereabouts, which the people brought down with them, every time they came there to fish; and that if it was not late, they could catch a dish for their suppers, and would send me some too for mine.

I thanked them, and told them, I wished I was there.

They said, They wished so too, and then they believed I could make shift to get up to town; though even then I should find it troublesome enough.

I told them, I should not mind the trouble, so it was but possible; But, said I, how must I contrive to get there?

One said, They would contrive, when the weather was fine, to carry me over the bay.

Another said, There was no occasion for running that risque, when the first fine day, they could bring down Antonia Riverio's boat, and carry me and all my cloaths, and other goods, up to the fuurno, from whence I might easily get to town, because the Governor to be sure would send a horse for me to ride up upon.

Another said, I needed not to fear a horse; for both the Governor and Priest had sent their men down to me, to invite me to take up my abode with them at their houses.

Ay, but, said another, speaking low, as if I was not to hear him, for my part, if I was the Captain, I should rather chuse to lodge with Singore Antonia Gumms, than with any one on the island, he having always a good stock of everything to eat, and more plenty than the Governor.

Ay, but, said another, the Priest has meat and fish oftner than Antonia Gumms, or anybody else on the island.

It's true, said another; but if the Captain lives with the Priest, he will beg all his cloaths from him, and you all know what a covetous man he is; we cannot make anything of a handsome cotton cloth cap, or have anything else that is either handsome or delightful, but presently he is begging it from us. Another said, That strangers were not reckoned to be so subject to, or to set so much value and esteem on the padres (*i.e.* priests), and especially English, as they did; nor even, if they were informed right, the Portuguese themselves: But that their priest's power over them must be imputed to their ignorance: And indeed there was all the reason in the world it should be so; because what little knowledge they had, they were obliged for it, they said, to the priest, as having no other means to obtain it, as he had no other means to obtain his, but by that book which the Portuguese instructed him in, and left with him, when they consecrated him a priest, and the bishop blessed him, with the full priestly power and authority to forgive and absolve sins; But though strangers had not that power of forgiving sins among themselves, saving the clergy, yet they believed they stood in no need of any information or knowledge from them, and therefore had not need of a priest for instruction, all the use or benefit which they had of him, being for forgiveness of their sins.

I told them, We never received forgiveness of our sins from a priest, but always sought it of God alone, through Jesus Christ: They said, Except God or Christ personally or sensibly spoke to me, and let me know that He had pardoned me, they did not know how I could be satisfied that ever I had absolution or remission of my sins, and consequently, for want of that knowledge of being certain whether I was forgiven or not, I should never know of my being pardoned, and must certainly be always full of fears and doubts, whether I was in a state to qualify me for heaven or hell; but for their parts, they could not be unprepared of a certainty of qualification to go to heaven, unless, by their own negligence, they did not repair to the priest for absolution of all their sins.

I told them, It was very well if they could purchase a remission of their sins at so easy a rate, and in so satisfactory a manner; They said, Yea, that they could, and the Priest dared not deny absolving any man of his sins, provided he confessed them to him; and it would be their own fault, if they concealed their sins, that they were not all pardoned.

But, continued they, We do not doubt, but when you come up to town, that the Priest and you will have abundance of discourse about these matters, from whom you will have a better account than we can give you, especially if you can speak Latin, as most of you strangers, and more especially you that are pilots, can.

After this conversation, it beginning to grow late, those that left us, wished us a good night, promising to return in the morning, and bring me some fish to eat, and so departed: And we that stayed behind, passed our time in discourses on my condition and circumstances; and having made a good fire of the pieces of the wreck which they had brought on shore, some of them lay down about it, or where they could best, to take their rest and sleep.

Domingo Gumms and his brother, Basil, with Franklin, sat up with me by the fire, and I took this opportunity to tell them, That I should be glad to hear the remainder of Signor Carolos's relation of his adventures; and that, as I supposed they had all frequently heard the same, and that therefore it would be no novelty to them, I hoped they would not take it amiss, if I desired him to continue his narrative in my own tongue; because it would otherwise occasion a deal of circumlocution, as I did not understand several words in their language, and should be obliged to interrupt him often, for an explanation of them. They replied, That they had, indeed, frequently heard him relate his adventures; but that nevertheless, they were so very extraordinary, that they should never be tired in hearing them; But, however, since it would contribute to my satisfaction, they would take pleasure in attending to his talk, though they should not be able to understand him: And hereupon, turning to Franklin, they said, *Pray, Singore Carolos, oblige the Captain with a relation of your adventures, or what else you think fit; and, as he desires, in your own native language.*

I said, *No, I should make shift to understand the most, or at least a great part of it, and what I did not understand, rather than make an interruption in the story, I would wait another opportunity, or stay until I had a more perfect idea and understanding in the country language.*

Mr. Franklin said, *He believed he could express himself in such words, as both they and the Captain could understand tolerably well.*

They answered, *No, he would infinitely more oblige them to relate it to the Captain in his own language; and therefore desired him to proceed, if I so pleased.*

I told them, *It would not be good manners for us to divert ourselves in a language which they understood not, and would be no less than an affront to offer; and especially as I knew that it was purely out of respect to me, though undeserved at their hands, that they were thus deprived of their natural rest, as well as of the diversion which they might have at their own homes; and that it was the least that I could do, to endeavour all that in me lay, to be diverting to them, although it were to baulk my own satisfaction.*

They said, *No, they could divert themselves very well; and besides, they should take more delight to hear us talk in our own language, though they could not understand a syllable of it, for the novelty of it, by far, than it would be to hear it in their own; and desired him to continue his story.*

Hereupon I desired Mr. Franklin, if he pleased, before he proceeded, to favour me with an account of the nature and dispositions of the inhabitants of this island, because at present it might be of more concern and use to me to know, in order to regulate myself among them, without giving them any cause of offence, and ingratiate myself in their favour, by all means possible. As for the farther description of the island, or the productions of it, I said, We would refer that till another opportunity, or till I could satisfy myself ocularly, as not being of so much importance at present, as the other would, because the ignorance of their humours, customs and manners, might occasion me to disoblige them.

He was very ready to comply with my desire, and said, That the people were affable and friendly, and very free of communicating anything they possessed one to another; but in an especial manner to a stranger, as he could assert by his own long experience: That they were not inclinable to be soon affronted; and were very merry and chearful in their way; and if I could be pleasant and chearful among them, it would inhance their esteem for me, and they would take much more notice of me, than if I behaved myself after a dull and melancholy manner, or affected solitariness. I said, *How can a man in my condition be merry? Surely, if they were to see me merry, or brisk, they must needs think that I not only lost little or nothing, but that also, I was got into a country that exceeded mine by far, or else, that I must be a fool, and incapable of a true sense of my misfortunes.*

He told me, *It was their little sense of what a misfortune was, as having but very little more thought or consideration that way, than the beasts of the field; nor the least notion, unless in a very dark and confused manner, of any thing beyond the extension or limits of their island; and for that reason,* continued he, *they have so little notion of misfortunes, not having anything themselves to lose, that all of them reckon your greatest misfortune to be the loss of your cloaths, and your present confinement here, in not being yet able to get up to their town: For the rest, they look on it no otherways, than as though one of them had spent two or three days at fishing, and had lost their hooks and time, and caught nothing; for as to that part of the misfortune, of being absent from your native country, though to them it would be the greatest hardship in the world, yet they think it is nothing to us strangers, as they call us, because we are so used to it: Neither is it in mortal power to convince them of the contrary: For all which reasons* (*though I am very sensible that you must needs have a deep sorrow for your present misfortunes*), *as well as indeed for the sake of your own health, you must endeavour, as much as you can, to be chearful; for I know, by my own woful experience, that nothing impairs the health more than a settled grief.*

I told him, *It was very true, and I was not myself insensible of it, as having experimented it before this time.*

After we had discoursed a little upon this head, I desired him, if he pleased, to finish the account of his adventures, as well while he was in Guinea, as also what occurred till his arrival on this island.

He said he would, and hoped it would be a means to divert me, and help pass the night away the better; and began, saying,

'I need not relate to you over again, what I have already done, and therefore shall proceed where I left off. The notion that I had, that there was gold within-land, and that most of the mountains abounded with it throughout all that vast tract, more especially between the latitudes of twelve or thirteen from the northward and southward, to the Equinoctial Line, and perhaps as far southerly as that land reaches, made me very solicitous to be sent up the country by King Thome; and what strengthened my curiosity, was the opportunity now offered, which would not leave them the least room to suspect that it was designed upon the account of making any remarks or inspection, either into the constitutions, polity, or strength of the inhabitants, or of the nature, productions, or riches of the country; of both which, as far as ever I could learn, the natives, especially those within-land, are very jealous, and by that means are unacquainted either with strangers, or their manner of trade; and by the other blacks bordering on the sea coast, this notion is kept up as much as possible, perhaps to deter them from venturing down to the sea coast to vend their commodities; they prepossessing them with the fear of being carried off by the whites, and likewise of the great subtlety, as well as power, which the Baccaraus, or whites, are masters of; insomuch, that the most part of those inland nations do suppose, that it's entirely owing to their country being yet undiscovered by us, that they have hitherto remained secure from being totally subjected to us; and that whenever we come to know the riches and value of the country, and its exceeding populousness, we shall immediately seize upon the country, and carry them into slavery in foreign countries at our pleasure. They believe, that all the whites think their inland countries are nothing but wild and barren desarts, frequented only with ravenous and voracious beasts, of which they have a mighty notion that we stand very much in fear; and tell the inland blacks, that this is the reason the Baccaraüs do not venture far up the country; which notions, said Franklin, I believe have been infused into them by the nations who live along the sea coast, out of policy to ingross the whole trade into their own hands; it being also usual with them to tell strangers, on the other hand, that there is no gold in the inland country, and that it is all contained in the sands and shore of the rivers on the coast: They have also notions, that the Baccaraus have a new world, where they intend to reside; but it wants a great deal to be done to it, to make it fit for their reception: That they send all their most valuable things from their old world thither; the labour of which is carried on by the negroes which they yearly carry from Guinea: That they want prodigious numbers of slaves to work in that new world, which they believe the whites will all remove into as soon as it is got in order: That this new world is an inconceivable degree better than the old one; but that it will be an exceeding length of time before it can be fitted for the Baccaraus to go into: That during all that long time, all those blacks which are yearly carried away off the coast of Guinea, must work and slave very hard, without any intermission or redemption, until the new world is completely fitted up in a very beautiful manner, and the Baccaraus are all settled there; and that when that is done, they will have no farther service for the blacks and will then send them home to this world again, and never more come to this old world, which the blacks will be left to inhabit, without ever being molested by the whites more. This happy time they earnestly wish for, that they need not stand in fear of being made slaves. They believe, that the Baccaraus trouble not their heads any farther, than to carry them from Guinea to the new world; and that then they leave all the work of fitting it up to be done by the negroes, whom they deliver over for that purpose to the power of certain fittezas[1] (*i.e.* demi-gods) who have the charge of managing, ordering, and contriving to make it as pleasant and delightful as is possible: That these fittezas set the negroes their tasks, who are prodigiously fum-fummed (*i.e.* beat) by them, if they do not perform them well.'

Franklin said, 'His being resident among them so long, gave him an opportunity of being acquainted with these notions of the inland negroes, which might perhaps be new to me, as well as to others, who had only touched on the sea coasts; for which reason, he said, he had mentioned them to me, as a novelty that might divert me.' He then proceeded to tell me, 'That he advised King Thome, in order to prevent any jealousy or animosity between himself and Governor Plunket, to send him away to the king of his acquaintance, and to inform the Governor, that that king came to visit him, and finding a white who could speak so much of their language as to be understood, he had prevailed upon him to permit him to go along with him, promising him his favour, and liberty to return whenever he pleased; and that to confirm the same, he (Franklin) would write a letter to Governor Plunket, to assure him, that in a little time he would return, and wait upon him.

'This advice, he said, pleased the king, who ordered it to be given out, that he was gone with King Bembolu to his town to abide with him a small time; and that he wrote a letter to Governor Plunket, and the rest of the English factory at Sierra Leon (having brought no less than two quire of paper from the pirates; which he would rather have wanted cloaths than been without), in which he declared, That having been taken by Roberts the pirate on the American seas, they not only deprived him of his vessel, but forcibly detained him as a

[1] Fetishes.

prisoner, and so strictly watched him, that he never had an opportunity to make his escape till he arrived at Sierra Leon, where he got a deliverance from them: That if he had fled for refuge to them, they were too weak to defend him from Roberts, who was so formidable a pirate, that he could have destroyed their settlement for giving him protection; which made it very happy for them, as well as himself, that he had put himself into the power of the negro prince, instead of that of the factory: That he was now going up in the country with King Bembolu, to reside with him a small time, and hoped he should have opportunity to make such discoveries, as might be of use to the whole factory, and to the trade of the English nation in general; and concluded, with wishing him and the factory health and success, etc.

'This letter, continued he, I left with the king; who, after he had consulted his nobles, sent me to the afore-named King Bembolu, attended by four of his guards, with his staff of state, which serves as a credential; and the blacks that accompanied me, were to satisfy him in all things that were necessary, and to tell him, that I was a potent Baccarau prince, who was a great friend to the negroes, and had come thither to settle trade, after a more amicable way than hitherto had been carried on between the Baccaraus and blacks, etc. That he was seven days on his journey to King Bembolu's town, which, as nigh as he could compute, was a journey of about ninety or a hundred miles, to which he travelled on foot, stopping by the way at several of their towns, where they were used very courteously by everybody that they met: That for the first four days he observed nothing of any consequence; but after that, perceived gold among them in a very great abundance, but dared not make any enquiry about it, or seem to take much notice, as not very well understanding the common speech, nor being able to place any confidence upon any one, in the short time they stopped anywhere as they went: That as soon as he had eaten or smoaked, unless he lay down to sleep, they were for going; but if he lay half the day, and feigned himself asleep, they would let him lie undisturbed: That he understood afterwards, that those who attended him, had orders to give him no opportunity to make any remarks or observations of the country, and more especially to carry him the desart way as much as they could, and to see that he did not write at any time; for though the king had taken all his paper from him, telling him, he would have no occasion to use it till he came back, and that he would lay it up safe for him till he returned, for fear, as he understood afterwards, that he should take notes of the country, etc., yet they had an opinion, that he, as well as all the whites, had a fitteza (or genius) who would bring him paper, at his call, or anything he wanted: That therefore his attendants were directed, if they saw him have any paper, and offer to write upon it, to deliver him up instantly to the King of Aucadingo, who, it seems, was an enemy to them, as well as to all whites. It was also given them as a caution, that if he was honest and good, and had no design, they would perceive it by his not writing; but if otherwise, he would call to his fitteza, who would not fail to assist him with paper, or what else he should have occasion for: And that in this case, they should not offer any violence to him themselves, but immediately deliver him up to the aforesaid King of Aucadingo, on whom alone the fittezas of the Baccaraus had no power to act or hurt. At length, continued he, we arrived at King Bembolu's town, or court, call it which you please; and after the blacks that conducted me, had shewn the staff of credit, and told their errand, we were received with abundance of respect and honour and there was gazing enough upon me, I being the first European that ever was remembered to have been up at that town.

'I was mightily made much of, said he, both by King Bembolu, and his nobles, who shewed me everything they thought might contribute to my diversion. But having committed everything that passed of conversation, and what I observed of rarities, etc., to paper, I shall not take up your time with repeating them now; referring myself to what I have written, which I will shew you when you can get up to town, which I hope will not be long.'

Why, said I, *I cannot be satisfied how I shall do to get up to the town, if it be so difficult as you all represent it to be.*

He said, *That I need not fear, but in a day or two, if we had anything of fine weather, but they would bring the boat round here, and carry me up to Fuurno, where I should have a tolerable good way, which though very steep*, said he, *yet it's very passable, even for horses; although I question whether any horse in England would be able to get up from thence to town, and yet that's the best road reckoned in all the island.* And indeed so it is.

Well, well, said I, *I shall not much mind whether I have a horse or not, so I can but make shift to scramble up anyhow; I only wish*, said I, *I was gone from this place.*

I asked him, *Whether the inhabitants knew how to manage a boat? or, Who it was that would order the boat down?*

He said, *That it belonged to a man called Antonio Riverio; but he believed that the Governor would see to get some hands to bring it down for me, as soon as it was fine weather.*

I told him, *If he thought it would be anything difficult, or troublesome, that I would rather venture to swim across the bay, with the mast or boom, guided by three or four of the blacks, than give them too much trouble, or tarry the uncertainty of their coming.*

He said, *It was very possible I might go over the bay very safe, in the manner I proposed, or even without mast, boom, or anything else to help me, more than the blacks alone, though the bay were ten times as wide as it is: But*, continued he, *you need not at all doubt of the boat being brought down for you as soon as the weather permits; for I will go to town myself to-morrow, and will speak with the Governor, and likewise with Antonio Riverio for the boat; and if nobody else will, I am sure Domingo Gumms, and his brother, will come with me; but I rather fear I shall have more offer their service to go in her, than she will be able to carry, or I care to encumber myself with.*

I asked him, *How big the boat was?* and, *How many it required to bring her down?*

He said, *It was but a little bauble of a thing; two men could carry it very easily, when it had been some time out of the water and dry; but that he had known six, seven, or eight people in her at a time.*

Ay, said I, *because they did not matter half a farthing, whether she sunk or swam with them, because they could always save themselves by swimming, if at any time they were put to it.*

He said, *It was true enough; for they would hardly venture in her farther off the shore, than they were sure they could save themselves by swimming, if occasion so required; Nay*, said he, *and I believe was it never so good a boat, and never so large, it would be the same.*

What sort of a boat is she, said I? *or did they make her themselves? Why*, said he, *when you see her, you will say you never saw such a thing in your life; but she does well enough to go a fishing with; and I have been with her myself, and four more, as far as the little islands, which you saw as you came along to this island.*

Why, said I, *sure they would not pretend to swim from the little islands to this island.*

He smiled, and said, *If it were not for fear of the voracious fish, of which there is great plenty about these islands, they would not fear swimming a great way farther;* and speaking to Domingo in the island language, he told him what we were talking of, and how I thought it impossible for a man to swim from the little islands (Guy's) to the Island of St. John's: At which Domingo laughed, and said, *That if it was not for fear of the fish, he could swim to the Island of St. Philip.*

I told him, *I thought it impossible for him, or anybody else, to swim one quarter so far, notwitstanding I knew that all, or most black people, swam very well* (it being eight large English leagues).

He said, *I was very much mistaken, it being possible for a man, provided the cramp did not take him, to be in the water several days.*

I told him, *I thought half a day, or less, would have been time enough, and more than enough, to spend the strongest man in the world.*

He said, *I was much mistaken.*

Mr. Franklin told Domingo, *That I was something fearful*

of going in the boat to Fuurno; who answered, *That if the boat was to fill with water as soon as ever we turned the Salt Point, he would engage, with the assistance of one more, whom he could pick out, to carry me safe up to the Fuurno.*

I told him, *It might be so; but I would much rather be carried round in the boat, than put him to the trouble, or myself in the danger.*

He said, *As for the trouble, he should think it none; and as to danger, I run none; yet he would much rather that I went round in the boat because, that in the oversetting or filling of the boat with water, I might chance to lose some of my things.*

I said, *Ay, and your boat too. No,* said he, *we should not lose our boat neither, except it was very bad weather, and a lee current; for,* said he, *I am sure in fine weather, I and three more could bring that boat safe into the Fuurno, if she was to be filled with water, and half way over between here and St. Philip's:* He added, *That Franklin knew what he said to be true; who was,* he said, *the knowingest man on the island; nay, and did believe, there were not many white pilotos that knew so much of the sea, or how to govern a boat in the sea, as he did; and therefore, if Singore Carolos would go up with him to-morrow, he would go and ask Antonio Riverio for his boat, and get as many good hands as Singore Carolos should think sufficient, if I could dispense with Singore's absence so long; or, if not, he would go himself, and get the boat down, and so bring us both up together, with all my things.*

I thanked him, and told him, *If Singore Carolos pleased to give himself the trouble to go, and come with him, I should not only be very willing, but should also take it as a very great favour.*

Mr. Franklin said, He would go up with Domingo to bring down the boat for the more dispatch. After which we fell into other talk, sometimes about one thing, and sometimes about another, till at last Domingo, with his brother, and all the rest of the blacks, fell asleep: After which, upon my desire, Mr. Franklin reassumed his discourse about his last adventures, and how he came to be placed on this remote island. But as the relation of them would too much break in upon my own history, and indeed require a volume of itself, I shall at present pass them by, and return to what more immediately relates to myself.

After our long discourse, I began to grow sleepy, and laid me down on the rock, by the fire side, in order to take a nap, and Franklin did the same, and so we fell fast asleep; Domingo in the meantime awakening, took care of the fire, and was so kind, as to raise my head softly, and, without waking me, laid it in his lap, which might be one good reason of my not waking till the morning.

About eight or nine o'clock in the forenoon, came down from town a parcel of the natives, to the number of twelve or fourteen, two of whom were sent by the Governor, with a side of wild goat, a couple of pompions, a water melon, a little calabash of milk, containing about a quart, and with his service, promised me, that he would send me more on the morrow, or next day, if I tarried so long; but hoped to have me up to town in a day or two.

He understood (they said) what a difficult place I was got ashore at, it being impossible, as he was informed, for me to climb up the rocks from where I was; besides, if it were, he would by no means have me, for fear I should tumble down and lose my life, the rocks being, as he was informed, so rotten, that I could not be certain or secure, either by foot or hand-hold; and was sorry that I could not swim over the bay, which if I could, I might then travel up to town, which though it might seem to me a difficult way, yet it would then be without any danger; but he would not have me be troubled at that, for he had borrowed a boat, which was the only one they had on the island fit to swim (for he had a boat himself, but she had lain, it seems, two years on the dry land, and was then in a manner all to pieces; neither did they know how to repair her; though afterwards I put them in the way; but concerning this, he did not send me any account now, but I understood it afterwards); but he sent me word also, that the owner would let the boat come for me, on this condition only, that Singore Carolos himself should go in the boat; for else he would not trust his boat to the management of the blacks, for fear of losing his boat. And therefore (continued the Governor's man) Singore Governador would have you, to get Singore Carolos to go up to town to-night; and if it should be fine weather to-morrow, you may be brought up to the Fuurno.

I told him, I thanked his master, and would speak directly to Singore Carolos about it, who was standing by all the time, and heard all our discourse; and preventing my asking him, said, I need not give myself the trouble, for he was resolved, as he had given me his word last night, as did also Singore Domingo Gumms, to have gone up to town, in order to have borrowed the boat of the owner Antonio Riverio himself, and likewise to have got some more blacks to assist him and Singore Domingo, to bring down the boat from where she was for me; but was glad the Governor had done it to his hand, not so much upon the account of saving him the trouble, which, in respect to whom it was for (meaning me), it would not be any; yet, as it was the Governor's act, it would prevent any heart-burning or jealousy. Why, said I, what jealousy or heart-burning could it occasion to you, to endeavour to get me out of this melancholy, disconsolate, as well as dangerous place, where a man is not secure one moment from being dashed to pieces, by the rocks and stones so frequently tumbling down? and surely, continued I, in English, these people must be of a very dangerous, as well as barbarous principle, to be angry or displeased with any person, for endeavouring to rescue one from the almost hourly danger of death, as we all are threatened with, by the so often tumbling down of the stones from the mountains.

This mostly happened early in the mornings, and late in the evenings, which gave me very good ground to believe the reason which the blacks gave for it, as they said by ocular demonstration, which was, that it was the wild goats going to their dens and caves on the edge of the mountain, whose foot was at the top of the rock under which we were; for the land rises something like those draughts, which are drawn to represent the Pyramids of Ægypt, the foot of one mountain being, as it were, the top of another, till you descended to the sea; and thus they rise one above another, till you arrive at the middle of the island, which is the highest; and which, though at a distance off at sea it appears with a rounding head, yet when you are on the top of it, it then seems indifferent flat, yet declining till you come to the edges, which then goes down steep, something like St. Paul's cupulo, rising as it were out of the body of the church, and at every height of pillars, and ends in a roundish flat head, supposing the cross, etc., not to be there.

Domingo Gumms being also present when Mr. Franklin spoke to me, and at all our discourse, said it was time to be going to townwards.

To whom Mr. Franklin said, It was time enough after they had got their dinner. Domingo said, There was nothing here but only pompion and water melon to eat, which they could get up at town, except the milk which the Governor had sent the Captain, which he thought would be a pity to rob him of.

Mr. Franklin said, He was sure that some of those that went to the Piscaree Picuana, would come and bring some fish with them for my dinner, and he would stay and eat some fish and pompion with me before he went to town. Domingo said, He was afraid it would be too late to stay their coming, and after that the boiling of the fish and pompion.

To which Mr. Franklin said, Then he would not stay the boiling of either; but would cut some pompion and roast, and if they brought the fish before it was enough, he would take a fish and broil it to eat with the pompion, and if they did not, he would eat a piece of pompion, and then walk with him to town; And, said he to Domingo, What need you be in such haste? You know if we were to go away from hence, to get up to Porto de Cauvra by day-light, we can get well enough up to town by night, and it will be more pleasant to walk then, than in the day, when the sun shines so hot.

Domingo said, As for their getting up, he did not fear that, and for his own part, he could get up better than most of the blacks on the island, and even in the night, if necessity required it; but he was urgent to get up to town before night, to speak with the Governor and Antonio Riverio, that he might procure such hands, as he thought proper, to launch the boat in the morning before day, in order, if the fair weather continued, to be back with me to the Fuurno, before the day gale came on.

To which Mr. Franklin said, That as for their coming back to Fuurno on the morrow, it would be impossible, before the day-breeze set in, and as they must hale the boat ashore where they could find a place out of the danger of the sea staving her at high water, so they must wait all night to take me, and my things, in the next morning at day-break; otherways, they would not be able to row up to Fuurno before the day-breeze set in, by reason that the rowl or set of the sea, even in a calm, was always to leeward; and therefore, he would rather come down in the afternoon, when the day-breeze blew strong down, because the wind would drive the boat faster than they could row in a calm.

Domingo said, He knew best what could be done; but that the boat being but small, if I thought well of it, they that intended to go up that night, would every one carry some of my things with them.

I thanked them very kindly; but said, I had nothing now left me, what with the pirates, and the sea, that was worth their taking the pains to carry with so much jeopardy.

Yes, said he, you have still enough left you, to be the richest man upon our island.

At which I smiled, and said, Then the island is very poor.

He said, That he was sure I had more cloaths, than any two on the island, not excepting the priest himself.

I said, I never had less in all my life.

He said, That might be, and told me, That if I, and Singore Carolos, thought well of it, he would then also carry my little boy with him up to town.

I told him, I did not think it proper nor safe, and would rather the boy went up with me when I went.

He told me, As for the safeness, he would engage the child should go as safe as he did, and would take it upon himself to carry him up, and the child should come to no disaster, but what he should participate of, and Singore Carolos should be the judge.

I told him, If he could get the child up those rocks, which they all along represented to me so difficult to ascend, and who, in a manner, was helpless, surely I might, with a little of their assistance, make shift to get up.

He told me, No, for the rocks were so steep and difficult, as well as rotten and dangerous, that I should never be able to get up.

Why, said I, then how can the child get up? for I am sure I can climb up much better than he.

Why, says he, I can carry him upon my back, and that I cannot do you.

But, said I, I should think I could get up any place that you could carry such a big boy as that.

He said, No, and if I would not believe him, he bid me ask Singore Carolos.

To which Mr. Franklin made answer, saying, It was true what Singore Domingo said, for he could with ease and security, he was well assured, climb up where neither himself, nor I, could, nor would care to venture.

Truly, said I, unless I was sure of the boy's going safe, I would not let him go by any means.

He said, I need not fear, if Domingo took the charge upon him, for then he was sure he would sooner suffer a disaster himself, than the boy: Why, said I, I do not see any advantage in sending the boy up now, and, I think, he may as well go round in the boat, when I go round; for he could be but little weight in the boat.

Franklin said, That was true enough; but still he thought, since they desired it, it would be better to let the boy go up now; and perhaps, my refusing might be taken as if I mistrusted them.

I said, I did not much fear but they would do as well as

they could; but was not willing the poor child should run any more hazard, than I did myself.

He said, As to the hazard, he was satisfied there could be none; for if Domingo was not sure of carrying him safe up, he would never undertake it; who, to his knowledge, was so sure-footed, that there was none on the island could, or dared venture to go where he could; nor could a wild goat escape from him, that he had a mind to catch; and it was his opinion, That I had best send the boy up now.

Well, said I, in God's name, I will venture, and if you find any difficulty in getting the boat for me, I will then try to get up myself.

He said, I need not fear the boat's coming for me the first opportunity of fine weather.

Said I, Don't you reckon this fine weather that we have now?

Yes, said he, and if it continues as it is now, you need not at all doubt, with God's leave, the boats being down some time to-morrow.

I said, I wished and hoped it would, and thought it best for them to go the sooner on the account of the boy, that they might be past the most dangerous part of the way before it was dark.

Mr. Franklin said, They had time enough; but Domingo said, It was better to go now, and then they should have daylight all the way; as likewise, that it would be something tedious carrying the boy at his back.

By this time, they beheld some of the blacks, who went from us the preceding night (accompanied, as it proved, by the three men I had brought with me from St. Nicholas), coming with some fish; whereupon Franklin said, he would broil and eat a fish before he went.

Domingo said, He would not stay upon the boy's account; and pressed me to let him carry him up then; so I yielded: And Mr. Franklin told Domingo, That as they did not go one way, he being forced to swim over the bay before he could ascend the rocks, and Domingo going with the boy right up, he might be going on, and as soon as he had eaten his fish, he would follow him; and considering that he had the boy to carry, he believed he should overtake him, and whichever of them first arrived at the first Curraal de Vauca, to stay there till the other came.

To this Domingo consented; and taking a cotton sash, he bound the boy with it on his back, and four more men accompanied him, and took some of my old rags, and some of the painted lineing of my cabbin, which was saved as afore related, and away they went; and after Mr. Franklin had broiled and eaten one fish, he also departed with two or three blacks who chose to go his way, promising his utmost diligence to bring the boat, or let me see him, if any accident happened to hinder his coming with it. The Priest's and Governor's men went also away to town.

I then turned myself to the three men I had brought with me from St. Nicholas; and the first salutation I had from them, was a weeping and howling after the negro manner, to testify their sorrow for my misfortune, as also their respect to me; and made abundance of protestations on that head; for it seems the inhabitants had very much blamed them for their leaving, and not assisting me.

I told them, It was very well; and it being neither a seasonable time or place to upbraid them, I made as though they were not much blameable.

One of them, whose name was Manuel, told me, That since it pleased God that I had escaped with my life, notwithstanding their baseness in so leaving me, and not assisting me, which he was heartily ashamed of, and should never forgive himself for; and having given over all hopes of ever seeing his native land, wife, or children, he therefore would dedicate his remaining days to my service; and that it was with that intent he was come down, and was resolved not to go up till I went, and desired that I would take him no otherways than as my servant, or slave.

I thanked him, and told him, That I only desired to be esteemed as a friend by them, and by all the natives of the island.

To which all present answered, That I need not doubt the friendship of the whole island; and they believed me to be so good and honest a Singore, that I could not fail of being beloved by all people wherever I came; and Manuel desired me not to use any compliment to him, but to take him as he had freely offered himself to me, and was resolved to be no otherwise than my slave as long as he lived.

I thanked him, but told him, I was in no condition of providing for myself, much less to have servants to provide for. He told me, He did not offer himself with that view, but rather that he should work and provide for me; and that it was his full resolution, not to leave me while he lived: For all which I thanked him; and so fell into other discourse, needless here to relate, till our fish and pompion were boiled, which was towards sunset, whereof I made a hearty meal, every one forcing upon me three or four times the quantity of what each of themselves had, and being served on a broken piece of calabash, or, for want of that, on a clean flat stone gathered off the beach; and they were so respectful, that not one of them would presume to eat with me, except Nicholau Verd, who once took that liberty, for which he was roundly checked by all that were then present; and though I often importuned them to let me eat with them, or some of the ancientest of them, yet they never would accept of it; but modestly replied, That black men were made to serve white men, and that it was honour enough to wait on the whites, without being their companions, or equals.

I must confess, it put me even to the blush to see such humility, as well as hospitality, amongst those innocent and ignorant poor creatures, when I considered how vastly they exceed us in those virtues, who pretend to so much learning and knowledge: And in particular, their veneration for age is extremely laudable and worthy of imitation; they paying a great regard to their elders of all ranks.

After eating, we passed our time away as well as our circumstances would permit, being particularly edified by the charity, morality, and kindness of those persons, whom, though we count savages or barbarians, far exceed the generality of us Christians, to our shame be it spoken, though we pretend and really have so many greater advantages over them.

I was very uneasy about the boy, and longed to hear of his being safe got up the rocks; and the morning proving fine weather, as did also the night past, gave us all reason to expect the boat down; but in vain.

About noon it began to blow fresh, and some of the blacks swam over to the Salt Point to look out for the boat, and took their fishing geer with them, and came back in the evening with a good mess of fish.

I do believe, that I did not more long, or wish for the boat, than these kind-hearted creatures did, but it was all in vain; and what made us the more impatient, nobody came down from town to tell us the reason.

About duskish two of the blacks went up to know the occasion of it; and we passed the night as well as we could.

Next day about noon, came down two men from town, who told us, That Singore Antonio Riverio had lent the boat, and that Singore Carolos had sent Domingo Gumms, with hands enough down, and promised himself to follow them: That Domingo went down accordingly, and lay all night at the boat, and not seeing Singore Carolos come, he launched the boat into the water, and waited till the sun was up; but no Singore Carolos coming, he sent a man up to town to know the reason of it, who, upon enquiry, found, that Singore Carolos went from town about the first cock-crow, and that they thought he had been down at the boat, or a good part of his journey towards where I was, before then; But, continued they, we have as bad news as all that to tell you, which is, That one of the two men that left you last night, can't be heard of: He that went with him says, That when they went in the water, one said to the other, Let us see which of us can swim across the bay swiftest; and that having out-swam his consort a pretty way, all of a sudden he could not hear him; and that he turned, and called him several times, but receiving no answer at all, he made the best of his way in a fright to the other side of the bay, and so got ashore, and travelled in the night up to town;

and says, That he does not know, whether it was the cramp took him, or whether it was a fish devoured him; but however, it so terrified them, that never after any of them would venture to swim over that bay.

I expressed my concern hereat; and asked him, Whether he had heard anything of the little boy? He said, Yes, he was got safe up, and the Governor would fain have had him live with him, but Singore Antonio Gumms would not let him, but kept him with himself, saying, he had most right to do so; for that his son Domingo had brought him up with great hazard and difficulty, and hoped the Captain would not only let him continue with him, but also would himself take up his abode with him; and had ordered Domingo, and all his sons, as they tendered his future favour, not to neglect their utmost diligence to get the Captain up, as soon as possible.

I was very glad to hear the boy was safe, and heartily wished myself with him.

I heard nothing farther till the next day in the afternoon, when Domingo came down, and confirmed to me what the man had told me the day before; and that Singore Carolos had ordered him and the men down, and promised to follow them that night: That thereupon he launched the boat in the morning to be the more ready, and when to his surprize he came not, he sent a man up to town to know the reason, who brought him word, that he had set out from the town about cock-crow, and they thought he had been with us; and, continued he, we waited till almost night, and then haled the boat up on the land again, and so went up to town, where we had an account, that Singore Carolos was taken so bad on the way, as he was coming down to us, that he was like to die; and that it was by meer chance he was found, and was brought up to town on an ass, being so weak, that two men were forced to support him: He added, That the townsmen were just going, if he had not come up, to send them word to hale the boat up, if he had launched her, and come to town again, for that Antonio Riverio would not trust the boat without Singore Carolos; after which, said he, my father would have me come down to acquaint you, and desires that you would rest contented a little, till it please God Singore Carolos is better, which if he is not in a little time, we will make shift, by some how or other, to get you from hence, etc., And withal, says he, my father gives his service to you, and bid me tell you, that your little boy is safe with him, and hopes he shall have the honour of entertaining you both, when you come up; and although he is not Governor now, yet he might have continued so long as he pleased, and does not doubt, but he shall be able to entertain you as well as any one upon the island, etc.

I returned him thanks for his unmerited favours; but was not a little troubled at my disappointment of the boat, and the more by reason of their aversion and fear to swim over the bay, occasioned by the late disaster; by which my hopes that way were cut off: However, I passed the following night as well as I could, neither wanting company, nor enough to eat of the best the island afforded.

CHAPTER EIGHT

NEXT morning I told Domingo, I had a great mind to try to get up the rocks. He disswaded me all he could, urging the impossibility, as well as danger. I told him, I was sure I could get up anywhere, where he was able to get up with such a great boy, as my boy was that he carried up. He said, I could not. I told him, If they would assist me, I would try, and perhaps I might do better than they imagined; and if I found that I could not, which I should never be convinced of till I tried, then, said I, I must desist, and be contented as well as I can, till it please God some other means offer.

Domingo said, He was afraid I should get so high, that it might be very hazardous to get me down again; and was positive I could not get quite up, nor any one upon the island with shoes on. I told him, I would very readily pull my shoes off, after I had gone as far as I could with them.

Some of the blacks present said to Domingo, Let us go and assist him; you see how desirous he is, and perhaps his eagerness may enable him to do better than we think for.

Domingo said, That I myself could not be more desirous to get safe up, than he was; but he knew the impossibility of it; but however, said he, to please the Captain, and to let him see that no endeavour shall be wanting, let us go six or eight of us, and try what we can do.

So away we went, and Domingo led the way. It was low water, and we walked on the beach, along by the foot of the rock, about three or four large stones'-cast, till we found one of the best places to mount at, though God knows bad enough. Domingo sent a young fellow up first to try whether the way was passable; who soon mounted up out of sight, and was gone a little above a quarter of an hour, and then returned again, and said, he had been a good way up, and that place was better to go up at, than any other they had yet found out. Domingo bid me stay a little, and he would go up a little way to view it, that I might not be forced to come back, perhaps after I had got up some part of the way; for, said he, we are often forced to do so ourselves. He accordingly went a little way, and came down to me again, and said, it was much the better way of any he had seen yet. The rock was pretty steep, but not right perpendicular, about the height of St. Paul's cupola, or higher; after which, it seemed to overhang as much as the lower sloped in; but they told me, that after I got up there, there was a good path in some places; so up we got, and I found the hold that we had with our feet was so little, that I was forced to pull off my shoes, and they supporting me below, that my feet should not slip, and them that was got above me, when they attained to any place that they could secure themselves (which they could very well do, when they got a place to fix their feet upon two or three inches broad), then they would reach down their long staffs for me to take hold of, and hale me up, those below shoveing me up with their hands; and when I was out of their reach that way, then they would shove me up with their long staves, till I had attained some place to hold and secure myself with my feet and hands, while they shifted higher, and fixed themselves to assist my ascending another degree.

When I was about half way up the first rock, I began to sweat with fear: I looked down but once after I had got any thing high; but I believe, had I not been supported, I should have tumbled down: My very sight dazled; nor is it possible for any one to conceive how it is, except those who have been in the like cases, nor they neither have the idea so lively or striking afterwards.

At last we got up to the first resting-place, which, as I told you before, was as high or higher than St. Paul's cupola, at London, from the bottom of the rock, and we had then a flat pretty even path, which looked like a gallery, only wanting rails: We walked along that path, which was about three foot broad, for about half a quarter of a mile, or more, sometimes descending, but mostly ascending; and in some places so narrow and dangerous, that they were obliged to pass some of them first, and then reach the end of their staves to me, while those behind bounded me to with their staves till I got over.

When we had wandered to the end of that vein, as I may call it, the rock was in a manner perpendicular, and we could hardly find a place whereon to fix one's toe, or tops of one's fingers, which put a stop to my journey: They searched all about to find a way passable for me, but all in vain, and had like to have proved fatal to some of them; for as they searched, and climbed, a great piece of a rotten crumbly rock tumbled down; and two of them, of which Domingo was one, had the narrowest escape that ever I knew or heard of; which was thus, One of them was got up a pretty height above the other two, on a pinacle or piece of a rock that stood without the rest; and one of them thrusting and striking at it with his staff, to see whether it was hollow, or would bear him, as is their usual practice, there tumbled down a huge piece of rock that was right over those two, who, like two rats, were clinging to the rocks with their feet and hands: But as Providence would have it, it rouled offwards, without doing them much damage, save the fright, and a few scratches, occasioned, as I suppose, by some of the small stones that dropt down after the great piece of the rock was fallen; but it raised such a dust, that the air, for as far as we could discern, was all, as it were, in a thick smoak, and it made such a terrible noise, that I thought all the rocks over us were coming down upon us; and I verily believe, it was half a quarter of an hour before the tumbling pieces of the rocks reached the bottom, for so long or longer I heard the sound of them falling; for we were then got a prodigious height up, and, by our turning and winding, quite out of sight of the sea, it being along the edge of the mountain, where the gathering of the waters is from the inland in the rains, and so passes down to the sea, making deep gullies where the rock is soft, and where not, descends in great falls.

After all was quiet, and the dust laid, we knew not what to do, neither seeing nor hearing any of the three that were gone before us to discover the way; at last, one of them that was with me, after recovering of his fright, said, That he believed Domingo Gumms, and the other two that were with him, were killed; and that it was their being on that rock, that made it tumble down: When presently, we heard a whooping and hollowing, which we answered, and as soon as they had again descended down that precipice, which they had so dangerously strove to ascend, they came to us, who all this time sat still, squeezing ourselves as close to the rock as we could, for fear any more should tumble down. When Domingo came to us, he was very much rejoiced to see us all well, thinking that we had been closer after them, and that we had been killed by the rocks that tumbled down; and said, He thought it was one of the greatest dangers that ever he was in; And, says the man that was a-top, that tumbled the rock down, I thought that Domingo, and all of you were killed; and the noise of it was so great, that the very rock trembled where on I stood, and I expected every minute it would tumble down, and me with it; but, said he to me, if you was a little higher than where you are, you might get up more easily than what you have already passed; but that it was impossible, as he thought, for me to get to the place where he stood when the rocks fell; neither would he himself venture to go there again.

Domingo said, He would rather than anything that I was down again; and that I must not pretend to strive to go any higher.

I told him, Except they could find a better way than this we were now in, I might as well lie down here and die, as attempt it. Neither, continued I, have I any hopes of getting this way; but sure, said I, that was a better way that you went, when you carried the boy at your back, than this that we came now.

He said, He thought that way was rather worse as to climbing, only that the rocks were something stronger and firmer than these; But, said he, don't be cast down nor discouraged at this; the worst jobb we have now, is to get you down again, the which, when accomplished, you need not doubt your getting up to town, whether Singore Carolos be well or no: And, continued he, I wish Singore Carolos had tarried down with you, and I had gone without him for the boat, which, had it been so, you would have been at town before now. As for getting you to town, added he, I am not a bit concerned;

for I do not fear having the liberty of the boat from Antonio Riverio myself, if Singore Carolos should not be able to go in her; but if not, I will take her whether he will or not.

Then, said I, they will blame me if any misfortune should happen to the boat. He said, No, he would take all that upon himself, and knew himself able so to do, and give any man upon the island a knock on the pate that should offer to check or stop him, excepting Singore Antonio his father, and Singore Padre, the Priest; But, said he, we must now make it our present endeavour, to get you down again to the sea, and then leave all the rest to me; after which, you yourself shall be judge, whether our family, or the Governor, or Priest, or any on our island, deserved most to have the credit and honour of entertaining you at their house; and hope you will do the honour to those who are most careful of your welfare.

I told him, I was very sensible I could neither honour nor credit anybody, by giving them the trouble to maintain me, but should rather take it as an honour, as well as charity, done to myself, that any one on the island would contribute so far only, as to prevent the boy's and my starving, until it pleased God of His mercy to put into our hands an opportunity of getting into our own country again.

He told me, He would have me not to doubt, that all the island, as well as the inhabitants, was at my service.

I told him, I had no reason at all to doubt of their goodness and hospitality towards me, having received proofs enough already, and a very remarkable one but now, by their but late narrow and miraculous escaping the losing of their lives, in endeavouring to serve me; and hoped the fright of that would not deter them from affording me their further assistance, without which I could expect nothing less than inevitably to perish here, among these hideous, frightful, and dismal rocks.

Domingo told me, That all the difficulty that I should encounter with more, would be in getting down again to where I came from, and after that he would have me be easy, and leave the rest to him.

God knows, said I, how it will be; but, come life, come death, I must submit to it; and have this satisfaction, that if I do perish, I perish among those whose desires and endeavours have not, and, I believe, will not be wanting to extricate me, as far as they are able. At which the kind-hearted Domingo, with a voice of concern, and tears in his eyes, replied, O Singore Capiteen, I have begun to assist you, and will lose my life, or get you up safe to town.

Every one present expressed themselves in the same manner, though not in so tender an accent, as Domingo; and so we set out to return the same way that we went; and when we were arrived at the end of our unrailed gallery; and some of them were about descending the rock, where we had first ascended, Domingo called to them to stop, and said, He would not trust the Captain to go down now, that the rocks were more crumbly; as indeed I afterwards found by experience they were, occasioned, I suppose, by the scorching of the sun, which, as it were, calcined them, and made them more apt to crumble and break; whereas in the night, they seemed to attract from the air a kind of gluten, which cemented and rendered them more strong and firm: Whether I have properly accounted for their being stronger in the night than in the day, I cannot tell; but that they are so, is confirmed by experience: For which reason Domingo would by no means let me attempt to go down till morning, when the sun was but just risen, enough to dry up the dew from the surperficies of the rocks: And so we pitched on the broadest and most convenient place for us to make our abode in till the next morning; and then Domingo, and two more, went down and brought a stick of fire, and some of the wreck wood, with some pompion and fish; and there we took up our lodging that night: And in the morning, with much difficulty, as well as hazard, we got down, and came to the old place again.

Soon after, Domingo, having rested and refreshed himself with a little fish and pompion, took his leave of me, and, with some of the blacks, went up to town to get the boat down for me, and bid me expect him, if the weather was good, the evening following, or the day after; but yet if it should happen so that he tarried longer, not to be out of hopes, or impute it in the least to his neglect; for he assured me, no endeavour or diligence of his should be wanting: This, he said, he could boldly aver for his own part, and believed, that no one on the island, but would contribute their assistance to it, to the utmost of their power.

I thanked him, and them all, and told him, I had no reason in the least to doubt what he said, and bid him give my humble service to his Singore Pay (*i.e.* his father), to the Singore Padre, and Singore Governardo, and to all the Singores in general, not forgetting Singore Carolos: He said, he would; so away they went.

Manuel, whom I told you of before, had set his resolution, never more to part with me, unless I brought him to his home and family, nor then neither, unless I would: The time that I was gone, he had got all my rags and cloaths, and had washed them; as also every rag of the sails that was as broad as my hand, and had them spread to dry; and as they dried, he folded them up, and laid them in a hole in the rock, where neither the sea, dust, nor dew, could come to annoy them; and told me, That he was not in any great hopes that I should have been able to have got up; but was in great fear that any disaster should happen to me, by reason the rocks were so difficult to climb up, as well as dangerous, which he had shunned, by his swimming; yet he heard so much from those that passed that way, that he had little hopes that I could; but wished heartily, that I might, and had washed, and was a drying all my things, in order to bring them up after me, as soon as he heard that I was safe up.

I thanked him; He said, I owed him no thanks; that it was but his bare duty, and as such, he did it, etc.

It was almost calm, and as the sun drew to the meridian, it fell quite calm, contrary to what it is on the weather side, as well south-east, and north-west sides of the island, where the nigher the sun approaches the meridian, the fresher the gale blows; but on the south-west side, the contrary; though sometimes, especially if it be calm in the offing, even a faint trade, between the hours of 10 m. and 3 p.m. you shall have a fine sea breeze at south-west; and such a breeze would have been very refreshing to me now.

The sun, as I said, was extreme hot, darting his rays against the solid rocks, which reflected upon us an inconceivable heat, so that by its stronger light or fire, it not only dimmed, but had like to have quite extinguished the weak lamp of my life.

For it so inflamed my blood, that, with other causes concurring, such as the badness of food for some time past, and drinking no liquor, but that fiery spirit, rum; my great fatigues, colds, heats, etc., and now my feeding altogether, and of a sudden, on watry food, such as pompion, water melon, bananas, etc., and instead of rum, drinking cold rock water; with my labouring and frights striving to scramble up the rocks; the former setting, as it were, my blood all on fire, the other chilling, and, as it were, stagnating it; of both which, I had a sensible perception.

All these together, I say, threw me into such an illness, that it was the wonder of every one, and the great mercy of the Almighty, that I recovered from it.

I found myself very much out of order, but was afraid either to conceit myself so, or own it to anybody else: They all saw an alteration, and asked me, Whether I found myself ill or no? I told them, I was indifferent, but thought it was the heat of the sun that made me a little faintish; they said, They believed I was not a little, but a great deal ill; for, says Manuel, your face is as red, as the very fire, and I will let you see it yourself, and away he goes, and fetches me some clear sea water in a calabash, and held it for me to behold my face in, which I could almost as well see, as in an ordinary looking-glass, and I was really surprized to see myself; it was just as if I had got a surfeit, or like one when the smallpox first comes out; and upon examining, I found, that all my body was the same.

My head was ready to split, and I thought my eyes would

have started out, and at last I was forced to bind something about my head; and I could hear them talk one to another, that I had an exceeding high and strong fever; some already concluding I should die, others hoping not, all wishing that I was up at town; and Manuel crying, and cursing his consorts, laying all the blame on them, by whose base neglect, he said, came my misfortunes, and the grief which occasioned my present illness, etc.

My distemper increased so, that I was not able to sit up, but was forced to lie along on the rock on pieces of sails, etc., with which they made a bed for me as well as they could; and in the evening, seeing me so bad, they all left me but three, of which Manuel was one; who would have had the other two have gone up also, telling them they could do me no good now, and that he alone was sufficient to look after me, and only wanted them to come down, one or two, every day, to bring down necessaries, and daily give an account at town how I was; but they all said, No, they would always leave two with him, as well for company, as to assist him, or to send away to town upon any extraordinary occasion; so away they went.

I was very ill the whole night, and a great part of it was delirious, and so continued the day following; in the evening, Domingo, and some more, came down, and was very sorrowful to see me in such a condition; most of the afternoon I was pretty sensible, and perceived several of the blacks weep, and especially Manuel and Domingo, who often wished, that I had not fallen sick before I got to town, when they should have been better able to take care of me, and keep me from the cold.

Domingo told me, That Singore Carolos was still ill, but much better than I, and was mighty sorry when the men that came up last night, brought word of my illness; but did not believe that I had been so bad, as he, to his great grief, found that I was; and that Singore Carolos, he hoped, would, in a little time, be better; and as soon as ever he was able, would be down to look after me; and that the Governor and Priest, as likewise all the people in general, sent word to me by him, That they were all ready to serve me, and that I should not want for anything that the island afforded; but more especially his father, Singore Anthonia Gums, who would have come down before now, but that he is a heavy old man; and so would the Governor, but that (as I had heard before) he was sick, and still was in a weak condition; and the Priest being a fat, heavy, corpulent man, he could not climb up or down the rocks, as he believed, so well as I.

About the time that the goats go to their dens, there came down a great many stones and much dust where we all were, without doing any considerable hurt to any of us, though there happened several stones to fall pretty nigh me, and a good deal of earth and dust upon me; one large stone fell, I believe, within half a yard of my head, which frightened them more than me, for my sickness was so extreme, that I was but very little affected with any apprehension of danger; but Domingo and Manuel could not be easy till they moved me to a place, which though to them seemed less dangerous, yet it was much more inconvenient, there hardly being room for me to extend myself, and the least turn would have rowled me of; which, although the fall would not have been very great, as not being above four or five foot above the beech, yet it being all stony, it was not only possible, but also very probable, that I might be hurt; and at high water, there was about a foot and a half, or two foot water, especially at spring tides, and moderate weather, the sea did but little more than come up to the rock; but my good attendants took enough care of me, two of them keeping by me all night, and if I offered but to turn, they would be ready, and ask me if I had a mind to turn, which if I said I had, they would turn me with as much tenderness, as a mother could do her tender babe; and so they tended me by turns till they thought the goats were all got out from their dens, and that the danger of the stones tumbling down was over; and then they removed me where I had something more room, and also contrived a sort of an auning or shade for me from the sun; after which, Domingo giving Manuel charge to tend me well (as also to remove me before the sun got below the tops of the mountains, and place me where I had been last night, for fear of the goats tumbling the stones down on me, and in the morning to move me again), he went away to town; at whose arrival, and news, they were very sorry; and Mr. Franklin told them, That I should be much better, if I lay better; and Domingo having a cotton hammock, which his father had of the pirates when they were at this island, he asked Mr. Franklin whether that would be of any service to me, who told him it would, and bid him carry it down, and shewed him how to hang it.

Domingo came down again that night, and his brother Basil, with some other of the blacks, and brought with them some milk, pompion, etc., and the hammock, which had been fixed ready for hanging up, at town, by Mr. Franklin; and they found means to hang it up at the side of the rock by some nobs that stuck out, and just high enough, that the sea could not flow up to me; though when it blew hard, that the sea rowled in, and beat in against the rocks, the spray would oftentimes fall into my hammock, and make me as wet as if I had been dipped in the sea.

They catched two quails, which they had knocked down in the way as they came along, and some others brought down a couple of fowls; neither wanted I anything at all the time I was there, nor after that I could be got upon the island; and Manuel constantly tended me night and day with a tenderness that is not common; besides it was very seldom, but what there was some of the inhabitants down with him.

I was pretty much delirious, insomuch, that sometimes, as they have since told me, they were forced to stand in the water, when it was full sea, to keep me in my hammock, their tenderness not permitting them to tye me down; neither would they, during the whole time of my illness, tell me anything I did, or what I said in my raving fits, because, as they afterwards told me, they would not discourage me.

I had a tolerable bed to lie on, made up of pieces of sails doubled, and laid in the hammock, and my bed-tick smooth over that; but they had taken all the feathers out and flung them away, because they were wet; on that was spread a cotton cloth, and another cotton cloth was laid over me, and on that my rug, which they had also saved; so that considering where I was, I may say I was extraordinarily accommodated.

A high burning continual fever held me near about a month; after which I was less delirious, but extreme weak, not being able so much as to turn myself; and in the spring tides I used to be often wet with the spray of the sea dashing against the rock where I hung, and then in the morning they would take me out of my hammock, and spread the things and dry them; and during the time that I was out of the hammock, one or another used to lay my head in their laps, or sometimes set me on their laps leaning against their breast, or any way which I found most easy; and I believe I was troublesome enough to them.

I shall trouble the readers with one instance of the strength of my delirium: One night, when the water was down, so that the beach was dry, I had a notion came into my head that I could very easily go up the rocks, and thought, in my imagination, that I had seen a way never discovered by the natives, which I thought I could very easily get up; and looking about me, designing to get away without anybody's discovering me, I pleased myself to think how I should surprize all the town to see me there, who would be apt to think I had some supernatural help. I thought I was so strong, that I was able almost to do anything; and every one being sitting about the fire on the top of the rock, which I could see as I lay in the hammock, I got out without making any noise, and was going along as easy as I could, that I might not be discovered, when Manuel spying me, came running to me, and asked me, Where I was going? I told him, I was going to town. He said, He wished with all his heart I was able. I told him, I was able enough. He said, No; and begged me to go with him back to the hammock. No, I told him, I would go to town. He said, That when I was well, I could not get up; and how could I pretend to it now I was ill?

I told him, I was as well as ever I was in my life, and as strong (and indeed so I thought I was), and was resolved to be up at town before daylight. He desired me to go to my hammock, and stay till daylight, and then I should see to walk better. I told him, I had lain so long in the hammock, that I was tired of it. Then, said he, come and sit down by the fire with us till day, and we will all go together. For, said he, you know that not one of the islanders will venture to go up the rocks in the night. Pish, said I, I know a way that never a one on the island knows. Pray, says he, let me persuade you either to go to your hammock, or come and sit down by the fire with us. I said, No; I was strong and well enough, and perfectly knew every step of the way. How can that be, said he, and you never was up that, nor any other way on this island, in your life? No matter for that, said I, I have been shewn the way, and have seen, that if I was to go it a thousand times, or oftner, I could not know it better than I now do; and therefore am resolved to go now, while I have the knowledge of it so fresh in my mind, lest God Almighty, who has shewn it me, may perhaps take away my knowledge to-morrow; And, said I, it signifies nothing your talking, I will go to town now, while I can, and will not any longer tarry here. Well, said he, if you are resolved to go, I will go with you, and I will put a cotten cloth about you, that you may not catch cold (for I was all this time standing stark naked). Well, do, said I, and bring a stick for me, to have in my hand to keep off the dogs when we come into town, for I reckon we shall be there a good while before day. Ay, said he, and will help you to walk. No, said I, the way that I shall lead you, you may walk it very easily without a stick; but I would not have you shew it to anybody, that they may admire how we got up, and the more for coming up in the night.

He said, He would not; and brought a cotten cloth out of the hammock, and borrowed a stick of one of the blacks who was sitting at the fire, telling them where I was going, and what I said. Some of them said, I was light-headed; others, That God was a great Friend to white people, and out of compassion to me, had perhaps sent His angel to shew me, in a vision, the way. Ay, said another, but there is no such easy way from hence up; nay, nor any where on the island from the sea side, as what he talks of. Well, but, said another, God can do all things; maybe He hath sent His angel to make the way so easy for him; and a great deal more such innocent foolish talk, which I heard of afterwards.

Manuel soon returned, and brought me a stick as I had desired him, and a cloth, which he tied about me after the negro fashion, and away we trudged; I being, I thought, as strong and hearty as ever I was in my life: But we had not walked above a stone's-cast or two, before my delirium began to leave me, and with that all my imaginary strength, so that I was unable to help myself; and Manuel had enough to do to set me on my legs again, and began to persuade me to go back with him to the fire, or to lie down in the hammock again; but I would not hear anything that way, but bid him go his way to his consorts, for that I could find the way to town without anybody's assistance, and shoved him from me; who letting me go, I dropped down through extreme weakness.

Hereupon he called to his consorts at the fire, who presently came, and among them carried me to the hammock, where I lay quiet enough.

I believe this was the last strong raving fit I had, being for the most part sensible after that; and then I had been laid up better than a month, and was very weak.

I lay three days and nights, they told me, without opening either my eyes or mouth, only when they forced it open with a knife, etc., to pour broth or milk down my throat, and never stirred; so that they very often thought I had been dead, till they felt my heart beat, which they would every now and then.

When I awaked from this lethargy, I was just, I thought, as though I had risen out of a sweet sleep, not thinking, nor they telling me then, it had been a nap of three days.

It was a little before that, that Mr. Franklin, being something recovered, came down to see me; but was gone before I awaked out of that long sleep, and strictly enjoined them, before he went, to be sure to take care of me, while any life remained in me; but as soon as ever they perceived me dead, to send directly to him, and he would, if able, come down. He was of opinion, That I should never recover; but wished that he had seen and spoke to me before I was so bad, that he might have known where to write to my friends, that they might have the satisfaction to know when, where, and how I died; he said he could not stay with me, not being well recovered, and found it prejudicial to him to lie open, exposed to the dew, and therefore went up again.

Domingo also came down often, and most of the time that I was ill, every night almost, there were two, or three, or more companions with Manuel.

I continued still very weak, but sensible, and sweat so every night, that in the morning you might have wrung all the cloaths about me, and yet remained so cold and clammy, that I could not be warm all night, do what they could to cover me: The blacks said, This extreme sweating was a good sign, and that my distemper was going away in those sweats.

When I had lain about six weeks in that condition, it pleased God it held calm for two or three days together, and Carolos and Domingo, with three others, brought the boat down; but about an hour, as near as I could guess, before the boat came, a terrible accident happened, which gives me still the greatest concern; for a great piece of rock tumbled down, right over where my hammock hung; and it being low water, and a fine day, poor Manuel was sitting on the beach, a little way off from me, on whom several of the great stones fell, and made a woful spectacle of him, by smashing him as it were almost to a mummy; my hammock hanging close to the side of the rock, the piece of rock, and stones, which came tumbling after it, rowled off, clear of my hammock, excepting some few, which scratched and rased the skin in several places, and gave me a slight contusion in my left arm, a little cut on my left thigh, and bruised the outside of my left ankle, which was the worst, and pained me above two months after.

It happened luckily that there was not any body else there at that time; for there had been four with Manuel the preceding night; but they seeing the day before had been calm, and that the morning promised the same for the ensuing day, two of them went up to town at break of day, to remind my friends to get down the boat, and the other two went a fishing.

When the boat came to the beach, poor Manuel was the first spectacle they saw; and looking farther about, they saw me lying down on the beach with my hammock almost covered with dust, and in so weak a condition, that I was not able to move, and almost unable to speak.

The first that came to me, asked me, when he saw my eyes open, for till then, he said, he thought I had been dead, in a very sharp tone, How came Manuel to be killed so?

I answered as well as I was able, That I could not tell; and by that time Mr. Franklin and the rest came up to me; and when he saw that I was alive, and spoke, he said, He was very glad; and asked me, How long Manuel had been dead? I told him, I did not know of his death; but I believed it was about an hour since I heard the rocks fall, which beat down my hammock, and, I believed, had hurt me a little.

Domingo said, What signifies asking him questions? Let us get him down to the boat before any more falls, and thank God he has so narrowly escaped; so away they took me, four of them, and carried me down to the boat, and put what they thought worth carrying away, into it; and away we went, and got up to Fuurno about two hours before sun-set, where they brought me ashore, and laid me in a little cave, upon a bed which they made me of dried grass which they gathered, and covered me with the rug and cloaths they brought up in the boat; and kindled a fire at the mouth of the cave.

They told me, That they did not, when they came away, design to have come back to Fuurno till the next morning; nor, they believed, had not, if it had not been for that unlucky disaster of the rocks falling and killing Manuel, and hurting me, and therefore expected no horses down for me till morning; at which time Domingo said, His brother would be down with a horse from his father, and hoped I would do their father the honour to lodge with him.

I can't tell whether it was with the joy of my deliverance from that dismal place, or how; but I found myself more hearty, and could speak so as to be intelligible without straining, or making me so faint as it used to do for some time past.

I told Domingo, That it could be no honour; and that I should give abundance of trouble to whosoever entertained me; and I thought I owed more obligations to him than to any one on the island, and therefore, since he was so good as to desire it, I would give him that trouble and charge.

He told me, The Governor, he believed, would send a horse for me also; but desired that I would ride up on his father's horse, since I had promised him to take up my abode with him.

Mr. Franklin told Domingo, That since I had given my word to lodge with his father, he need say no more about it, for that it was the property of the English nation, sooner to die than to go from it.

Domingo said, He believed it; and went away directly to carry up the joyful news, as he called it, of my safe arrival at the Fuurno. Next morning betimes he returned, with several of the blacks, and his brother, who brought a horse for me: The Governor also sent a man and horse for me.

My fever had in a manner left me; but I was so weak, that when I was set on my feet, I could not stand a moment without being supported; and Mr. Franklin said, That the Governor's horse was the quietest, as well as securest to carry me, and the saddle was the deepest, and easiest for me to sit upon, and so proposed that I should ride up on that, which Domingo with some reluctancy, for fear the Governor should take it as an obligation for me to live with him, complied with, upon my repeated promise that I would take up my abode at his father's; and after they had well girted and secured the saddle, they set me on the Governor's horse; and, for the greater security, tied my feet under the horse's belly with a cotten sash, much as they do a criminal; the pummel of the saddle afore being as high almost as the pitt of my stomach, and it was as high behind; and they fastened me so, that if I had been dead, or asleep, I could not fall: They then put the horse in the path, and turned him loose, and bid me not fear, for he knew his way home; and away went the horse afore a good pace, but did not trot; and never stayed till he came to the Governor's hut door, who, with several of his relations, and a good many others, was ready to receive him.

I was up some time before the blacks; and the Governor welcomed me with all the signs of joy imaginable, and excused himself for not coming down to me at the Salt Point Bay, by reason of his illness, etc., but now I was come up, he would endeavour to make amends to me for that, etc., and told me, his house, himself, his family, his friends, and all that the island afforded, was at my service, and he himself would be to me in the room of my Manuel whom I had lost, and which he was very sorry for, since he heard, he said, he was an affectionate and faithful servant; and ordered to unloose me, and take me down off the horse.

I told him, I was extremely obliged to him, and all the Singores on the island; and, if he pleased to hear me without being angry, I would give him my reasons, why I could not possibly take up my abode with him, without incurring the displeasure of Singore Padre to both himself and me, and what the consequence of that might be, I believed him to be a better judge than myself; which was, that Singore Padre was the first that offered me his house, as he was the second: Now, continued I, if I should lodge at the Padre's house, I suppose you would have taken it ill of me, and I am informed, that if I lodge at your house, he will do both you and me all the prejudice that lies in his power.

Ay, said he, I know that he loves me but from the teeth outwards; I have been upon my guard a great while; I know he is spiteful and malicious enough, but I do not value him though he's a padre; but it may be, that out of malice he may, some way or other, privately do you a prejudice, but openly he shall not; and though for your reasons given, I could agree to your living with any one else on the island, yet I never shall agree to your lodging at the Padre's. I know, said he, his eagerness to have you live with him, is not out of respect to strangers, but for what he can get from you.

Nay, said I, he can expect nothing from me, I having been robbed of everything before I came here.

Yes, yes, said he, you have cloaths, and he will be glad to get some of them.

Well, says I, if you will be contented for me to live at another house, I will give you my word I will not live at the Priest's.

He said, So it were with one that he thought would take care of me, he would.

I replied, That to avoid giving any offence, or, at least, as little as I could, to any party, I thought it best to go to Singore Antonio Gumms.

He said, I did very prudently, as we whites always did; and he liked Singore Antonio very well, he being a good man and having a better house by far to entertain me in, than his; but hoped, when I was able to walk abroad, that I would not be a stranger to his house.

I told him, I should not: At which he seemed satisfied.

By this time the people who followed me came up; and though the Governor was swayed so with the reasons that I gave him, so as to be satisfied with my going to live at Singore Antonio Gumms', yet some of his friends present were not; and began to say one to another, that this was owing to Singore Carolos, and to Domingo Gumms, and that Singore Carolos ought to be chastized for his insolence; who being but a stranger should take that liberty to perswade the Captain not to live with the Singore Governador.

Domingo overhearing them, said, It was false, to say that Singore Carolos had any hand in perswading Singore Capiteen to live at his father's; it was he himself that did it; and his father was as well able to accommodate Singore Capiteen as Singore Governador was; and his father was Governador when Singore Luonell Gonsalvo (that was the present Governor's name) was but a boy, and might, if he pleased, have been

Governor now, but that he was old, and would not take the trouble upon him; and that man that should say that Singore Carolos had a hand in perswading the Capiteen, he had a faukade ready for him; and immediately drew out a long sharp-pointed knife.

Mr. Franklin told them, That he did not perswade me either to one house, or another; but that I had promised, at the repeated request of Domingo, to go to his father's, lest I should disoblige either the Governor or the Padre.

Notwithstanding this excuse, one of them up with his stick to strike at Mr. Franklin; but Domingo gave him such a rap on the head with his stick, that he laid him down as quiet as he had been in his last sleep, for some minutes; which put them all into such a ferment, that the Governor, fearing it might be of no good consequence to me, got me into his house; leaving orders to apprehend and make a prisoner of him, who first lifted his stick to strike Mr. Franklin, as being the first breaker of the peace; And this, indeed, was the most prudent way he could have acted, to prevent a commotion among them; and this intirely put a stop to their forming parties, which they were going to do.

After I was brought into the house, the Governor shewed me the bed which he had made up for me, in hopes that I would have remained with him; but he was, as he told me before, satisfied (to prevent giving offence) at my living with Singore Antonio, whom all the island respected; but since I was alighted he would have me stay at his house till the cool of the evening, and then he would send me down to Singore Antonio's; so I was laid on the bed, which indeed was extraordinary, considering the people and country; for there were four posts drove into the floor, in the form of a long square, and four pieces of wood tied to them with banana cords, which formed the head, feet, and sides of the bed, and three or four sticks laid across, and tied at each end to the two pieces that made the sides of the bed; over that was laid a hurdle made of large cane reed, being the same sort which is brought out of Portugal, etc. Over the cane hurdle was good store of dried banana leaves, laid after the same manner as the poorer sort of the native Irish do their beds of straw; over the banana leaves was laid a banana mat, and on that two white cotten cloths as sheets, with a thick blue-and-white cotten cloth over all, as a rug or quilt.

I have been the more particular in describing this bed, because beds are not usual there, they all lying on the ground, and, as he told me, it was of his brother's contrivance, who had lived some time at St. Philip's, and had been once at St. Jago, where he saw those sort of beds there, used by the Brancas (*i.e.* Portuguese) inhabiting there; and said, He was sure there was never another bed upon the island of that sort, except one that his brother made for Singore Padre; and he would keep it always ready for me, against I was recovered, in hopes I would pass a night now and then with him; which I said I would, so it gave no offence. He said, He would beg that favour of Singore Antonio, who, he was sure, would not deny him.

The prisoner who had begun the fray, was bound hand and foot, and put in the Governor's house, and so remained till next day; and upon all parties becoming friends again, he was set free.

I had a fowl boiled for me, and I supped a little of the broth; and in the cool of the evening I was carried down in my hammock, by the inhabitants on their shoulders, it being fixed on a pole by Mr. Franklin. I was joyfully received by Singore Antonio, who told me, Since I had been so kind to come to live with him, notwithstanding I had been so importuned by the Priest and Governor, he reckoned himself and all his family so highly obligated to me, that all that they could do for me was much too little. And, indeed, he made it appear that what he said was sincere; for during the whole time that I continued ill and weak, which was about six weeks more, the good old man would trust neither his wife, who was also a good, tender and motherly old woman, nor any of his children, nor even Domingo, either to make up my bed, which was done every night, or to lift me out while it was made, or to serve me with my victuals; but did all himself; often telling me, that it was the greatest honour he ever had in his life, to be my servitor.

My bed was of the same fashion of that which I described before at the Governor's; for the old man, as soon as he had any assurance of my coming to his house, went to the Priest's, to see how his bed was made, and by that pattern fixed one for me; after the Brancas fashion, as they called it.

During the time of my illness, every day some or other of the inhabitants would come to see how I did; but never hardly any of them came without bringing something for me, either a fowl, some bananas, Indian corn, and banana cakes, pompion, water-melons, etc., according as they had; but Singore Antonio very seldom let them come into the house, excepting some few of the better sort, for fear of disturbing me, but received their offering at the door, and there answered them how I did, and returned them thanks for their presents on my behalf.

The Priest paid me a visit the next day after I came up; and the Governor used to come and see me almost every day; and every two or three days sent me, sometimes a quarter, sometimes a side, and sometimes a whole carcass of a wild goat.

After I began to gather strength, that I could dress myself and sit up, they used to be admitted in; for then Singore Antonio thought, he said, that company might divert me, and do me good.

When I came to be able to eat pretty well, and could take a walk out in the air, which was about two months after I came up to town, I told Singore Antonio, that I began to be pretty well, I thanked God, and all the good people of the island, and in a particular manner himself, and Domingo, who, under God, was a great instrument of saving my life; and that now my stomach was pretty strong, I would endeavour to eat as they did, viz. pompion, feeshoon, parched Indian corn, etc., and that I reckoned I had destroyed his stock of fowls already (which was the largest stock that any four on the island had besides himself). He said, I had not destroyed his stock, for they were not his fowls that I eat, but my own. I told him, It was his goodness to make them so. He said, No; they were my own property, and were given to me by the singores, who came daily to see me in the time of my sickness: And, says he, How many fowls do you think you have yet left alive? I told him, I could not tell; neither did I know that I had any. Why, said he, you have more fowls, I believe, than I; and calling his Singora Muritia (which was his wife's name), he asked her, How many fowls the Captain had left alive? who told him fifty-one, or fifty-two. I was in amaze at it, and said, I was indebted to all the singores of the island more than ever I should be able to pay.

He smiled, and said, That to help any one that was in need, but more especially a stranger, was a duty incumbent on every one; and that if any of them should ever happen to be in the like circumstances in my country, it would be then a duty in me to do the same for them; and he did not doubt but I should have been of that opinion, if I had never been on this island, and received kindness from them.

After I was able to walk abroad, I had every day invitations, till I had visited all the inhabitants' houses or huts on the island, except the Fiteseers' (*i.e.* witches) houses; against which, my landlord, as also the Governor, and the Priest, gave me a caution, neither to eat, nor drink, nor have any intimacy or acquaintance with them, but as little as I could.

The first visit I paid (for which I asked the Governor's leave; and praying him not to be offended at it, which he readily granted, and promised not in the least), was to the Priest, who took it very kind, that I had done him the first favour at my first going abroad; the next was to the Governor; and after him to Singore George Gonsalvo, who had formerly been a Governor; and then to the rest in order, according to their seniority, as my landlord Antonio Gumms directed me, whose advice in that affair I wholly followed.

*

THE Cape de Verd Islands were first discovered by the Portuguese; but I could not learn from the natives the exact time, nor by whom; but there were then no inhabitants on any of them, nor cattle of any kind.

The Portuguese settled first on St. Jago, which is not only the largest of all the Cape de Verd Islands, but the most fruitful: from whence, in process of time, they peopled most of the others; some of which, they were forced to quit again for want of sustenance, occasioned by extreme droughts, and want of rain, which rendered them so barren, that of late a great many souls were famished to death: This drought has continued for this sixteen or seventeen years at Bona Vist, and the Isle of May, and longer at the Isle of Sal; and none of them of late have had the rainy seasons so kind as formerly; but the high lands have always the most; and the natives will tell you, that the mountains draw, and gather the clouds together, until they are so ponderous, that the air being unable to bear their weight any longer, they break and fall down in rain; but the low islands, such as Sal, Bona Vist, May, etc., not having such high mountains to detain and gather the clouds together, they blow over, which, they say, occasioned the drought there, more than at the other islands.

The Portuguese, who first settled on these islands, and particularly on that of St. Jago, had slaves from Guinea; and, as it was an usual thing with them (and is continued to this present time) when a man or woman died, to set one or more of their slaves free, which they do as a meritorious act of atonement for their sins; and the climate being more agreeable to the constitutions of those blacks, than to the European Portuguese, they increased much faster, and found means to get themselves transported to the neighbouring islands, where they could live more free from the oppressions of the whites, who used them after the Spanish or Portuguese proud and lording manner, which did not so well agree with those but lately manumitted blacks; and as they improved in those islands, some of the whites settled there also; but after the trade to Guinea, and the East-Indies, became common to other nations, and the Portuguese trade declined, and dwindled away, as at this day, to a trifle, to what it was at first; the blacks all the time increasing more than the Portuguese, they claimed an equal degree of liberty and freedom with their masters, who thereupon mostly returned either to St. Jago or to Portugal; and those that remained, were both poor, and few, and were then necessitated to allow the blacks, if not to be their superiors, yet, at least, to be their equals; and marrying with them, the succeeding generations became by that mixture, from mallattoes, to copper-coloured negroes; so that now you shall see as great variety of negroes on those islands, as is contained on the whole coast of Guinea.

The King of Portugal claiming these islands by right of first discovery, as soon as he found them thus inhabited, gave them to such of his lords, as he thought fit, excepting St. Jago, and, of late, St. Philip's, which are governed by men commissioned by him, who are commonly Portuguese born.

As the King of Portugal has not much profit from these islands, although he hath made St. Jago the clearing port for all ships trading from any part of his dominions, to that part of Guinea lying between Cape de Verd and Sierra Leon; so he is not at much charge in keeping them, there being no fortification on any of them, save St. Jago, and St. Philip's, and on them, none of any strength, except that at the city of St. Jago, which was built by the Spaniards, when Portugal was subject to Spain; neither is the King of Portugal at the charge of keeping any soldiers to defend them, the natives being obliged to serve in their respective islands, but not out of them, which is all the acknowledgement they pay to the crown; neither are they able to pay any other taxes. And this may serve for a general account: I shall now proceed to a particular account of the Island of St. John.

This island is as fertile for pompion, water-melon, potatoes, bananas, maiz, and feshoon, as any of the Cape de Verd Islands; as likewise for cows, horses, asses, and hogs.

With respect to the inhabitants, who do not reach to the number of two hundred souls, the natives are all black, and the most innocent and harmless, as well as ignorant and superstitious, of all the islands.

This island hath not been inhabited above two ages,[1] which might be the reason of giving it the name of the Island of Brava, or Wild Island; for Brava, both in the Portuguese and Creole tongue, signifies wild.

It was, for several years, only inhabited by two black families, who lived wholly in heathenism, until, about sixty years past, a famine raging at St. Philip's, some of the poore sort of blacks procured themselves to be put on the Island of St. John, by a Portuguese ship, who were joyfully received, as well as relieved, by their fellow blacks the first inhabitants, who, having much increased the stock of goats, cows, and especially hogs, which the Portuguese had placed on all the islands when they first discovered them, those first inhabitants, understanding the Portuguese brought their fellow blacks from St. Philip's, purely out of compassion to prevent their being starved, freely offered to load the ship with hogs, as a reward for their charity; which so thinned their hogs, that by the time the ship was loaden, they had but few left, and so they catched and killed, or tamed the remainder.

These blacks which came from St. Philip's, soon begot in them the notion of property; so that he that could kill, catch, or tame most, had most; and soon reduced all the cattle on the island to *meum* and *tuum*, except the goats, which, to this day, remain wild; but are claimed as the property of the lord of the soil, as are all the wild goats on the islands.

After these blacks had been some time settled on this island, the St. Philip's merchants having a large boat, managed by a Portuguese sailor, whom they had hired, and used to send to St. Jago with cotten cloths, when the Portuguese ships missed coming to trade there; one of the priests of St. Philip's, out of

---

[1] Generations. The island had, in fact, been settled in 1680 by negroes from the neighbouring Isle of Fogo (St. Philip) and from Madeira. In 1566 it had only three or four inhabitants.

godly Romish zeal, to try what he could pick up among the poor shepherdless blacks at St. John's, got the proprietors of the boat to send her with him over thither, and he making known the pious occasion of his coming, and his power of pardoning their sins, and thereby sending them easily, and yet certainly, to heaven, let their actions be never so bad; and the impossibility of their going thither, let their actions be never so good, without a sacerdotal or priestly admittance by absolution; and a great part of these notions being also instilled into those first inhabitants, by their brother blacks, who lately came from St. Philip's, the pious padre had little more to do, than to baptize them as they were, without instructing them much further in the principles of religion, it being sufficient to believe that they were Christians by their baptism, and, that they were sure to go to heaven, and, at the Resurrection, to be changed white, etc., and so he mumbled over a Mass, which neither they that heard it, nor he that read it, understood; whereby he got what he went for; for those blacks which came from Fogo, or St. Philip's, having taught the others how to spin cotton, which naturally grew there, and to wear it (they before going stark naked, as most of the negroes on the coast of Guinea do), the reverend padre got cloths of those that had them, and single breadths from others, cotton thread, or yarn, from others, cotton from those that neither had spun nor wove, and from others indigo, which likeways then grew common, though it does not now; from others hogs, fowls, etc., the good pious padre refusing nothing that was brought him, which he thought worth receiving, and when he had got as much as he thought he could well manage to get back in the boat, he took his leave of them, and prepared for his return; the poor deluded souls waiting on him down to the Fuurno, where his boat lay; and he, in return of their kindness, freely gave them a parting Mass in a cave there, which, ever since, goes by the name of Fuurno de Padre.

Accordingly he took his leave of them, telling them, *That what they had given was to God, and that he was God's steward, or receiver;* and, indeed, not only there, but in all the rest of the islands, the people are persuaded, that whatever is given to the priest, is given to God, unless they particularly dedicate it to some saint, in which case, they think they lay an obligation on the saint to whom they make the present, to stand their friend; and for which saints, the priests are also the receivers, as well as of God: He promised, however, to return again, to give them a further absolution for what sins they should commit in his absence; and so he returned laden home, and visited them yearly, or as often as he could, or found it would answer; until after some years, as he was giving his benediction, and saying a Mass for them in the aforementioned cave, having not above thirty auditors (for it seems they began to suspect, for all their ignorance, that the principal motive of his pretended piety was avarice, and therefore did not now so universally attend him down to the boat, as at first), the cave fell in, where the pious padre remains with all his auditors, without being able to finish his Mass, until this day.

They were heard groaning for three days after; but the rocks and great stones which fell in, and stopped their coming forth, could not be moved to let them out; and it was happy for the rest of the inhabitants, that their zeal was not so vehement as at first; for had they been all there, the same fate would have befallen them, and the whole island must have been entirely depopulated.

The boat-men perceiving their pious master fixed, and no possibility of his coming forth, made the best of their way home, where they gave the doleful account of Singore Padre's, and his most zealous auditors' imprisonment; and so the black flock of the Island of St. John's, remained without an absolving pastor for several years, which gave them such an opportunity of mingling the pagan and Romish superstitions so radically (making good that old chymical axiom, *That like easily unites and incorporates with its like*), that to this day they remain unseparated.

Some years after, the King of Portugal sent a ship at his own charge, to carry the bishop, etc., round the islands, as well as all the coast of Guinea, for a general visitation, who, out of his most reverend piety, placed a fellow there to be priest; and when I was there, the then priest was the fourth, and, I don't doubt, was a pattern of his predecessors, or, it might be, exceeded them in learning; for he could make shift to read in his old missal book, which, I suppose, the reverend bishop gave him when ordained to that function, which he calls and believes to be the *Scriptura Sagrade* (*i.e.* Holy Scriptures), and told me so himself; and when I told him, that it was not, but that that appellation was alone given to the Bible, his answer was (for I had told him before, that my country was separated from the Romish Communion, on account of the tenets they held in contradiction of the undoubted Word of God), *That to us the Bible might be the best book that we had, because it was certain that when we apostatised from the Holy Catholic Church, that that Holy Book of the Mass, which far exceeds the Bible, was not given us by the Holy Pope, it not being lawful for any to look into it, but priests lawfully ordained by a Roman bishop.*

I urged, *His not knowing for the most part what was contained in it, it being in Latin, a language which he did not understand, any more than I, that never read it.*

He told me, *He did not think that was any imperfection in him, unless he was of a higher order; and that to be able to understand it, was so sublime a mystery, that it was not, that he knew of, taught to any black priest;* and added, *That he knew enough,* viz. *What he should read to baptize, and marry; as likewise for the principal holidays, and for Sundays; and whether he understood or not, God would never fail blessing the effects of those Sacraments:* He also said, *That he could say or read the office for consecrating the Body and Blood of Christ, and transubstantiating the water into that true Body and Blood, as often as he read the words of the Consecration, with an intent to make the Sacrament; though he did not, he confessed, understand the meaning of one word that he read;* He urged the same for the Absolution, and Redeeming out of Purgatory, by the Absolution Office, and the Masses for the dead, and a great deal of such stuff;

but notwithstanding all his high pretentions, and the ignorance of his flock, there are several of the thinking sort of these poor innocents, that reverence him only from the teeth outwards, as we use to say.

He baptizes, marries, and buries; but the natives have intermixed with those rites, some of their old heathenish superstitions, such as washing before baptism, decking the bride with flowers, and a garland, on the marriage-day giving her bodily worship, stripping her of all at night, and putting earth on her head, in token of subjection, sprinkling the graves of the dead with water, and sometimes with the juice of water-melons, and abundance of other fooleries.

There hath been formerly a great deal of ambergris found about this island, but very little now; there was a Portuguese about thirty years past, that was banished from Portugal, for some crime by him committed, for a term of years, who got him a little sloop, or shallop, and traded with her among these islands, and lighted on a piece of ambergris of almost an incredible bigness, with which he purchased his freedom to return to Portugal again, before the term for his exile was completed; and, moreover, if my relator spoke truth, purchased himself a plentiful estate, and never after went to sea; the man's name was John Carneira, and the rock near to which he found it, which was between the two little islands, is at present called by his name by the natives, as well as by the Portuguese.

This island abounds with fish, especially about the little islands; where also, some tortoise resort at the season of laying their eggs; but they are not much regarded for food, either here, or at St. Philip's, or at St. Jago, and yet at all the other islands, they are accounted their most delicious food; and, indeed, so they are.

I now began to be pretty strong and hearty, and used to go out with the natives a hunting and fishing; the last I used often to be at, as being more diverting and less fatiguing.

I had nails enow saved out of the pieces of the wreck, to have supplied the island perhaps an age, or more, with fishing-hooks; for all that the natives had saved and knocked out with stones, they brought to me, after I was come up to Singore Antonio Gumms; for the Priest had told them, That if they kept any thing that they had saved, of what kind soever, from me, God would certainly take vengeance of them, and they would never thrive, nor prosper in any thing that they undertook; so that I had every bit of iron which they had hazardously and painfully saved, and brought up; as also every piece of board, or any thing else; which was all of service to me, as in the sequel of this story you shall hear.

Our manner of fishing was thus: We used to go from town before day, so as to get down to the sea-side before the sun was very high, to avoid his scorching heat in our journey down the rocks, and took with us a calabash or two of water, according as our company was, more or less, also some pompion, bananas, etc., for food. Our fishing utensils were long canes for fishing rods, and cotten lines, which they made and twisted so well, that I think they exceeded any of our hemp or flax lines made in England, both for strength and durableness. We made use of stones, for want of lead, to sink our lines, and did well enough, because in most places where we fished on the rocks, there was little or no tide run.

Our hooks, as I hinted before, were made by the old bungling smith, of old nails; though I generally made my own hooks, and also for the family, whereof I now was a member; for I could borrow a hammer and a file of the old farrier, as they called him, whenever I would, and I think my hooks far exceeded his; but a bended sharp-pointed nail, without any other preparation, would have been sufficient; for the fish in those parts were so voracious, that if you were not very watchful, and quick, they would swallow the hook down into their belly, which they seldom let them do, endeavouring always to hook them in the mouth, to prevent their cutting their lines with their teeth, as almost all the fish thereabouts have large and sharp teeth, rather like ravenous land animals, than our fish on the coast of England; and when at any time they hale a fish up that hath swallowed the hook, if it should chance to cut the line and escape, they would blame the fisherman, and impute it to his want of skill, or carelessness, or both.

Our bait was generally crabs, which they were very dexterous at catching; and when we could not catch crabs, we used to take limpits, or any other shell-fish we could get upon the rocks; and when we had caught a fish, we generally made bait of that; though crabs was the best and surest bait we could use.

They always brought wood down with them for firing, which they gathered as they went along, to boil our fish, and roast our pompion, etc., with, and used to be out sometimes three, four, five, or six days, according as we caught fish, or our inclinations led us.

They gathered salt on the rocks, which was made by the heat of the sun, of the sea-water, lying in the holes of the rocks, being either cast up in the hollows of the rocks by the spray of the sea beating up against them when it blew; or when it was a clear sun-shine day, at high water the sea would fill some hollows of the rocks; and after the sea was fallen, before it came up again, it would all, if the hole was shallow, be a dry salt; but if deep, then the salt would lie at the bottom; or, if too deep, those hollows that the sea flowed up to, could not, in so short time, kern any salt; but those hollows or holes which were above the flowing of the sea, and filled with water, I have known it all converted to salt, or rather all the water exhaled by the sun, and only the salt left in the hole; and have observed it two foot thick of salt, and to the quantity of about four bushels, or more, in a hole which did not exceed five or six yards square.

I am apt to think that there is a certain quality in some rocks that helps, and in others, that hinders the salt's kerning; for in some I have seen water that has stood so long, that it has been all vapoured away, leaving behind only a sediment as muddy water does, but very salt, and sometimes a thin crust lying on the sediment, sometimes resembling the crust, or cream that lies on the top of the water when you wash or purify tartar, and commonly called cream of tartar, but extreme salt and strong, even to a corosiveness; whereas other rocks shall yield one-third or one-fourth part of salt, in proportion to the quantity of water contained in those hollows.

The natives used to get their salt in a readiness first, as much as they thought sufficient for that day's use, and then all hands went to fishing; and in the evening they used to gut, split, and salt what they caught, and let them lie in the salt in heaps all night; and in the morning, after the sun was up, they spread them in the sun to dry, turning them as occasion required; and when they were hungry, they dressed some fish and pompion, which we never wanted whenever I happened to be with them; but if not, they very seldom carried any, contenting themselves with a little boiled or broiled fish while abroad, and that seldom oftner than once, towards night, after they had done fishing.

At those fishing-places which were easy of access, and often frequented by them, they used to leave an earthen pot, which was free for any to use who came a fishing, and that for the sake of the fish-broth, which they esteem much beyond any broth made of flesh.

At night they repose themselves in the hollow of the rocks; being always careful not to lie exposed to the falling of the night-dew; and they would gather dry grass, etc., and bring it down to lie on.

When we had caught fish enough, or was tired of our sport, and had a mind to go to town, they would send one up for an ass, to come as far as it could, and the rest would bring the fish up at their backs to the place where the ass was, which they loaded with it up to town; and they would always oblige me to ride down as far as the beast could go, which was also brought for me to ride on up again, with the ass that was to carry the fish up.

When we were come up with our fish, they used to send to their friends and relations such a quantity as they thought fit, who used to do the same to them again: And this was our manner of fishing at the Island of St. John's.

One thing I forgot to observe, that we always, each of us,

was provided with two lines, one, which was the smaller, we had fixed to our fishing-rod with a little hook, for catching the lesser fish, and had our large lines and hooks ready by us, when we saw a large fish, which we feared would be too heavy for our small hooks and fishing-canes; and sometimes, when fish did not bite, they would swim away to a more convenient place, when they could not otherwise get along for the smoothness and steepness of the rocks, and swim back again with a much larger quantity of fish, than they could carry on the dry land, or be able to hale out of the water without help.

As to their hunting, the privilege of killing the wild goats is intirely the Governor's, without whose leave, no one dare hunt; and this was a law made by the Portuguese when they first peopled these islands, and put a breed of cattle on them, to prevent the breed from being utterly destroyed.

This is the principal privilege or advantage the Governor hath; who also commands the peace, and decides the little differences which sometimes happens among them, and can, upon their not submitting to his decision, confine them till they do, in an open place, walled round like the pounds which are in some parts of England for imprisoning cattle, when they are caught trespassing on their neighbours' ground; but instead of a gate, they generally lay only a stick across, and those innocent criminals will stay there, without attempting to go out, as if they had been in the securest prison in the world; except when some of the highest spirited amongst them, happening to be overcome with passion, and inspired with revenge against those that have offended them, fly out in their rage; who, however, as soon as caught again, are, by the Governor's order, tied hand and foot, and a sentinel is set to watch them, and prevent their escaping again, till they agree with their antagonist, ask the Governor's pardon for going out of prison without being cleared, and remain in prison such a space of time, as the Governor thinks his crime hath deserved; which is the utmost punishment the Governor hath power to inflict: Nay, if one kills another, which hardly happens in an age, all the Governor can do, is to confine him till he pacifies the relations of the deceased by the mediation of his friends, who are bound for the criminal's appearance, when a judge comes authorised from Portugal to do justice: Which never has been yet, as far as I could learn from the natives.

Sometimes when it is a small crime, especially if it be a senior person, the Governor confines him only in his own, or some other house; and this is reckoned a great favour; for to be imprisoned, is accounted such a great scandal among them, that Tyburn itself is hardly so much dreaded by our criminals in England, as those open prisons are by them. But to proceed: When the Governor has a mind to make a general hunt, all the islanders are summoned, and all the hunting-dogs are called. These are between a beagle and a greyhound, not unlike the mongrel greyhounds we have in England, but shorter legged, and clumsier, with large ears hanging down.

At night, or when the Governor thinks fit to leave off hunting, they meet all together, and the Governor parts the venison among them as he pleases, sending what he judges proper to his own house, with all the skins; and after he comes home, he sends a piece to one, and a piece to another, of those that are old, or that were not out a hunting; and the skins he distributes among them as he thinks convenient, or as their necessity requires, reserving the remainder of the skins for the lord of the soil.

They have a report, that the King of Portugal has lately given their island to one of the ladies of his court: But how they came by this information I never could tell; however, most of the he-goat skins were laid by for her, in a house built for that purpose, according to their report, ever since the Portuguese first brought them hither, and which is called by them Casa de Fazendo (*i.e.* a warehouse). And here they have lain so long, that many of them, as I observed, were almost reduced to dust.

Sometimes the Governor hunts for his private diversion, and then he sends only to such a number, as he thinks fit, to accompany him; and sometimes he only sends, and does not go a hunting himself; and then, all the venison is brought, together with the skins, to his house, where he distributes it as he thinks fit; and there is none allowed to keep hunting-dogs but whom he licenses, and those are called *caussadors*, or huntsmen.

CHAPTER TEN

*

I MADE enquiry from time to time when any ship had touched on the island, and was informed, that only two ships had touched there in seven years' time, the one an Englishman, who bought some hogs of them, and the other a Portuguese, who anchored in a bay called Ferrier, and landed his cask to fill water, but was blown off, and left his water-cask behind him; as also one black, a native of St. Nicholas, who swam from them, and gave an account, that they had some more of his countrymen on board, whom they were carrying to Brazil for slaves.

Mr. Franklin and the rest informed me, that French ships often used to touch at St. Philip's, and now and then a ship came to trade there for mules, and that the French frequently used to come over in their boats to buy fowls and hogs; but of late years they had discontinued that practice, which made them conclude, either that no ships had been there trading lately, or that they supplied themselves better at St. Philip's, than they could at St. John's.

Hereupon, I would fain have had the Governor to let me mend up his old boat to go over to St. Philip's, and offered to be the carpenter myself, and also to find nails, which, as I mentioned before, I had a great quantity of, and likewise to make her sails of my jib, etc., but he would not consent to it, *For fear*, he said, *that I should come to any mischance, by reason the boat was small, and the wood very much decayed and rotten: Besides, he had heard*, he said, *that the channel between St. John's and St. Philip's, was very turbulent, with great seas, strong currents, and violent gales of wind.* All which was very true; yet I would freely have run the hazard, if the Governor would have let me mend his boat; but he still denied me for the reasons above mentioned; but however told me, *If I understood how to build a vessel, I might build one new, large, and strong, there being wood enough on the island, and he doubted not but all the inhabitants likewise would assist me, as much as they were capable: And*, continued he, *Singore Carolos hath often told us,*

231

that he could build any vessel, if he had conveniences: Now you have nails enough to build a large vessel, I believe, and we have three or four hatchets among us, and you have an adz which was saved, and you need not do any of the laborious work, but leave that for us, and you, and Singore Carolos only do that part of the work which our ingenuity won't reach to. We have wood enough, and several of us can handle a hatchet, so as to cut down fig-trees, split them, and hew boards out of them, and I will engage to provide you with boards enough, or what other sort of timber you would have; and my brother, who put up the bed for me, who, I told you, had been at St. Jago, is a good carpenter, though I won't pretend to say, like your white carpenters; but yet he can work very well, and makes almost all our doors on the island, and has besides made stools for the Padre, which also several others on the island can do; and the chair which you have seen at the Padre's house, shows that he is a workman.

I told him, I was afraid I should not have nails enough; having only six or seven hundred broken and whole, besides a great many large spikes, some bolts, and other iron-work, which they had saved. He said, *He thought I was the best judge in that case; and that if I wanted, I could instruct the old farrier, who was also ingenious of himself, so as to make me some nails out of the old iron. But,* said he, *you shall promise me to make one large enough to carry you over the channel of St. Philip's safely without any danger, and that cannot be less than twice the bigness, at least, of my boat; therefore,* continued he, *you shall not make her less than twice as long, and twice as broad, and twice, or more, as deep as mine was, that the great seas, in passing over the channel, may not be able to fill her.*

Why, said I, *to make a boat twice the length, breadth, and depth of yours, would be to make one a great many times bigger than your boat;* but all the geometry that I was master of, could not convince him of that.

So at last we concluded to build; and when we had taken a general survey of the whole island, to find what tools were on it fit for our occasion, we mustered up three small hatchets, a thing like a butcher's cleaver, two gimblets, one about the size fit for a twenty-penny nail, the other a very large spike gimblet, a small pin-mall, one claw hammer, one like a cobbler's hammer, and a double-headed hammer about three pound weight, besides what the smith had.

So after we had fully concluded upon the matter, all the inhabitants were summoned to meet before the Governor's house, which accordingly they did, the Governor making a speech to them, showing them the cause for which they met, and how charitable and good a work it was to assist me, and withal, how it would redound to their credit, etc.

They answered, *That he could not be more ready to ask, than they to grant; and that they were wholly at my call, when and where I pleased, and that I might always command them as my servants and slaves. They were very sorry*, they said, *to think of my leaving them; but when they considered how mean I lived here, both for food and raiment, as well as perhaps the want of other things which they might be ignorant of, they could not be so unjust as to desire me to continue in that misery, which they were sensible I underwent while there with them: That they wished their island yielded those necessaries, as well as pleasures and delights, which my country did, and then perhaps they would keep me with them per force, and think they did not wrong me; but, as it was, they could not in reason persuade me, much less force me to stay with them.*

I told them, *I thanked them kindly, and hoped I should come back one time or other, when I had it in my power to make them some retaliation.*

They said, *They desired none, my good opinion of them was all they wished for, and for the continuance of that they would do any thing that was in their power.* They said, *That since they had but three hatchets, all them that could use them, would take their turns day by day, that the hatchets might never be idle, and those that could not exercise the hatchets, must carry down the boards and timber, after hewed and a little dried, to the place where I had a design to build the boat at.*

All this was accordingly put in execution, neither would they let me work at the cutting of the trees down, or splitting, or hewing them into boards; but bid me reserve myself against I came to build the boat, to do that part which they could not.

They had an ingenuity peculiar to themselves in splitting the trees after they felled them, which was thus: When they had cut down the tree to that length which would serve to work it for a board, which seldom exceeded seven or eight foot, though sometimes by chance, they run twelve or fourteen foot in length, they would lay the piece along, and chock it fast with stones, that it might not roll, and then they would chop a channel, or gutter, as narrow as they could, and deep; after which, they would turn the piece of timber, and right opposite to the first, they would dig in another gutter with their hatchets, as deep as they could, the whole length of the piece, and then they would get wedge-like stones, that were so thick, as to fill up the breadth of the gutter, before it touched the bottom; then taking great stones, as big as they could lift, and standing close to the piece of timber, they would throw them down with all their might, on their stone wedges, which they so often repeated, till the piece split, which would not be long, provided they made their gutters deep enough; and they would be sure always to split as straight as they made their gutters. After they had split their piece of timber, they would hew away the flat sides as even as they could, which, for the most part, was pretty tolerable; and then they would hew away the other side, until it was of the size which I ordered them, which was two inches; for they could not be expected to hew them so straight, or even, as a saw would cut them; nor could I ever get them to hew by a line; for though, they said, that might be a guide to whites, yet, they never being used to it, it rather hindered them, than any ways helped them to cut straight.

After we had got a good quantity of boards made, there fell out a lucky hit to help our design, which was a large piece of wreck, drove down close along the island, on the north-west side, and by the current setting round, brought it under the lee of the island, and, by good luck, the sea breeze setting in, brought it to the shore near a place called Scio, where some people were fishing, who made shift to secure it, while they sent others to get more help, and call me, they thinking it had been a whole vessel, and that I could contrive some way to free her, and fit her up to go to my own country in.

I saw it was only a piece of a ship's quarter, but had no convenient place to hale it ashore to secure it there, because of the rocks; wherefore they proposed to float it down to Scio, unless they met with any convenient beach to hale it ashore upon before; so they made fast lines to it to tow it by, and launching it off clear of the wash of the sea, away they swam with it, to the number of between thirty and forty, and, with great difficulty, got it into a little cove, between Scio and Piscarree Picuana, where they haled it to the shore; from whence they sent to inform me of it.

I made all the haste to them that I could, and finding we had not help enough, I sent up to the Governor and Priest for more, which they procured, and came down themselves; and at the same time, I sent for some ropes that had been left where I had been shipwrecked, with which we haled it up as high as we could, and went to work to break it up as well as we could with stones, instead of malls; and saved all the nails, ironwork, and all the plank and timber which we could; and after two days working upon it, we got it broke up so as to be able to hale all of it that we thought would be to our purpose, clear of the sea, which afforded us a good quantity of boards, timber, nails, spikes, bolts, with all the mizen chain plates, bolts, with the mizen mast, and standing rigging, the which I concluded should be my keel, and resolved upon this cove to be my building-place; so after we had secured all that we could, or thought worth securing, we went up to town, and I would have gone about building forthwith; but the Governor, and some others, told me, That I had better let them make me boards enough before I took the people off from making them; for that they were now fixed at it in several gangs, and if I took them off, it might be some difficulty to get them to it again and that besides, they could not be making boards, if I began to build, because there were not hatchets enough for us to work at both; besides, the wood would be drier and lighter to work, as well as to carry down from the mountains where they cut them, to the place where I designed to build; and therefore they rightly advised, it would be better to let them cut boards and timber enough, and rather more than less, before I began to build.

This advice was not to be neglected, and in the mean time, I got all the ropes, boards, and my boom, which yet remained at the place where I was wrecked, and every thing else that I thought might be of use, to my building-place, which was a small league from the cove where I designed to begin the work.

I was not without many doubts and fears of my ability to build this boat, having never in my life done any thing of that kind, nor any thing else of carpenters' work, and thought to myself, if I should not be able to go through with it, and especially now they had taken so much pains about it, and were all confident of my ability (though I all along told them, that I never had done any thing of that kind, and was no carpenter), yet I was afraid it might occasion them to lessen their esteem of me, and, perhaps, slight me; but then I thought to myself on the other hand, that no man was born a carpenter; that it was necessity which put mankind on many inventions at first; and that I had a better foundation to go upon, than any of those could have, that first set about it, having seen a vessel begun, and built from the keel: All these considerations, I say, encouraged me to proceed; and since I had gone thus far, I thought myself obliged to use my utmost skill to complete it.

After all was done ready for going to work, I acquainted the Governor, etc., with my resolution to begin, who wished me success; and he, and my landlord, assured me, that I should be constantly supplied with provisions, etc., which was faithfully performed; and so I went down with six or eight of the best carpenters the island afforded, accompanied with others, who employed their time in bringing, carrying, and assisting in what they could, and going daily, some of them, to the adjacent rocks to fish for us that were at work; for they had all, both carpenters and others, brought down their fishing-gear with them; and every day we had some that came from town with pompion, etc., who would stay, and let the others go up that had a mind; so that we had always hands enough down (besides the Singores carpentaras) to do all the drudging work, as carrying, lifting, and holding, as well as to catch us as much fish as we could eat.

The Governor came down the day after me, and brought a line with him, which was about twenty foot long, it being the length of his boat, and told me, *That he understood by Singore Carolos, that I designed to make my boat but little (if any thing) bigger than his; which, if I did not, he would forbid all the people to assist me any farther; for that he, and Singore Carolos too, were of opinion, That I should only cast myself away through my earnestness to get off the island.*

I told him, *I thanked him for his care, but would have him believe, I knew what was fit to venture in, as well as Singore Carolos: And if Singore Carolos is such an understanding man,* said I, with a little warmth, *why does not he come down, that I might have his assistance, to advise and contrive how it should be?*

He said, *Singore Carolos was not well, and was very sorry that he was not able to come; but was in a great fear that I would make the boat so small, the sooner to get finished, and get off the island, that I should drown myself.*

I told him, *I would engage to make her big enough to go almost any where in her.*

He said, *Then I must make her many times bigger than his boat; but let me make her as big as I would, he would engage me boards, timber, and help enough.*

I thanked him, and asked him, *How big he would have me make her?*

He said, *At least twice as big as his own boat.*

I told him, I did design to do that; and he desired me to show him how long I designed to make the keel. I measured off thirty foot, though not designing her nigh that length, only to satisfy him; and he measured with his line, and finding it ten foot more than the length of his boat, he said, *That would carry but half as much more than that.*

I told him, *The way that I should build her, she would, at that length, carry four times as much as his boat;* but he would not believe me: Whereupon, I said, *That if, after the boat was built, she did not carry above twice as much as his, I would give her to him, and tarry upon the island till a ship came.*

Well, then, says he, *I will take you at your word; if she does not carry as much more as my boat, without the keel being any longer than the length of this line and half, you are to stay with us till a ship comes.*

Well, said I, *it's a bargain.*

So he borrowed a line from one that was by, and measured the length, and half length of it, and cut it off, and gave it to his brother, who was one of my carpenters, and bid him be sure *not to let me make it a bit shorter; for he would not have me to take so much pains, and the vessel not to be fit to venture in at last.*

He had brought a goat down with him, with pompion, and some ears of Indian corn, milk, and cuscuse, which he gave us, and in the evening went away.

I measured the keel out twenty-five foot, which, they insisted, was not the length I had proposed to the Governor: I told them, *They should see, when it was finished, that I was a better judge of that, than any one on the island, assuring them, That a vessel of that length, would carry three or four times as much as the Governor's boat; and that if we made it any bigger, for want of nails, and other necessaries to fasten and secure her, the very weight and bulk of her, would make her liable to be staved to pieces, the first sea that she encountered with.*

They answered, *They believed what I said to be true, and was sure I knew better than the Governor, or anybody else on the island, even than Singore Carolos; and therefore, as it was I that was to venture in her, I ought to do her my own way; and that way which I thought was securest.*

I desired them *not to take any notice to the Governor, but that she was as big as he would have her, till she was finished:* Which, they said, *they would not.*

I went on with my work, but was at a sad loss for a saw,

which some of them hearing me talk of, said, There was an old saw on the island, but they thought it would not cut; I desired them to get it for me, and it might be that I could sharpen it; they said, they would; so I bid them to borrow also, one of the smith's files, and bring it down with the saw; which they accordingly did the next day.

The saw was very old, but it was not altogether so much eaten with rust, as one might have expected it to be, having been kept dry: and in those hot countries, if iron be kept from the dew and dampness of the sea, it will last a long time before it decays with rust.

I sharpened it with the file, and set it as well as I could, so that I made it cut tolerably well, which they all much admired at, saying, *That none of the people on the island, could find the way to make the saw sharp; and that they believed, it exceeded the ingenuity of Singore Carolos, though he was very ingenious, and, till I came among them, they thought no-body could go beyond him; but they saw,* as they said, *I could far outstrip him, as he outstripped them.*

I told them, *That Singore Carolos was an ingenious man, and, as I might do some things better than he, so I did not doubt, but he could do a great many things better than I.*

No, they said, *they would not believe but I could do every thing better than Singore Carolos, etc.*

I believe I had nigh half finished, before Mr. Franklin came down to me, and he had been ailing all the time. He told me, *That if he had been well, to have been with me at the beginning to have assisted me, it would, he believed, have been something more forward; but that the people were so unwilling that I should go from them, that they seemed some of them to say, That he was partly the adviser and contriver of my making this boat; And some of them,* says he, *owe me an ill will about it; but the less for my not being with you; for that other-some believe it to be wholly your own contrivance.*

I told him, *When I went up to town, I would clear him of all that, and thought, if it was so, that he had better go up to town again, to avoid their causeless suspicion.*

He said, *Now he was come down, he would stay and assist me two or three days.*

I told him, *I should be very glad of his company, provided it would not be prejudicial to him.*

He said, *For a day or two, it could not, and his time among them would not be long; for he had determined,* he said, *to go with me in the boat.*

And, indeed, he had given me this assurance before, which was one great reason of my building her; for to have a boat without hands, would have been the same, in effect, as to have no boat at all.

The person also, who had swum away from the Portuguese ship when it put into this island from St. Nicholas, had promised to go with me; and likewise those that came with me from St. Nicholas; as also Domingo; and so did several others, whom I had no great dependance on, though I had on those I have now mentioned.

Mr. Franklin lost much of his credit by this trip, which I was sorry for, but could not help it; for he, it seems, had oftentimes said, That he could build, etc. And as for the theoric part, he might, I believe, understand it very well, being a man of a good genius, as well as a man of letters, having had, I believe, good and gentleman-like education; but for the want of the practical part, he was more awkward than my black carpenters by far, which they presently perceived, and were not a little proud of it, though I did my endeavour to blind his defect, as much as I could, by telling them, *That he was feeble, and that his hand shook, through weakness occasioned by his illness,* which passed off well enough.

By this time, my black carpenters were grown so dextrous, that by giving them a mould with them, they would go up and hew me out boards to answer the winding and rounding at the bow, or abaft, and likewise timber, and would cut or hew any thing to fit, I thought, better than I could, though they did not think so themselves; but the witchcraft was, the lines and sweeps; for I had made me a pair of wooden compasses, which I sometimes used; and I never saw any thing so wondered at, as at my setting up the stem and stern-post, because I used a plummet to set them upright.

I made use of the wreck boards which we had saved, along the body of the boat, where it did not require much bending or winding; for they were so dry, stubborn, and stiff, that they would sooner break than bend much.

Our nails began now to diminish apace, so that having nailed the vessel indifferently secure at the bottom, I was forced to fasten only the butt-ends, and here and there, where necessity required, was obliged only to pin, or trunnel them with our large spike gimblet, which, as cases then stood, was the best shift we could make.

The length at the keel was near twenty-five foot; the length between stem and stern-post, thirty foot; breadth at the main beam ten foot; depth about four foot ten inches; I laid a half deck abaft, a little above eight foot in length; a fore-castle from the stem-aft, something above seven foot; I laid in four beams that I double kneed, fastening the knees with spikes; the main beam had three knees at each end, whereof one of them was a standing knee; I bolted them with some of the smallest bolts pointed, and boring the length of our spike gimblet, we forced the rest by driving the bolt red hot.

After we had skinned her, there were still boards enough to deck her; but for want of nails (which, at the latter end of our work, grew so scarce, that we were forced to make use of all the broken points of nails) I frequently took a point of a nail, which was but little more in length, than the thickness of the plank, and after I had drove it up, I drove a broken stump of a nail upon that, till I had drove it half way in the plank, to take the better hold of the timber.

What now concerned me most, was how to make her tight: I had some old spare ropes, of which I made oakum; but I found cotton and moss did better: My method to try how the caulking held, was in the evening, after we had left off work, to heave water hard against the seams within side, and where I perceived the water to go through, I caulked it over again.

I finished my mast, and fixed the rigging; and the pieces of the jib of my former sloop made me a main-sail, but too narrow by a breadth and a half; but there was no help.

My fore-sail and jib, were patched out of the pieces of the main-sail, and of cotton cloth, which was given me by the natives, some contributing one piece, some another; some bigger, some smaller.

My boom I made of my old gaff, by scarfing a hand-spike to it.

My rudder irons, I made thus; I got three eye-bolts, and with heating, I sharpened their points, and drove them into the stern post, up to the eyes, which served in the room of braces, or gudgeons, call them which you please.

My pintles were made of broken bolts that had lost their heads, which I bended thus ⎯⎯⎯⎯⎯ , and having pointed one end, I drove it into the rudder, first making a way for it with my spike gimblet, for fear of splitting my rudder.

Having got every thing in order, and fixed, I was resolved to make a trial of her, though I much feared my caulking would come out at sea, having nothing to bind or secure it with; and accordingly sent word up to town that I was all ready, and desired they would come down, and lend their assistance to launch the vessel, which the more help we had, would receive the less damage.

Accordingly they all came down, with the Priest and Governor, and some women.

Two or three days before, four of the blacks, with Nicholau Verd, went and made fast a rope to my anchor, which lay in the Salt Point Bay, and not only that, but haled the palm out from under some rocks that it was hooked in, and swam it, I believe, a stone's cast, or better, and let it go again when they saw it clear of rocks: I was forced to take their words for their unhooking it from the rock, but being on the tops of the rocks overhead when they did it, I was an eye-witness of their bringing it up to the surface of the water, and floating it away so far; which I was very much surprised at, believing it impossible for four times the number to have sustained the weight of the anchor, which, besides the stock, was two hundred three quarters, and the stock then being so much water-soaken, could not weigh much less than one hundred weight.

The people, as I said, being all come down, we launched her very well; but she made a prodigious quantity of water, as much as two hands could keep free by constantly baling. I stopped several places where it weeped in; but could see nothing of a constant leak, except under three of the floor timber heads, which I could not come at to stop; neither did it seem to me that half the water that we baled out, could come in at all those places where we discovered it to leak; however, I chinched it as well as I could; and then I consulted with Mr. Franklin which was the best way to come round to Fuurno, that being the best place on the island to take in provisions, and to hale her ashore at, there running, in fine weather, but little surf, or suff as seamen call it, in that place; and I proposing to take up the anchor in the Salt Point Bay in my passage to Fuurno, which I could not do without the vessel: But withal, it was something hazardous to attempt that way, for fear the vessel would not work, which one might reasonably doubt, considering the builders and tools, as also the smallness of the sails, which though so well cut as to stand tolerably well, yet were little more than half enough for the vessel; and if we should, by that way of proceeding, put off of the island, it would be in a manner, impossible to fetch the Island of St. Philip's, and then we should be exposed to the wide ocean, and have a long run before we could fetch any land, in a leaky and open boat, and with very little provisions.

I had indeed made me a wooden hillick, which I fastened to a stone, as the Newfoundland fishing-shallops use, by means of my shrouds, which I had saved, and now spliced together, to the quantity of about twenty-five fathoms; but I did not think this sufficient to supply the place of an anchor, which made me very desirous to recover that in Salt Point Bay.

Mr. Franklin advised me *not to run such a hazard on the account of getting the anchor;* and said, *He believed I might get one more suitable for my vessel, and also with a new hawser to it,* which the Portuguese had left behind him at Ferrier, when he was blown off from the island, and left his water cask behind him.

I told him, *That would do better, if we could find the anchor, though I supposed the hawser would not be much worth, after it had lain so long in the water.*

He said, *That he was on board the Portuguese ship when the anchor was carried out, and that it was but a small hatch anchor, and the hawser was new, and he was sure it could be found; and that several of the blacks, as well as he, knew whereabouts in the bay it lay: That it had a buoy to it; but the buoy rope was so short, that it did not reach the surface of the water at low water, but might be seen under water in fine weather.*

Hereupon we asked some of the blacks, who told me, *They had seen the buoy since I had been on the island, and did not know but it might be there yet; but whether it was or not, they were sure they could find the anchor.*

The negro who had swam off from the Portuguese, told me, *That he was on board of the Portuguese when he drove off: That his great anchor came home, and the hawser broke at the windlace, or somewhere within board;* for, he said, *he could not tell me so clearly, not knowing the proper terms; but he was sure the hawser broke within, and that there was a great deal of it left with the anchor: That when they moored with the small anchor, it was let go in shallow water, and the buoy bore; but when the gale of wind came on, that she brought home the great anchor, the little anchor came home, and dragged into deeper water; so that the buoy rope being short, it did not bear; and when he found that the ship was driving out to sea, he jumped over board, and swam ashore: And that several times since, he had seen the buoy, etc., and was sure he could find the anchor, unless it was buried in the sand, though there was no buoy to it.*

Hereupon I concluded to go round by the Ferrier to the Fuurno; for that way I run no hazard of being blown off, by reason I always had some of the island to leeward of me; but whether it was my laying open the danger of being blown off by going the other way, or how, I can't tell; but Mr. Franklin found means to excuse and put off his going with me in the boat till I got to Fuurno, and then too, as you shall hear in the sequel of the story.

I prepared every thing ready, and made four oars, by scarfing two pieces together in each oar, for I could not get pieces long enough without doing so; and being a calm day, we rowed along shore, and got to Ferrier Bay very safe, and with very little trouble, save the labour of rowing.

This good success, which crowned our first attempt, so encouraged the blacks, that I believe forty, or more, proffered their service to go with me.

When we had been there a day or two, finding her still continue leaky, I concluded to hale her up, and sent up to town for help; who accordingly came, and we got her up, and then we went to work to put in a good deal of water, to see where it came out, thereby to discover all the leaks.

I found one great leak, which was a knot hole, just at the scarff of the stem to the keel, which run as large as a beer barrel tap: I was glad when I saw it, and stopped that, and the other leaks; but all my seams wanted caulking again; for the oakum and cotton hanging out of the seams, made a comical sight at a distance; and what to do I could not tell: However, I made it all in as well as I could; and intimating to some of the blacks, that if I had tallow to lay on the seams, it would not only keep the oakum from washing out, but would also make the vessel a great deal more tight, they said, *They were sure, if I asked the Governor, he would order a general hunting match, and kill a good quantity of goats, and save the tallow for me.*

So I concluded to leave some hands with the boat, to keep her from shrinking by wetting her often in the day, and as the water leaked out, or dryed up with the heat of the sun, to replenish it by putting water from the sea into her; which they promised they would, and I showed them how high I would have it kept, viz. to cover the floor timber heads, and so I came up to town; and as soon as I had acquainted the Governor, he not only promised me what I desired, but seemed angry because I was not so free as to ask it at first. I told him, *That I had been so troublesome to him, and all the singores of the island, that I would not put them to this till I found the necessity of it, and impossibility to do without it.*

This was so far from being a sufficient reason to him, that he was the more angry, and said, *That he and all the singores on the island were at my service, as well as every thing that the island produced, and I had so many repeated proofs of it, since I had the misfortune of being placed there, that he thought it a great fault in me to conceal from them any thing that I stood in need of that the island afforded.*

Having concluded a general hunting, they killed about forty goats; but it being the time of year when they yielded but little tallow, out of them all we did not get, I believe, more than four or five pounds, and above half that was skin.

The Governor asked me, *If that would do?* I told him, *It must, since we could not get any more; and that the goats yielded so little, that it was not worth while to kill any more; but would make that do for the worst places in the bottom; and thanked him for what he had done.*

He told me, *I need not, he hoped, doubt of my being welcome;* but asked me, *If cows' tallow would not serve instead of goats'?* I told him, *Every bit as well.* He asked me, *Whether hogs' fat would do?* I told him, *No, it was so soft, that with the heat of the sun warming the water it would wash off.*

He said, *He was sorry for that, because the hogs now were fat, and he could get enough of their fat; but was afraid the cows would yield as little fat as the goats; but however,* he said, *he would look out one of the fattest of all his cows, and kill it, and according as that proved, or I wanted, he would kill more.*

I thanked him, and told him, *I would go down and use what I had, and in the mean time, desired him to send me the fat that the cow yielded;* which he said he would: so down I went, taking the negro who swam from the Portuguese, with another called Fum-fo-roon (who also had been on board the Portuguese, but not when he drove to sea, and had likewise seen the buoy under water, since I came to the island), and two or three more.

When I came down, I found that my blacks, who I gave in

charge to keep the boat wet, had been very diligent, and I believe had not let her dry in any part of her all the time I was absent, insomuch that she rather swelled than shrunk; but however, now I was resolved to let her dry, and shrink her seams, and so caulk her all over anew; for by caulking her so much as I had done, I had improved very much in this art, so that I could now caulk better, and, as the caulkers term it, make the oakum not only stand fairer, but also firmer; and some of my black carpenters were not much behind me, though I always tried their work after them.

My divers did not seek for the anchor the first day, as being weary of their journey down; but the next day, to the number of twelve, they swam off, and I believe might be five or six hours in the water before they found it; and were going to give it over, when Fum-fo-roon accidentally playing with some of the others, at their usual game of plunging, and striking with their feet, in imitation of the thresher and grampus-fish, and diving from him that struck at him, he happened to strike against the buoy, which was about a fathom under water, there being so much more water there than the length of the buoy rope.

He immediately rose up, and hollowed out as loud as he could, *The anchor! the anchor!* At which they all flocked about him; and those who were with me on the shore, hearing him, and seeing the rest flocking to him, they all jumped into the sea, leaving me alone, and went to help them.

The anchor was buried in the ground, which is thereabouts a tough clammy stiff owse, or clay, covered over with soft owse and sand mixed, and they were a long time getting it out of the ground, but at last did; and then they attempted to get the hawser, which lay buried in the owse, and after abundance of striving, and lowering the anchor down upon the ground again, to rest, at last they brought it to the shore, which, from the place they first took it up at, wanted, I really believe, very little of a mile.

I was very glad when I saw the anchor and hawser, which had been but very little wore, and was then fresh and good, being a four inch and half hawser, and about forty-five fathom long.

Both anchor and hawser were very fit for me, both for size and length; the anchor, I believe, weighing about one hundred and a half.

I gave them abundance of thanks: They said, *I was heartily welcome, and wished they could do more for me, etc.*

The same evening, the Governor sent me down about four or five pounds of tallow, and a piece of beef of about twenty pounds, and acquainted me withal, *That that was all the tallow the cow afforded, and was the fattest he had; but if I thought I should want any more, and would send him word, he would send me down a cow alive the next day, and the blacks should kill and salt it for me, to keep it in the boat as a store, etc.*

I accepted of his offer, which I found was the best way to ingratiate myself into his favour, for you can't affront them worse than to refuse their offers; and I made the less scruple, because I really wanted the tallow, and the beef was far from being an unnecessary present; and accordingly I had one of the fattest cows he had, sent down, which, in the cool of the evening, was killed; out of which I had five or six pounds of tallow, and the beef, which was good spending meat, we salted, first cutting out all the bones, except the ribs, the better to keep it from tainting, and dried it in the sun.

The boat being now dry and shrunk enough, I went to work, and caulked her as well as I could, and had as many blacks as I could trust to help; there being always enow of them down every day, to catch as much fish as we could tell what to do with, and every one that came down always brought something with him, as pompion, water-melon, bananas, ears of Indian corn, and cuscuss, which is Indian corn first pounded, and then boiled over the steam of fresh water, till it becomes a mass like boiled pudding, and then it's cut or broke in pieces, and dried in the sun, and if well dried will keep some months; something resembling a sort of bread (but much coarser) made in the Mediterranean Sea for seafaring persons, as our sea bisket is in England; so that laying by what we could not eat, I had a stock, by the time the boat was fit to turn into the water, that a man might, if the vessel would have performed its part, make shift with for as great a run as Barbadoes.

After I had caulked all, I got some ass's dung, and burned it to black ashes, and while it was yet a-fire, I put a quantity into a wooden thing like a mortar, which they have there for pounding their maiz, etc., and on that I put a sufficient quantity of tallow, and made one of the blacks pound it with a wooden pestle, till it was well incorporated, and then it would look as black and shining as jet, till it stiffened by cooling and standing; which again might be made soft as putty, by beating well in a mortar.

The service that this black ashes of ass's dung did, was this, that after I had laid it on the seams, and rubbed it in well with my fingers by drawing it along the seam, it would, in a little time, so harden, that the sun, for all his heat there, did not melt it, neither would it wash off again with the water; besides another service, as great as any, it did me, though I did not know any thing of it then, which was, that it kept the fish from eating it off the vessel; which I came to find out thus: after we had launched the boat, the tallow, some how or other, was rubbed out of a seam, a little below the water's edge, which, by heeling her, I brought out of the water, and put some clean tallow in the seam; but in less than half a day, they eat all that unmingled tallow as clean off, as if there never had been any laid there, while they never touched that which I had mixed with the ashes.

After I had as well caulked my frigate as I could, and paid all the seams' rents, etc. with tallow and ass's dung ashes, which reached no higher than the ballast mark, I got her launched; and after twenty-four hours' swelling in the water, she was tolerably tight, insomuch, that morning and evening was sufficient to bale her.

Having ballasted her, and fitted every thing ready, I waited now only for a moderate light gale to beat round; and at length I obtained my wish, and getting every thing on board, set sail with no less than sixteen blacks, and more would fain have accompanied me; but I was sadly puzzled with my raw mariners, none of them knowing how to bear out the foresail, to help her to stay, nor well how to row with a lee oar to cast her about; so that every time I had a mind to put about, I was forced to veer, which lost a great deal of ground; besides, we were much too light, not having ballast enough in; so that by the time the windward current was done, we had not got above a league to windward of Ferrier, and were half a league, or something less, to leeward of a little cove, where I had designed to have stopped for the next day's flood, if I could have reached it; but perceiving it was in vain to attempt it after the windward current was done, I was a little concerned at it; but yet was not a little proud that I had gained thus far, and could make sure of where I came from, with the pleasure of running back again before the wind.

They did not perceive our losing ground so soon as I did, and would not be persuaded of it, nor of the disadvantage of a lee tide; and were very certain, they said, that I could get to the cove well enough.

I was willing to humour them, who had so often run the risk of their lives to serve me, knowing that we had time enough to get into Ferrier, and moor before night, and could run no hazard of being driven to leeward of it, before it would be evident to them that we lost ground upon the lee tide; and therefore I made a couple of trips off and on, till they saw themselves that we lost considerable every trip, and then they freely consented to bear away; which we did, and anchored and moored where we did before in the Ferrier.

We were met there by several blacks, who had kept on the hills to see the boat work, who said she went bravely, like a fowl flying for swiftness.

I took in some more ballast the next day, and staid two or three days; and having a fit opportunity to my mind, both for tide and moderate weather, I beat up, and my mariners being something more handy than at first, so that they could help to stay her with a lee oar, we got, by the time that it was high water, under the leewardmost of the little islands, where I stopped till the next morning; and taking the advantage of a windward tide, I made two or three small trips under the islands, till we got abreast of the windward of most of them, which I did (the weather being moderate) more to exercise and divert my mariners, than any necessity; for the wind being far northerly, as it mostly is there, when it's fine weather, I could have weathered the Point of Ghuylungo, which is the weathermost point of St. John's, with one trip.

Having got the length of the weathermost of the little islands, I bore away afore the wind for the Fuurno, and arriving there, was welcomed, with abundance of joy, by the blacks, who had all the day, with inexpressible pleasure and satisfaction, been on the rocks, seeing us under sail from our weighing, till we got in.

I moored there; and being now secure, I went up to town to take my final leave, as I then thought, of the inhabitants, and to thank them for all their kindness to me; who all contributed to supply me with provisions, etc., for the voyage, with the same good-nature and cheerfulness, which I had experienced so fully on many occasions, and stored me with pompion, feshoon, maiz, and every thing else that the island afforded, in great plenty.

Having passed four or five days among them, I prepared for my voyage to St. Philip's, where I was in hopes to have found an opportunity of getting a passage off, sooner than from St. John's Island; but when I was ready, to my great surprise, Mr. Franklin would not go with me; and gave me such reasons for his refusal, as I was forced to acquiesce with.

I took my little boy on board with me, who, till then, had been up at town; neither had he been down with me all the time that I was building the boat, being too young to do me much service on that occasion.

CHAPTER ELEVEN

*

EVERY thing being ready, and on board, we sailed from the Fuurno, and arriving at St. Philip's, I put all ashore that were to go ashore there, and staying three days in that island, I stocked myself with provisions and water; after which I sailed, and in about ten days' time, I beat up to St. Jago, and, had I not been acquainted with the set of the current, I might have beat till now, before I had got up to it in that boat; I fetched a bay at St. Jago, called, Rivero des Bharkas, where I anchored; but finding that there were no ships there, and had not been for some months, except one Ostend India ship, called by the inhabitants, *Nau India des Imperio*, and finding there was a great scarcity of salt at St. Jago, I concluded to go to the Isle of May and take in salt; for I was near half full with pompion, maiz, etc., and the St. Jago men told me, *That they understood, that the Isle of May was almost famished for the want of sustenance, as they had had a scarcity, more or less, for above fifteen or sixteen years, depending wholly on the ships that load salt there, for subsistance.*

Next day tide, I weighed, but could not get about the island that tide; neither could I find any place to venture to anchor at, to stop the tide; and being loth to bear down to Porto Facienda, I resolved to keep the sea all night, which I did, my mariners being become very expert.

Next morning the lee tides had hurried me far to leeward, and it blowing fresh all night, made a chopping sea set about the north point of the island, insomuch, that I could not fetch Porto Facienda, from whence I came the day before, and it was as much as ever I could do to fetch Terra-fall Road, where I lay two or three days, and fine weather presenting, I weighed, and stopped again the lee tide at Porto Facienda, and the next morning tide, I beat the tide an end; but was sadly puzzled then, to find a place to stop the lee tide, without which, I found it was impossible for me to get round the island with my dull-swift frigate.

It was day-light, and moderate weather, and I saw a little bay under my lee-bow, which seemed to me to be a sandy or shingly beach, into which I resolved to run, as long as I saw any prospect of safety, the water being clear enough to discern any thing before it hurt me, and my boat drawing about four foot water, or a little more; and if the worst came to the worst, and it would not do, I could but run off again.

Right against the bay were a great many rocks, some larger, some smaller, the largest of them not above a good stone's cast in length, and most of them above water, extending about half a league off from the shore: I run in, and keeping a good look-out, luffing for one, and bearing away for another; till at last, I got safe in, though with taking a great deal of care; for without that, it would have been very dangerous.

In a little time came down an elderly man, with four slaves armed with lances, attending him; he very courteously asked me to come ashore: I told him, *I was a little busy as yet, and had not well secured my vessel; but would wait on him as soon as I could;* and asked him, *If he pleased to accept of a water melon to refresh him in the mean time?*

He thanked me, and bid me heave it into the water, and he would send one of his slaves to bring it ashore; which I did, and two of the lance-men swam off and carried it ashore to their master, who sat under the clift of a rock in the shade, for the sun shone very hot; for though it was a fresh gale in the offing, yet in the cove, we had not a breath of wind, save now and then a light air would come down through the valley.

The grave gentleman spread his cloak, and cut the water melon, laying it in as great order, as if it had been a person of quality's table set with the greatest varieties; he called two of his attendants to him, and, I suppose, gave them orders what they should do: I could not hear, but I saw the two slaves make their master a very reverent bow, and went away.

I did not care much for trusting myself ashore with him at first; for that part of St. Jago consists mostly of banditti, who frequently fly thither from justice, and sometimes make incursions among the more civilised parts of the island, where, if they are catched, they suffer; but if they escape thither, they are secure; for no officer of justice dare follow them there, they assuming a privilege to themselves to oppose justice, even in case of murder: But after he so kindly accepted my present, which, with those people, is mostly esteemed as a token, or tye of friendship, I ventured ashore.

By this time the two slaves which he had sent away, came back, and brought a large calabash of milk, and a fine young full-grown goat, and very fat, which he presented me with; I received it with thanks, and told him, *I was sorry I had nothing on board worth presenting him with, in return of his kindness.*

He told me, *I had done that already sufficiently; for he took so much satisfaction in the honour I did him, by giving him my good company, that he did not know what he could do to make me a suitable retaliation: Besides,* said he, *the water melon which you gave me, I do not take it for such a slight present as you imagine; for the seeds I design to plant; and though it may not yield better melons than what I already have, yet, being sprung from the seed of a melon which came from abroad, it will always pass for a rarity.*

I asked him, *If he would be pleased to accept of a pompion of the growth of St. John's?*

He thanked me, and told me, *He would, but would have but one, which would yield him seed enough.*

So I called on board, and bid them bring one of St. Philip's Island pompions, and another that was brought from St. John's, which they did, and I presented them to Singore Jhuiss,[1] who told me, that was his title, but his name was Singore Jorge Vharela.

So taking our leave one of another, away went Singore Jorge to his house, and I on board, where I slept without disturbance.

In the morning betimes came down two slaves with a goat, and two calabashes of milk for me; and told me, *That their master would go up on a hill, where he could see me under sail.*

I got about the Bighude, which is the north-east point of the Island of St. Jago, about noon; the wind was north-east, light gales; and about two or three in the evening I saw the

[1] *Juiz*—judge.

Isle of May, and Monte Pinosa bore south-east-by-east; but the lee tide set us away to the southward apace: We fetched in, as nigh as I could guess, about the Calyete; but it being night (or rather morning, for it was between one and two when I got so close in, as to be obliged to tack off) and but a difficult place to go in at, I dared not venture in in the night; so I plied all night; but, by the time day broke out, I was got about midway between the Calyete and the Porto Englese, which is the road used by our ships which go there to load salt; for which reason it is so called; though the inhabitants have another name among themselves, viz. Yingdoss, and only call it Porto Englese when they speak to Europeans.

Finding it would be very tedious to beat up again, because the flood tide runs nothing at all there; but the ebb, which is the lee tide, sets strong, I bore away for Yingdoss, and anchored there in four fathom, in the middle of the bay: but no ships being there, and the surff running so high on the shore, that we could do nothing at that place, I was forced to weigh, and beat up to Kalyete or Paaseco, which lies to windward of Calyete; and this cost me two days; and finding that also not convenient for landing my things, and that it was a long way from the salt pans; after I had been to pay my compliment to Captain Vicente Alba vel Alva, who was come down to see me, I returned on board, weighed, and run down to the Calyete, and there anchored, and disposed of my things, and had salt brought to me there by the natives, for which I paid with some of my cargo that I had brought from St. John's and St. Philip's.

I cannot tell justly who was the author, but a notion my mariners all had, that I took in this salt, to carry it, and them, to Barbadoes, where they must be slaves during their lives, gave me a great deal of perplexity at this place: Neither was it in my power to convince them of the contrary, and accordingly they all to a man left me, and went ashore.

And now I was in a scurvy condition; I had bartered away almost all my provisions for salt; there raged a severe famine at this island, insomuch, that some of the inhabitants were ready to be famished; and I could not expect, if it had been in their power, that they would treat me as I was used at St. John's, or St. Philip's; and yet I had not help enough to get my anchor up, or venture to run for St. Jago, which then was very plentiful and fertile, though before, for three years past, they had suffered a sore famine also.

At length two blacks came and offered their service to go with me; one was a native of St. Nicholas, and told me, *That he came from thence about ten months before in an English ship; but the captain not proving so kind to him as he expected, he left him at this island, where he had been about eight months, and was almost starved since he came here; and if I would take him,* he said, *he would never leave me.*

Upon which I took him, being as glad of him, as he was of my provisions.

The other was a native of St. Anthonio, who also engaged to go with me.

The St. Anthonio man told me, *That I should make a better hand if I went to St. Anthonio with my salt; and to go from thence to the Isle of Sal, and take a gang from St. Anthonio, to kill turtle there, and sell them at the Island of St. Nicholas, which still was very scarce of provisions.*

I asked him, *How long he had been from St. Anthonio?* He told me, *About eight months;* so I concluded to take his advice, if the wind favoured, to fetch these islands; if not, I could but go to St. Jago at last, which I should always have under my lee.

So we sailed from Calyete in the evening, and stretched to the northward all night, with light winds, and a head sea; so that when the day broke out, the northermost point of St. Jago bore about west-north-west, about the distance of five or six leagues.

The light winds still continuing, in which my boat would do nothing with her small sails, I was afraid of being sagged down so to leeward, that I could not fetch either St. Nicholas, or St. Anthonio, wherefore I was resolved to bear away to St. Jago, which I did, and run for the north-east point; and finding a large fair bay, about two leagues or something more to the southward of the Bickude, I run in there, and anchored.

I let go my anchor about the middle of the cove, and the wind not blowing right in, but slanting along down to the bottom of the great bay, the vessel tailed towards the westermost point of the rock that made the cove; and after I had given a sufficient scope of cable, and brought up so nigh, that our stern was about the boat's length from the rock, it was pretty smooth water, but the flaws sometimes blew in pretty strong, though not so as to fear our ground-tackle holding.

The St. Anthonio man told me, *He did not like the place, for it was the wildest part of that quarter where the banditti inhabited.*

I told him, *They could not hurt us, we having no business ashore, and that I was resolved in the night to go;* with which he seemed to be satisfied.

They got the pot on, and went to work to boil some pompion and sherree (which is the largest part of the maiz when it's pounded, and when boiled, something resembles boiled barley), designing to make pap, and I lay down to take a nap while they got it ready; and had but just got asleep, when I was awaked by stones hove into the vessel, whereof some of them fell on the quarter deck, under which I lay. I asked, *What was the matter?* My folks answered, *They did not know; but a parcel of blacks ashore hove down stones, and called us all the ill names they could think of.* I put my head up the scuttle abaft to see, and as soon as they espied me, slap came several stones at me: I dodged under the deck; and as soon as they ceased heaving stones, I looked up again, and in the St. Jago creole tongue asked them the reason of using us so roughly? But they fell more furiously than at first to heaving stones, and some so large, that I was afraid they would sink the boat, calling me all the rogues, thieves, and picaroons, etc. that their malice was capable of expressing; and asking me, *Whether I had a mind to carry them away? And if I had there were slaves enough present for me; and bid me come ashore like a man-thieving devil, and they were ready for me, etc.*

I had no other remedy, but to shield myself under the deck again, till the gust of their fury was over, and they ceased to heave stones; my companions advising me, in their fright, to cut the cable, or get up the anchor, and hurry away out of that dangerous place, not considering that we could not stand upon deck to weigh the anchor, or to do any thing towards endeavour-ing to get the vessel away, either by sails or oars; besides, the wind blew right in on the point of the rock, and we had so little room, that the vessel, if we could or would expose ourselves, would be ashore before she could gather any way; and the rocks over us were moreover so high, that the vessel was, as it were, under them, so that those barbarians could almost tumble any stone on board, that they were capable of lifting.

As soon as I dared, I looked up again; I begged of them to cease heaving stones, and let me but speak to them; but they seemed to be the more exasperated at me, and one hove a stone so unexpectedly, as I stood with my head and from my breast upwards above the deck, that it had like to have put an end to my life, for it fell on the edge of the scuttle, and there broke to pieces; part tumbling down, the rest lying on the half deck. I dodged down, having received no hurt, but pretty much scared; but they tumbled the stones down so thick, that the half deck was almost covered with them.

The folks and the boy sheltered themselves forward behind the mast, and under the forecastle, the little boy frightened almost out of his wits; as indeed, so were we all.

Looking from behind the mast, after they had ceased heaving stones, to see whether they were gone or no, one of them hove a great stone, which struck against the mast, and there shattered to small pieces; upon which the boy dropped down under the beam, and I thought the poor child was killed, which he would undoubtedly, had the stone hit him; but he received no harm, only dropping down, either with the fright, or to shun the danger, or both; but he could not tell when I asked him after-wards, *What made him sink down?* but said, *He thought he should be killed; and that they all thought I had been killed by the stone that fell on the scuttle.*

THE BANDITS OF ST. JAGO

The quarter-deck being open, having no bulk-head, only at the head of my cabbin, so that I could see fore and aft, when I was under the half-deck; as soon as that storm was over, and they ceased heaving stones, I looked up again; for as soon as they were quiet, I began to fear they would swim off and attempt to board us, which I was resolved not to suffer them to do, as long as I had life or strength to oppose them. I no sooner raised my head in sight, but slam came three or four stones at me; but I prevented their hurting me by dropping under deck: Some of them came down the scuttle, and one of them glanced against my ankle, which, though I felt nothing of it then, yet it pained me some time after.

When I found their fury something abated, for they ceased heaving stones as soon as I dived out of sight, I looked up again, and begged of them but to let me speak to them. They called me all to naught, and said, *I was the devil that commanded the other devils, and bid me come ashore.*

I told them, *I would, if they would first let me speak to them.* They told me, *No; I must come ashore*, and fell a heaving stones again; at which I secured myself again under the deck.

Then they called to me; but I made no answer: They called several times; and at last, they said, *If I did not come up, they would tumble down rocks and stones till they filled or sunk the vessel.*

I looked up, and said, *They would neither give me liberty to speak, or come upon deck, without running the hazard of having my brains knocked out.*

They told me, *They would heave no more stones if I would come ashore.*

I said, *I would in a very little time; but that there was a sunken rock, whereon was not water enough yet for the boat to fleet over; but that, as the water was rising, I could in a little time put the boat to the rock, and then I would come ashore to them.*

This I only said to amuse them, to have an opportunity to appease them; for there was no sunken rock, it being steep too, at the rocky point of the cove whereon they stood tumbling stones upon us.

They bid me swim ashore. I told them, *I could not swim; but if they would have a little patience till the water flowed, I would put the boat to the rock and go ashore to them, or they come on board, which they pleased.*

They asked, *How long it would be?* I told them, *A very little time.* At which they seemed easy, and sat down on the rock.

I did not see above four there, but I could hear them speak to others, who were behind in a clift of the rock. I looked very narrowly to see if they had any fire arms, but perceived none; yet dared not to come up, standing in the scuttle, ready to drop my head down, if there should be occasion.

They asked me, *What countryman I was?* I told them, *I was an Englishman.*

They asked, *If I was sent there by the King of Portugal?* I told them, *No.*

They demanded, *What I came there for?* I told them, *I was leaky, and wanted to hale ashore to stop my leak; but as there was no convenient place, I designed to go to Porto Formosa, where was a more convenient place to hale ashore.*

By this time the others behind the rock came and sat down in sight with the rest: I told fifteen, and could not tell whether there were any more; but I saw no fire arms among them, and was the more confirmed in it, because I thought if they had any, they would have made use of them against us. They had most of them lances and long knives, such as that which Singore Jorge Vharela had, and some had swords.

They called to me again, and asked, *Why I did not come ashore?* I told them, *I would presently.*

They seemed very impatient; and told me, *If I deferred coming any longer, they would heave stones till they sunk the boat.*

I told them, *I had done them no harm as yet, except they reckoned my anchoring there was an injury to them: That they had done me a great deal of damage already, with their heaving stones in the vessel: That I came there with no design to injure them, nor any body else, but as a friend, and for that reason, I did not do myself that justice which was in my power to do, for the abuse which they, without any provocation, had treated me with: That I had fire arms and ammunition enough on board, to have laid them all dead; but supposing they might be mistaken, and believe me to be some other, who perhaps had deserved this ill treatment at their hands; That consideration,* said I (though I had neither gun nor powder on board; but since fair means would not do, I was resolved, if possible, to frighten them), *and the esteem which I always had for persons in your condition, has deterred me from hurting you hitherto; but if, notwithstanding, what I have said to you, will not prevent your future incivilities, I must be forced, though against my will, to do myself justice with the death of as many of you, as will presume farther to affront me.*

At this they set up a hideous hollow, casting stones as fast as they could, calling to one another to go home, and bring their Spring Guardas, and fight for their lives; I dived down as soon as I perceived them take up the stones, and shunned the danger; my men calling from afore to me, and telling me, *We could expect nothing from them now but death:* And indeed I cannot say that my expectation was of any else; but I was resolved to make the best I could of it, and bid my folks hold their tongues, and let me alone to manage them, and did not fear but we should do well enough.

As soon as their fury was over, and they ceased heaving stones, which lasted about half a quarter of an hour, their hearts I believe failed them, and they got all behind the rock. I looked up, but could not see one of them. I began to think they were gone; and looking sharp about, I perceived one of them peeping over the rock. I was just going to speak, when slam came a stone: I dived; but not finding that any more was coming, I looked up again, and took a piece of a fishing cane, which I had cut short for a walking-stick, and held it out as though it had been a gun, and called to them, and told them, *I was very loth to do them any damage; and if I did, it would be much against my inclination, because I had such an esteem for all their country, and was very well known and respected by some of the best singores on that part of the island.*

I still kept my eyes about me, lest they should go to their old work of heaving stones again: At last one of them spoke from behind the rock, and asked me, *If I knew any body that lived on the quarter of Terra-Fall?* (for all that end of St. Jago is called the quarter of Terra-Fall). I said, *Yes.*

They called to me again; but I could not perceive any body, by reason of the fear of my supposed gun, which I kept so that they could not discover the cheat, and asked me, *Who I knew in the quarter of Terra-Fall?*

I told them, *I knew Singore Juan Vharela, the padre, and several others* (whose names I had learned when I was at Porto Terra-Fall), *and likewise Singore Jorge Vharela the Jhuiss, who had been very kind to me, and with whom I had a very great friendship; and that I was to go to see him, as soon as I had stopped the leak of my vessel.* At which they all started up, and asked me, *If mine was the vessel that had been at Singore Jhuiss's porto?*

I told them, *Yes, I was the same; and was sure if Singore Jhuiss knew that I was there, and so affronted, that he would soon be there to assist me; and that it was the respect I had for him, and my other good friends in these parts, made me not to revenge myself on them, knowing that what they did, must certainly be occasioned through mistake.*

They said, *It was very true, and they were very sorry they had affronted me so; and took me to be of that sort of people called pirates, and were afraid that I was either come to take them away for slaves, or their cattle for food, or else, that I was sent by the King of Portugal, to apprehend some of them that were fled thither from the oppression of the Ovidore and the rest of the Brancas of the Cidade, i.e.* the Portuguese living in or about the city; the Ovidore being the King of Portugal's chief justiciary of all the Cape de Verd Islands, as well as of all the coast of the main continent of Guinea under his authority.

I told them, *I did not look like one upon either of those designs, having no more than two men and a little boy with me.*

They said, *They did not know but I might have had a great many men hid under the covert (i.e.* the deck).

I asked them, *If they thought so, how dared they to have come so nigh, for fear of being shot.*

They said, *They were sworn to oppose all that came to break the privilege of the place; and if I had fired at them, they would have kept close behind the rock, to keep us from getting up in the country, and in the mean time would have sent word up to raise the country. And,* continued they, *we have already sent up to town for more help, and likewise fire arms; but since we understand who you are, we will send up to stop their coming down, and likewise for something for a present for you.*

I thanked them, and continued talking about one thing or another, till the messenger came back that they had sent, who brought a calabash of milk, and a large cock and a hen: they held them up, and showing them to me, desired me to put the vessel to the rock to take them in.

I told them, *I could not put the vessel to the rock without danger of staving her.*

They said, *They would not have me come to any damage for ever so much; but hoped I was not afraid that they would hurt me.*

I told them, *No, not at all* (though I did not much care for trusting them).

They bid me send one of my mariners ashore for the present.

I told them, *None of my mariners could swim; that when I was at Singore Jhuiss's port, his slaves were forced to swim off with Singore Jhuiss's presents, and likewise carry what presents I made him ashore, because none of my people could swim; and when I went ashore to him, I was forced to put the vessel ashore; which I could do safe enough there, by reason it was a much better port than this; but if one of them would bring their present off, I would see for something to send with him ashore, in return of their kindness.*

They said, *They did not desire any thing; they were very sorry for the abuse they had given me, and thought they were highly obliged to me for being so generously reconciled to them, and hoped they had not done the vessel any damage.*

I told them, *They had not;* which if they had, I should not

I I

have told them; and said, *That I hoped they were not afraid that I would be so base as to do them any harm.*

They said, *No*; but yet did not seem very willing to venture to come on board.

At last a lusty grim-looked fellow said, *If I would put the boat in at the beach, so that he could wade in, he would come; but,* said he, *I can't nor I won't swim.*

It being now almost sunset, and the wind much less in the offing, so that the eddy-flaws were now but weak, insomuch, that I could easily, by veering cable, back her stern to the beach, and likewise there they could not do me much damage, as being farther from the rock, than as I rid; I told him, I would: So getting out two oars, and veering cable, and backing her stern too with our oars, till I could get ground with a short oar, I set her in as nigh as I thought fit, and then bid him come; who was got down the rock, and stood on the beach, armed with his lance, sword, and long knife.

I bid him leave his lance on the beach, as being troublesome as well as needless to wade off with. He, with a hesitating unwillingness, at last did, and waded off with his sword, knife, calabash of milk, and the two fowls, holding them up that they should not be wet, and waded till the water was as high as his navel, and then stopped, and bid me put the boat nigher in. I called to the boy in English, *Not to veer any more cable, and set her in till the cable was taut,* and bid my guest wade on.

He came, and by that time he was got to the boat's stern, was up to the arms. I told him, *The boat would not fleet any further in*; so he handed me the milk and fowls, and then would fain have got up with his sword and knife in his hand. I told him, *He need not fear to trust me with them.* He saw he could not get up with them in his hand, and yet was very loth to trust me with them; however, with abundance of diffidence, he handed his sword up to me, and endeavoured to get up with his knife in his hand, which they always trust to, as the surest weapon; but finding he could not, at last he handed that to me also, and then I gave him an end of a rope for a man-rope, by which he got up.

As soon as he got in on the quarter-deck, he saluted me with the usual formalities, and pretended they were very sorry for the rudeness that they had offered to me. I told him, *It was very well, I never bore any malice, especially when I was injured by a mistake, as I was satisfied this was.*

The fellow eyed his sword and knife in my hand, but was afraid, I believe, to ask them of me: I observed it, but did not seem to take any notice of it.

I was puzzled what to give them; and asked, *If they wanted any salt?* He said, *No, they had plenty of salt; for they could get enough to serve them, made by the sun on the rocks; but he had heard, that there was a great scarcity of salt at the city;* which I knew as well as he.

The fellow seemed to be very uneasy, and offered to take his sword; but I would not deliver it to him. He said, *He wanted to go ashore.* I told him, *He should presently.*

I had a felt hat, which I had purchased at the Isle of May, and having nothing else to give, I presented him with that, telling him, *That was all that I had worth giving; but wished I had one for every one that was ashore.* He said, *It was very well.*

I told him, *I had no particular knowledge of any of them, and therefore gave it among them all, for them to do as they thought fit with:* So he desired me to put the boat in again, that he might go ashore. I asked him, *Whether he could not swim?* who said *No;* and so I put the boat as nigh to the beach as I thought fit, and then bid him get into the water, and I would hand the hat and his arms to him, as soon as he was on the ground.

I fixed him a man-rope, and down he went by it; but by that time his feet touched the bottom, his chin was in the water, upon which he called out to put the boat nigher in, or he could not get ashore. I bid him let go the rope, and get ashore, and I would heave the things to him ashore. He did so; but muttered as he went, and I believe he never expected to get his arms again.

However, when he was got ashore, I hove the things ashore, and they all returned me thanks, and said, they would bring me a fat goat, and some more milk down in the morning. I thanked them; and it being almost duskish, away they went, bidding me adieu, telling me, that they would be down in the morning betimes. I said it was very well.

I have been the more prolix in relating this, because I do not know that I met with any thing in the whole of this voyage, that appeared to me more dangerous than this adventure at first did; and I can't deny but it gave as great a shock to my courage, as any thing that I can remember in the whole course of my life.

The night proving almost calm, I expected an off-shore land-breeze; and waiting till the morning-star rose, and no land-breeze coming, I drew up my anchor, and rowed out, not caring to be caught among the banditti another day.

So we rowed out till we got into the true wind, which was about the break of day, and I run down directly for Porto Formosa, and into the head of the bay.

CHAPTER TWELVE

*

I WAS resolved, if I could, to get to some of the Windward Islands, expecially to St. Nicholas, as well to shun the sickly season at St. Jago, as also having a prospect of sooner meeting with an European ship to get from the islands, the season of the year also concurring.

It was then the middle of August 1724; and about this time we saw a sail, which came into the road where I was, which proved to be a sloop belonging to Bristol, commanded by Captain — who had the Bishop of St. Jago, and the Visitador General, with their attendance, on board, and were going their visitation round the islands; and after that, the Visitador was to visit all the coast of Guinea, under the authority of the King of Portugal.

When they saw me, it daunted them, they thinking I was a pirate; for seldom, and very rare, any ships touch at these islands at this time of the year.

The captain, to be better informed, sent his yawl on board; and he told me afterwards, if I had detained his boat, or that he saw me get under sail, he would have stood off, and prepared for defence.

She was a stout sloop, had eight guns, and sixteen hands, and, if I be not deceived, the captain was a man of courage.

As soon as the boat came on board, I was not a little rejoiced to hear men speaking my native language; they asked me, *Where I belonged to?* I told them *what I was, etc.*

They told me, *Their captain gave his service to me, and desired my company on board.*

I answered, *That as soon as their sloop came to an anchor, I would go on board.*

They told me *what they were apprehensive I was, and that their captain was afraid to anchor, till he was better informed.*

I seeing they had no arms, did not much mistrust them; however, I did not care to venture, till I was sure; so I told them, *They saw what I was, but I did not know what they were; but would have them go on board, and give my service to their captain, and tell him, I would wait on him, as soon as he came to anchor, if he pleased to send his boat, for I had none;* so away they went, and, I suppose, told him what I said.

He immediately sent the boat for me again, to desire me *to do him the favour to come and anchor his vessel in the best birth of the road, for he was not acquainted with it, neither had he any one on board that was.*

When I saw the boat coming again the second time, I began to fear they were rogues, for he had a jack ensign and pendant flying, which made him look the more suspicious.

When the boat came on board, they told me their errand; so I went with them, and anchored the vessel in a good birth; the bishop, etc. was put ashore directly; after which, the captain and I had leisure to talk.

I gave him an account what I was, and the occasion of my being in that condition, etc. He was very courteous to me, and offered to do any thing for me, that lay in his power.

He would fain have had me gone with him, which I was very willing to do, till I came to understand the design of the voyage, which would no ways agree with what you may call humane or universal justice, neither was it safe; however, I shall not, as not thinking it proper, say any more of it; and this is the only reason why I have not mentioned the gentleman's name.

The reader may, perhaps, think it was piracy the gentleman was designed for; but I do assure him, it was not.

He had a good stock of every thing usually carried to sea, as wine, brandy, sugar, etc., and he was of a very free and generous disposition, and I fared, you must think, after another rate than I had done for a long time past; however, at first I was very cautious and sparing, both as to my eating and drinking, for fear it might stir up too quick a ferment in the fluid parts of my body, by the unusual addition of such hot active spirits, as good eating and drinking commonly produce; but notwithstanding my caution, the new diet, and spirituous drink, caused an agitation, or ferment, though insensible, till it came to the height of a fever, which increased daily.

I staid on board of him, till the bishop, Visitador, and all his passengers, were on board, and he unmoored, and short on his other anchor; for, he said, I should stay to the last minute that he stayed: He bid me take what things I thought might be useful to me in my illness, out of his medicine chest, which I did, viz. some Sp. Sal Armoniack, Tinct. Antimonii, Ol. Sulph. Camp. and some Theriac. Andromachi, etc.

After I had taken my leave, I went into the boat, and was put on board my own vessel; and as soon as they returned on board, he weighed, and sailed.

The evening following, I also sailed for St. Nicholas, which was the principal island for asses, and that was the first commodity ships came to trade for in those parts, and most an end a ship touched at St. Nicholas for asses, in the month of November, or December; and those that came in January, commonly loaded salt.

I made St. Nicholas in the morning about six of the clock; the wind was about south-west, and looked very dark and rainy, as well as windy-like, which made me loth to venture in, all the roads of that island being open to those winds; so I brought too, to consider what to do; we were then about four leagues off, I was very weak, but the cold and wet had abated the heat of my fever, together with the care and charge which I had upon me, as having no-body that I could trust.

After I brought too, it rained very hard, and blew, which held till about four in the afternoon, then the wind veering about to the north-west, north-north-west, and at last to the north, and clearing up, promised a fine, moderate, pleasant night; upon which I resolved to run in a cove, by the inhabitants called Porto Ghuy, which I judged better, as having less sea tumbling in, than at Paraghesi.

In the morning, the weather still continuing as above, as well as likely to be, fair and settled, I took up my anchor, and run into Paraghesi, and let go my anchor off, and an end of a rope fast ashore.

There were abundance of people down to receive and welcome me, who had been informed by some of those that had been at the Ghuy a fishing, that it was I, and that I had salt in to truck away for maiz; and several of them had brought maiz down with them to exchange with me for my salt; and they told me, *That most of the islanders would be down to exchange maiz for salt.*

You must know, that it being now the turtle-season, and the people of St. Nicholas catching and salting that amphibious creature, and using it more than any of those islands do; and having besides, no salt pans, and very little made on the rocks; and those rocks where that little is made, being so difficult, as well as dangerous, to go down, that very few of the inhabitants care for venturing, there being two men killed attempting to go seek for salt, while I was on the island; all these reasons made it a very valuable commodity on that island at this time: And they asked me, *How I would dispose of my salt?* I told them, *measure for measure,* which they agreed to, and all that had corn down, brought it on board, and shot it on the forecastle, I haling the vessel close to the rock, where it is two fathom and a half at low water, and at high water, at ordinary tides, the rock is about four or five foot above the surface of the water, and flat on the top like a key, which the inhabitants call Kaay, and is a general name they give to all convenient rocks for landing at.

The wind veering to the north-east, the sky towards noon became overcast, as it often is with the trade wind, and looked fair weather-like; but my fear and care being over, now I was got into a harbour, etc., I found, that as my dangers decreased, so the sense of my sickness returned, and what with the noise and cabal of those people, etc. I was forced to lie down: The boy also was ill, though nothing nigh so bad as I; and the natives said, *That it was better to have me ashore, where I might have a fire made me in a cave, which was in sight of the boat, and have a bed made me of dried grass, etc.* So my St. Antonio man, whom I always found to be a sensible, careful, as well as an honest, and affectionate man to me, said, *That if I pleased to entrust him, he would take care to measure out all the salt, and take the same measure of maiz for me, as well as if I was present;*

and that it would be more quiet for me to be ashore, where I might have a warm cave to shelter me from the wind and cold; and have a fire, and a good soft bed of dry grass.

I told him, *Whether I went ashore, or staid on board, I was so weak, that I must trust him; but if I was never so well, I should not question his justness, were it a cargo of twice the value of what I now had.*

The rest that were by, and heard my answer, without asking me, or saying anything to me, took me up, and carried me ashore to the cave, and got me a bed of dry grass, made a fire, and would fain have made me some pap, but I would not let them; I had a violent hot fever, and a little after I was laid there, the St. Antonio man came and told me, *The forecastle was full of corn, and a great deal on the quarter deck; and if I thought well of it, he was of opinion, it would be better to put the rest of the maiz in some clean cleft, or hollow of a rock, till I thought fit to put it on board. Adding, That there was maiz enough down to purchase all the salt, and that they might shoot the remainder in the hollow of a rock, and then he could measure them out their salt, and did not fear but to clear the boat of all her salt before night, which, if we did not, he was afraid a great deal would be wasted with the rain; for, he believed, we should have as much, or more rain, than we had the former night.*

I said, *If it turned to rain again, I much feared we should have a southerly wind, and then we should lose our boat.*

A young man, who said he had been taken by Captain Loe coming from Virginia, and some months past, had escaped from him at the Island of St. Vincent, while Loe was there a cleaning and refitting the *Merry Christmas*, a ship belonging to London, which he had taken coming from Virginia; this young man, who told me his name was George, and was born in Devonshire, said, He would lie in the vessel all night: I ordered them to save a barrel of salt, which I designed for presents to the priest, governor, etc., which they did, and bartered all the rest of the salt for maiz, and some feshoons.

The wind increased, and consequently the sea, which rowled right into the cove; and though there is an island or rock, which you would think might break off the fury of the waves, as being then right to windward of the boat, and in smooth water, and above the surface of the water twelve or fourteen foot; yet now it did not seem in the least to shelter, but the sea seemed to be rather worse by being broke, rowling in over the rock, which very seldom now appeared.

At last the sea with the wind increased so, that one would think it impossible for such a vessel, or even any one, to hold out, or resist the raging force of the wind and sea; which none can conceive, but those whose lot (or I might say misfortune) it is to be exposed to the raging force of those two elements together. Soon after the shore-fast gave way, and then she swung off, and rid in the stream of her anchor, and seemed to ride more easy, and play with the sea better; and rid so about half an hour, when a sea came foaming in, as though it scorned to be opposed, even by the high mountainous rocks themselves, and threatened to bear down all, as it were, before it, and to us seemed to swallow up the poor vessel; for we did not see her for about the space of a minute.

The consequence of it was, the cable broke, and that sea carried her up on the beach so high, that she lay undisturbed more than a quarter of an hour. As soon as she came ashore, they all got out of her, and in the fright run up the valley as high as the rocks would let them; but when they recovered from their fright, and saw themselves safe, they returned down again to the boat, which lay all this time quiet, as being out of the reach of the sea; George went on board, and might have saved several odd things, which I had picked up in the time of my peregrination in her; but while he was in her, a great sea rowled on, which was only the forerunner of a greater; for it only shocked her; but so frightened George, and perhaps it would have done the same to any other, that he made all the haste out he could, and brought nothing with him but a bottle of that wine, which my friend had given me at Bona Vist.

As I said, that sea that shocked the vessel, was a forerunner of a greater; for presently after George got ashore out of the boat, a sea came that staved her all to pieces; the blacks that were with me went down to them, and gathered all the pieces of boards, and what else they could, that the sea hove on to the shore; and one of them brought the boy up to the cave to me, where we remained till morning.

I was as wet all night, sitting on the rock to behold the boat, with the rain and spray of the sea being blown up by the violence of the wind, as if I had been come out of the sea; and it doubtless did me a great deal of harm, and perhaps was one great cause of that long and tedious sickness, which held me till after my arrival in England, and was a principal cause of my having leisure to write this history.

As soon as day broke out, by which time the weather began to clear up, and be more moderate, though a great sea still run, I could behold the ruins of my eight (I might say ten or twelve) months' labour, lying piled up on the shore. With the help of some of them, I was carried down the rocks, and viewed what was saved, which was most part of the wreck, some pieces of the sails, one of my iron pots, an ax, saw, etc.

There was one of them that was down, had an ass, and offered it to me to carry me up, and told me, *I had best get up before the sun rose too high; otherwise, as I was so weak, it would make me very faintish to go up in the heat of the day*. He added, *That if no other asses came down, they would make shift and carry the boy up after me:* So I was mounted on the ass, and three or four accompanied me up, and one or more ran up to town before, to give the padre and governor an account of my condition, and also of my coming up.

I was met on the way by Singore Nicholau Gonsalvo, with whom I had been acquainted before, whose father had been formerly governor of the island: he was sorry for my loss, I believe, with all his heart, and testified so much by his tears, and obliged me to promise to live with him till I had an opportunity of meeting with a ship to carry me off the island.

When I came up to town, I rid directly to the governor's house, who had made preparation to receive me; and as soon as the priest heard I was come, he came directly to welcome me to town, as well as to condole with me in my misfortune.

I told them, *I thought the greatest of my present misfortune was, my want of health; and as for the loss of the boat, or anything in her, I accounted it as nothing, she having already answered my design in building her, which was only to bring me off of that lone-some island, where seldom any ships came, to some part where I might expect to meet with one; and hoped I was as likely to light of one here, as any of the Cape de Verd Islands.*

The governor said, *He expected me to live with him, while I remained on the island.*

I told him, *I must beg him not to take it amiss; for not having any personal acquaintance with him, nor the reverend padre, I had already promised Singore Nicholau Gonsalvo, my old acquaintance, to live with him.*

By this time the victuals were ready, and brought to the table, which were fish, fowls, goat's flesh, Indian corn bread, plantanes, bananas, boiled pompion, etc., the fowls were baked in a pot, and looked very well, and as brown as if they had been roasted, and the venison and fish were boiled, there was also a calamow, which is a calabash cut in two, and serves them in the room of basins and porengers; and this was brought to me full of fish water, being reckoned by them the daintiest mess they can give to a sick or weak person; however, I could not drink or sup it, though I put the calamow to my head three or four times without tasting it, because I would not have them think I slighted the sick mess.

I eat a bit or two of the fowl, and after dinner lay down on a bed, which was on purpose set up for me.

In the evening Nicholau came up, and having carried all my things that he brought up to his house, he came to the governor's, and acquainted me with what he had done; and I took my leave of the governor, and went to my lodging,

My fever returned on me again, and burned and raged violently about eight days; and after that, especially in the night, I used to sweat cold clammy sweats, to such a degree, that my landlady one morning, to try how much sweat she could wring out, wrung the bed clothes, which were cotton, and she wrung more than filled a quarter of a canada, which,

274

of our measure, is about three-eighths of a pint; and doubtless there was more than that quantity soaked into the cotton besides.

I was in this condition about a fortnight after the burning fever left me, and then my sweats abated; and as they abated, which were very gradually, my strength a little increased; but I recovered my spirits much sooner than my strength.

Either the priest, the governor, the fradre, or one or other of the inhabitants, used to visit me every day; and when I was in my weak fits, they would never speak to me, only come and look at me, and ask my landlord, landlady, or whoever of the family was in the way, how I was, etc.

After I began to be a little hearty, my landlord asked me, *What I would do with the wreck that was saved?*

I told him, *He might do what he pleased with it, and supposed there could not be much of it left, if it lay down there all this time.*

He said, *He was sure there was not one piece of all that was saved diminished; for the priest had charged them all publickly at church, upon pain of excommunication, not to touch or take away the least bit of wood, or any thing else, and pronounced damnation to any one that would wrong me of so much as a nail.*

I told him, *If any of it would be of any use or service to him, to take out as much as he had occasion for, as having most right to it, and the rest I would give to my friends that I was most obligated to, as he would advise and direct me.*

He told me, *I had no occasion to give one bit away to any body; he could have sold it all while I was sick, but was loth to trouble me then, and would not dispose of it without my order:* And withal told me, *That the priest was minded to enlarge the choir, and would have occasion for all the wreck, and bid me try what he would give me for it; and if he would give any thing handsome, he believed it would be my better way to sell it to him altogether, than have the trouble to sell it in parcels to the people; and though I might make more, yet it would be too troublesome for me to go down to Paraghesi, every time that a man came to buy a testoon's worth of stuff; and if I pleased, he would first tell the priest about* it, and inform him that I was able to dispose of it, and that talking would not prejudice me now; and desired me, if I sold it to him, to except a piece which he made me understand was the boom, because he wanted it to make a ridge-pole for his house.

I told him, *I would, and if there was any thing more which he thought he should have occasion for, it should be also at his service.*

He said, *No, he wanted only that, and he would not take it till it was valued by a couple of men, and would pay me the full value.*

I told him, *I would not take any thing of him, and he was welcome to all, or as much as he pleased.*

He said, *If I would not let him pay me for it, as much as I could have for it of any body else, he would not have it; but bid me sell it with the rest to the priest.*

To please him, I was forced to say he should pay for it; and he spoke to the priest about it, who came to me, and after we had talked about it, the priest said, *He did not know the value of it; but he would send down two old men, who should value it according to their conscience, and what they valued it at, he would give me, if I thought it sufficient; if not, I might dispose of it as I thought fit, and he would give free liberty for any one to buy who had occasion:* Without which liberty, no body dared buy any thing that the priest bid money for.

When they returned, and gave the priest an account, he came to me, and told me, *He would give me 9000 reas, but I must not take the boom; for he knew,* he said, *I could not want it for my own use.*

I told him, *It was true; but I had promised a friend to save it for him; and if he thought it was not worth so much without that piece, he should, if he pleased, have them for nothing; but if I sold them, I would have no less than I told him for them.*

Well, said he, *then you shall have 9000* (which is twelve dollars, a dollar being reckoned there at 750 reas); So we agreed; and he told me, *I might have my money when I pleased.* I said, *It was very well.*

Some few days after he paid me; which made me richer than I had been for some years before; and I bought a large hog for a dollar and half, and had it killed. My landlord would have had me sold the maiz and feshoon which lay on the rock at Paraghesi; but I told him, *I would not; but bid him take what he had occasion for, and let the poor, or any that wanted the rest, take it.*

He took, I believe, about the quantity of five bushels, the whole of what was laid on the rock being about forty or fifty bushels; and then I gave liberty for every body that wanted to take the rest; which mightily raised me in esteem with the inhabitants, especially the poorer sort.

I recovered my strength a little; but presently after fell first into a quotidian, than a tertian ague, which kept me very weak; for my cold sweats, which I had the latter end of the cold or shaking fit, came again; but nothing to the excess that it was before.

I thus passed, or rather lingered my time away, till about the latter part of October, when, to my great satisfaction, I had news of an English ship being arrived at this island, and that she anchored in the port of Terra-Fall. It was late in the evening when I heard the news, and I immediately resolved to go down that night. My landlord persuaded me all he could to defer my journey till the morning, for fear of catching cold, etc., but I was fixed in my resolution; and while he and his son were gone to catch a horse for me to ride down upon, to my yet greater satisfaction, I had a letter from the captain, brought me by one of the blacks, who was down at Terra-Fall when the ship came to an anchor; for as soon as that was done, the captain observing people ashore, sent his boat to bring off some of them, or, if they were not willing, to give them an account what he was, and what he came to trade for, as likewise to inform himself whether there had been any pirates about the islands.

Several of them went off in the boat on board, who informed the captain of me, as far as they were capable of; and when they named my name he remembered me, though we never had had any personal acquaintance together; but the year before, at Bona Vist, he fell into the same pirates' hands that I had, from whom he heard of my being taken; and the blacks relating to him, my being shipwrecked at St. John's, of my building a balandra there, and of my losing her here, etc., he told them, *He knew me;* and asked them, *If any of them would carry a letter from him to me:* They said, *With all their hearts;* so he immediately writ to me, acquainting me *of his arrival, his designing to trade there for cotton cloths, money, or what else I would inform him that the country afforded that would be worth his purchasing; and that he had, he believed, a very good cargo for these islands, and referred particularizing, till he saw me, and should expect me down at the port to-morrow, if I was able.*

Next morning before day, the governor and I, and several others, went down; the priest was to come after he had said his Mass, which is every morning in St. Nicholas Church, unless sickness, etc. hinders; my landlord, poor man, could not come, being so bad with a pain in his back, occasioned by a wrench, and a cold upon that, that he could not sit an ass, which gave us both no small concern.

We got down about ten a clock, having been on the journey about eight hours; Captain John Harfoot, whose vessel was a brigantine about sixty or seventy tuns, saw us coming time enough to get ashore with the boat before we got to the sea side, and had got a sail ashore, and a tent fixed.

He received us very courteously, and was glad to see me, as I was more to see him there: After we had talked a while about trade, and I had given him several hints relating to it, he took us on board.

The priest came down about one a clock, for whom Captain Harfoot sent his boat. In the evening they went ashore, and so to town; but I staid; after which we had more leisure to talk.

I told him the nature and best method of trading, etc., so far as related to the disposal of his cargo; and he very kindly offered me my passage, and what entertainment his vessel afforded, for me and the boy, and told me the design of his voyage, which was to trade among the islands about two months, and then run for the Island of Barbadoes, where he was to meet a ship to take his cargo of cotton cloths from him;

and told me, as I knew it very well myself, *That when I got to that island, I might get an employ there, or, if my affairs required my going home, I need not fear something in my way; but if not, I was welcome to go home with him, if I so thought fit.*

I went up to get my cloaths, etc. and to bring the boy down, and take my final leave of the inhabitants; all which I chose to do personally, because I could be serviceable to his affairs.

I had spoke to him about George, and that I believed he would be glad to work for his passage to get off these islands, and gave him an account, as far as George had given me: The captain told me, that he had his full complement of hands, and had no occasion for any more; but rather than the young fellow should stay there, he would give him his passage; so when I came up to town, I told George, who seemed rejoiced at it.

I took my leave of the inhabitants, and the boy and I went down the same night, George following us the next morning; as soon as Captain Harfoot saw the little boy, he wondered how I came to take such a little child to sea, who, he said, was fitter for a nurse, than to do me any service.

I told him my reasons for taking him, as I have afore related; he commended me for it, but said, *He wondered how I could take care of the boy, and bring him with me in so many difficulties; and that a great many men would have left him at St. John's.*

I told him, *That I thought it would be an unchristian, as well as an inhuman act, to have left a child so, to be brought up in a manner like an infidel.*

He said, *That was true; but there were thousands that would have left him;* and said, *That I should find it very chargeable to get him home.*

I told him, *If I could, I would get him home, let it cost me what it would, at least to Barbadoes.*

Nay, says he, *it will cost you nothing for him to Barbadoes, for you are as welcome to his passage thither, as if it was your own vessel.* I returned him many thanks for his kindness.

When George came down, he haled the brigantine; Captain Harfoot asked me, *If that was the man?* I answered, *Yes;* he sent the boat for him; and as soon as he was brought on board, I observed his countenance to change, but I could not imagine the reason; however, Captain Harfoot soon made me sensible of the reason of George's dejection of countenance; which was this: the year before, when Loe took Captain Harfoot at Bona Vist, this fellow was on board the pirates, and, it seems, was as active as the rest in plundering and rifling; and George perceiving that Mr. Harfoot knew him again, it so daunted him, that he had no courage to speak. The captain, as soon as he had recovered memory enough, to convince him that he was certain it was he, said in a passion, *You impudent rascally villain, I admire how you dare come to ask a favour of me!*

The fellow looked very dejected, and told him, *That he was a prisoner on board with the pirates, and was constrained to do what he did, as not daring to refuse whatever they thought proper to command him.*

The captain bid him *hold his tongue, and tell them so that knew no better; and that if he had not the impudence of the devil, or his master Loe, he would not come to ask him any favour, etc.* Adding, *That if he was sure to find a man-of-war to put him on board of, before he went from the islands, he would give him his passage to it;* and turning to me, said, *If a body should take that villain on board to carry him to justice, and should meet any of his brother villains* (meaning the pirates), *a man could expect nothing but death;* and turning to George, who to all this replied not a word, he said, *I will send you ashore again; but if I meet with any of His Majesty's ships before I leave these islands, I will give them an account of you, and persuade them, all I can, to come and give you a passage to Tyburn; and hope ere long to hear of your master Loe's receiving his last reward, according to his deserts, at some such place.*

He then ordered the boat to put him ashore; and when he had done what he had to do there, he weighed, and we run for Bona Vist, where he tarried four days; from thence we went to the Isle of May, and tarried two days, and then proceeded to the Island of St. Jago, and anchored in Porto Praya, where we met with an English ship come from the coast of Guinea, with a cargo of slaves, wax, teeth, etc., bound for Lisbon. She slaved at Cacheu, and was there all the time of the rains: she was freighted by the Portuguese merchants, and had been very leaky after her arrival at St. Jago, insomuch, that they were forced to take out all her cargo there, to come at her leaks, some of the chief of which they stopped, and nailed lead over them. Their carpenter, and two doctors, and above half their company, died at Guinea. The captain was sick at St. Jago; but when we came in, he was recovered, but yet weak, as was almost all the remaining part of the company.

We got to Barbadoes, and anchored in Carlisle-Bay, Christmas-Day, 1724.

In less than three months after our arrival we sailed, and arrived at Lisbon, where I took the first opportunity of a passage for London, which happened with Mr. Alexander Baxter, master of the *Pricket*, a brigantine, who generously gave both me and my boy a passage to London, where we arrived towards the latter part of June, 1725.

My ague had followed me as a constant, though unwelcome attendant to the West Indies, and from thence to Lisbon, and about the middle of the passage between Lisbon and London it left me; but after my being about a fortnight ashore, it returned as bad as ever, and brought me so low, that I was uncapable of any thing but writing; which, by the perswasion of some friends, I undertook, and, by the blessing of God upon the medicines administered, I recovered my former health; but having then gone through a great part of this history, I resolved to compleat it, and found the doing of it much more tedious and painful, than at first I imagined it would be; the which ignorance, with my incapacity to go abroad when I began it, were the only inducements to comply with the perswasions of my friends, as I mentioned before.

And now I have finished my history of as much as I thought would be necessary or useful. It is my maiden work of a publick nature; and as I find this proves acceptable or serviceable, it may encourage me to a discovery of what hath occurred to me, in my past, or future observations, so far as I conceive they may be useful or delightful to my countrymen in general, especially to the merchant adventurers, and the gentlemen belonging to the sea, in particular: And if the reader finds as much satisfaction in the reading, as I have taken pains truly to observe and collect, I shall think my trouble well bestowed.

N.B. – The little boy, so often mentioned in the foregoing sheets now lives with Mr. Galapin, a tobacconist, in Monument Yard, and may be referred to for the truth of most of the particulars before related.

J. AND J. GRAY, PRINTERS, EDINBURGH

A LIST OF TITLES

THE

Saint Giles Library

One shilling and ninepence net
each volume

JONATHAN CAPE
THIRTY BEDFORD SQUARE
LONDON

FICTION

BIOGRAPHY AND AUTOBIOGRAPHY

TRAVEL, ADVENTURE, AND THE OPEN AIR

LITERATURE, LITERARY CRITICISM, AND ESSAYS

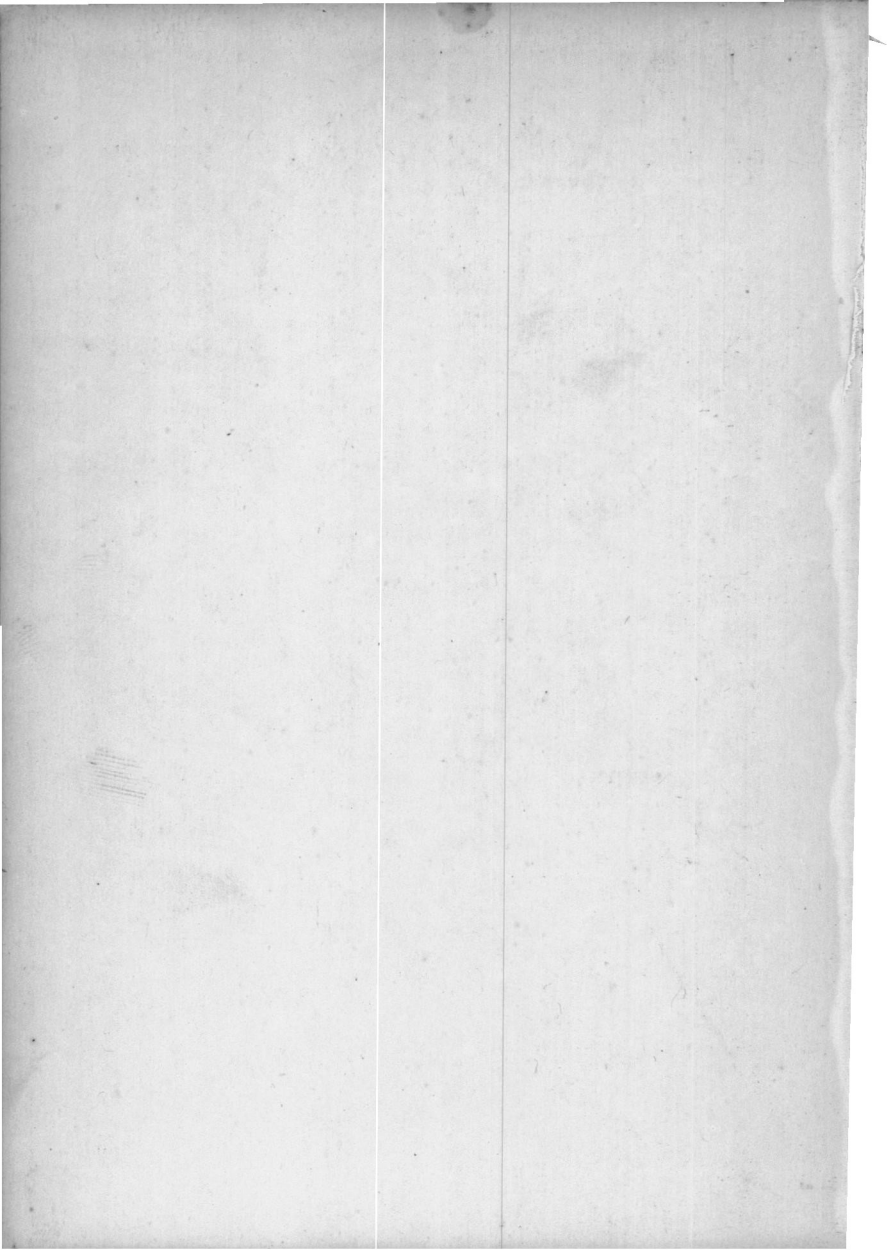